The Elementary Mathematics Specialist's Handbook

Edited by

Patricia F. Campbell
University of Maryland
College Park, Maryland

Aimee J. Ellington
Virginia Commonwealth University
Richmond, Virginia

William E. Haver
Virginia Commonwealth University
Richmond, Virginia

Vickie L. Inge
University of Virginia
Charlottesville, Virginia

This text was developed in part with support from the National Science Foundation (NSF), DRL-0918223 and DUE-0412324. All opinions, findings, conclusions, and recommendations expressed herein are those of the authors and do not necessarily reflect the views of NSF.

Fourth printing 2016

Library of Congress Cataloging-in-Publication Data
Practitioner's guide to being an elementary mathematics specialist / edited by Patricia F. Campbell, University of Maryland, College Park, Maryland, William E. Haver, Virginia Commonwealth University, Richmond, Virginia, Aimee J. Ellington, Virginia Commonwealth University, Richmond, Virginia, Vickie L. Inge, University of Virginia, Charlottesville, Virginia.
pages cm
Includes bibliographical references.
ISBN 978-0-87353-699-8 (pbk.)
1. Mathematics—Study and teaching (Elementary—United States. I. Campbell, Patricia F., editor. II. Haver, William E., editor. III. Ellington, Aimee J., 1968- IV. Inge, Vickie L., editor.
QA135.6.P68 2014
372.70973—dc23
2014024051

The National Council of Teachers of Mathematics is the public voice of mathematics education, supporting teachers to ensure equitable mathematics learning of the highest quality for all students through vision, leadership, professional development, and research.

Printed in the United States of America

Contents

Preface vii

Part 1: Setting the Stage 1

Chapter 1 3

The Role of the Elementary Mathematics Specialist
Patricia F. Campbell
University of Maryland, College Park, Maryland

Chapter 2 17

Research Findings
Patricia F. Campbell
University of Maryland, College Park, Maryland
Aimee J. Ellington
Virginia Commonwealth University, Richmond, Virginia

Part 2: Supporting Teachers 29

Chapter 3 31

Coaching Individual Teachers
DeAnna Moreau
Colonial Heights Public Schools, Colonial Heights, Virginia
Joy W. Whitenack
Virginia Commonwealth University, Richmond, Virginia

Chapter 4 51

Supporting Grade-Level Teams
Carolyn Doyle
Richmond Public Schools, Richmond, Virginia
Candace Standley
Culpeper County Public Schools, Culpeper, Virginia

Chapter 5 71

Supporting Groups of Teachers across Grades
Laura S. Domalik
Virginia Commonwealth University, Richmond, Virginia
Vandivere P. Hodges
Virginia Commonwealth University, Richmond, Virginia
Linda K. Jaeger
Richmond Public Schools, Richmond, Virginia

Chapter 6 91

Working with Resource Teachers
Karen Mirkovich
Prince William County Public Schools, Manassas, Virginia

Patricia A. Robertson
Arlington Public Schools, Arlington, Virginia
Jason A. Scherm
Westmoreland County Public Schools, Montross, Virginia

Chapter 7 103
Supporting Teachers' Work with Special Education Students
LouAnn H. Lovin
James Madison University, Harrisonburg, Virginia
Margaret M. Kyger
James Madison University, Harrisonburg, Virginia

Chapter 8 117
Supporting Teachers' Work with English Language Learners and Gifted Mathematics Learners
Susan Birnie
Alexandria City Public Schools, Alexandria, Virginia
Catherine Lamczyk
Stafford County Public Schools, Stafford, Virginia

Part 3: Supporting the School Mathematics Program 131

Chapter 9 133
Using Assessment to Inform Instruction on the Basis of Data
Denise M. Walston
Council of Great City Schools, Washington, D.C.
Sandra S. Overcash
Nonpublic Educational Services, Inc., Virginia Beach, Virginia

Chapter 10 149
Managing a School's Instructional Resources for Mathematics
Kim Raines
Fauquier County Public Schools, Warrenton, Virginia
Beth Williams
Bedford County Public Schools, Bedford, Virginia

Chapter 11 163
Serving as the Face of an Elementary School's Mathematics Program
Contina Martin
Portsmouth Public Schools, Portsmouth, Virginia
Fanya Morton
King George County Schools, King George, Virginia

Part 4: Other Considerations 175

Chapter 12 177
Turning Challenges into Opportunities
Sarah M. Minervino
Arlington Public Schools, Arlington, Virginia

Patricia A. Robertson
Arlington Public Schools, Arlington, Virginia
Joy W. Whitenack
Virginia Commonwealth University, Richmond, Virginia

Chapter 13 191
Defining the Elementary Mathematics Specialist Position
Debra J. Delozier
Stafford County Public Schools, Stafford, Virginia
Fiona C. Nichols
Portsmouth Public Schools, Portsmouth, Virginia

Chapter 14 201
Leadership Expectations and Negotiating with the Principal
Vickie L. Inge
University of Virginia, Charlottesville, Virginia
Carol S. Walsh
Middlesex County Public Schools, Saluda, Virginia
Jeannie Duke
Middlesex County Public Schools, Saluda, Virginia

Chapter 15 215
Induction to a New Position Involves Transitions
Aimee J. Ellington
Virginia Commonwealth University, Richmond, Virginia
William E. Haver
Virginia Commonwealth University, Richmond, Virginia

Chapter 16 227
Personal and Professional Growth and Development
Reuben W. Farley
Virginia Commonwealth University, Richmond, Virginia
Tracy L. Gaither
Arlington Public Schools, Arlington, Virginia
Vandivere P. Hodges
Virginia Commonwealth University, Richmond, Virginia

Chapter 17 237
The Principal and the Elementary Mathematics Specialist Work Together
Vickie L. Inge
University of Virginia, Charlottesville, Virginia
Debbie Arco
Hanover County Public Schools, Ashland, Virginia
Duffie Jones
Charlotte County Public Schools, Charlotte Court House, Virginia

Appendix A 255
Who Are Mathematics Specialists?
Virginia Mathematics and Science Coalition, Richmond, Virginia

Appendix B 257

The Virginia Mathematics Specialist Program

Megan K. Murray

The University of Hull, Scarborough, North Yorkshire, England

Loren D. Pitt

University of Virginia, Charlottesville, Virginia

Accompanying Material at More4U

Chapter 17

The Principal and the Elementary Mathematics Specialist Work Together

Preface

"Mathematics specialist" describes individuals employed in a number of different roles in schools across the nation. In this handbook, "elementary mathematics specialist" refers to an individual who has been granted release time from classroom teaching to advance the mathematics program in a K–5 school and provide school-based, collegial, professional development for teachers. This handbook envisions various roles for the elementary mathematics specialist, as described in chapter 1. Typically, the position of mathematics specialist is full time, and the individual who holds this title offers programmatic leadership for mathematics in the school, in addition to providing job-embedded professional development. However, in small schools, the elementary mathematics specialist may have some responsibility for teaching children for part of each school day or each week and may then assume the professional development and programmatic responsibilities of a specialist for the remainder of the school day or week.

Some schools and school systems give mathematics specialists other roles, following differing worthwhile models for using mathematics specialists to improve mathematics achievement, but this handbook does not address those models. In particular, for the purposes of this handbook, the elementary mathematics specialist is *not*—

- assigned to teach mathematics full time—all day, every day—to students in selected grades or at specific achievement levels in an elementary school, as the "specialized teacher of mathematics" or the "mathematics only" teacher;
- responsible for evaluative, performance monitoring of teachers;
- assigned full-time, all-day responsibility as a classroom teacher and in addition charged with providing professional development for teachers after the school day has ended for students;
- assigned as a full-time classroom teacher who is occasionally or regularly released from teaching responsibilities to work with teachers or to support a school's mathematics program for part of a day, or a few hours, each week.

This handbook has been developed as a resource for the mathematics specialist whose central role is to facilitate and support the job-embedded professional development of elementary school classroom teachers. This role includes coaching individual teachers, coaching small groups or grade-level teams of teachers, providing programmatic leadership for mathematics in the school, collaborating with and supporting other resource teachers, and serving as the face of the school's mathematics program. This handbook explores how mathematics specialists can be effective in all these areas.

The handbook's last chapter is intended to be particularly useful for an elementary school principals who is preparing to collaborate with a mathematics specialist, addressing how the principal and the specialist may work together to define and advance mathematics teaching and learning in their school. This chapter, "The Principal and the Elementary Mathematics Specialist Work Together" (chapter 17), also appears at nctm.org/more4u in a electronic version that can be printed out as a freestanding piece for specialists and principals to read and discuss together.

The National Science Foundation has supported research and development initiatives addressing mathematics specialists through funded projects awarded to Virginia Commonwealth University in partnership with the University of Virginia, Norfolk State University, Longwood University, the University of Maryland, and the Virginia Mathematics and Science Coalition (DUE-0926537, "MSP Institute: Mathematics Specialists in Middle Schools"; DUE-0412324, "NSF Institute: Preparing

Virginia's Mathematics Specialist"; DRL-0918223, "Researching the Expansion of K–5 Mathematics Specialist Program into Rural School Systems"; and ESI-0353360, "Mathematics Specialist in K–5 Schools: Research and Policy Pilot Study"). These projects encompass components to achieve the following:

- Develop and offer master's degree programs to prepare teachers to serve as mathematics specialists
- Work with school systems and school principals to deploy mathematics specialists effectively
- Conduct research on the impact of mathematics specialists on teacher beliefs and student achievement
- Disseminate the results of this work and these experiences nationwide.

The mathematics specialist initiative in Virginia has drawn on multiple experiences and materials nationwide, and, in turn, shares lessons learned in this handbook. With National Science Foundation support, this initiative has produced the following results:

- All partners developed and adopted a document titled *Who Are Mathematics Specialists?* (see appendix A).
- Six universities in Virginia collaboratively developed and began offering master's degree programs to prepare mathematics specialists (appendix B provides a description of the program as offered at the University of Virginia).
- Virginia's Department of Education and state legislature adopted a Mathematics Specialist for Elementary and Middle Education endorsement that teachers who hold certification in Virginia may add to their existing teaching license. The licensure expectations for this endorsement parallel the requirements for the master's degree program described in appendix B. To date, more than 400 teachers have earned the endorsement, and a new statewide professional organization of mathematics specialists has been launched in Virginia. This organization has sponsored two annual conferences, each attended by more than one hundred fifty mathematics specialists.
- Research has investigated and continues to study the impact of mathematics specialists on student achievement and teachers' beliefs about mathematics teaching and learning. One large treatment/control study has been completed, led by Patricia Campbell, lead editor of this handbook. Chapter 2, "Research Findings," describes some results from this study, including the finding that students in schools with mathematics specialists who had completed a mathematics specialist preparation program achieved significantly higher scores on Virginia's state mathematics achievement test in each of grades 3, 4, and 5 than students in the control schools. Two additional studies with treatment/control components have been undertaken and will be completed in 2016.

The chapters in this handbook were authored by individuals who have served as mathematics specialists, supervisors of specialists, principals in schools with specialists, instructors of courses in a preparation program for specialists, and facilitators of programs designed to support principals who have specialists placed in their schools. In addition, to ensure that the content and advice in this handbook addresses the reality of practice as experienced by elementary mathematics specialists, an advisory board was formed, consisting of practicing mathematics specialists. Two or more members of this board reviewed each chapter of the handbook for clarity, content, and relevance, offering suggestions for improvement. The chapters were subsequently revised in response to the feedback, and suggestions and reflections of these practicing mathematics specialists were added to the chapters. The following individuals from Virginia school systems served on the advisory board:

Ché Abdeljawad	Arlington Public Schools
Carolyn Doyle	Richmond City Public Schools
Amy Duffy	Roanoke City Public Schools
Candie George	Mecklenburg County Public Schools
Jennifer Hackley	Staunton City Public Schools
Stacey Lauffer	Culpeper County Public Schools
Sarah Minervino	Arlington Public Schools
Jason Scherm	Westmoreland County Public Schools
Elizabeth Sinclair	Arlington Public Schools
Candace Standley	Culpeper County Public Schools
Carol Walsh	Middlesex County Public Schools
Dana Witt	Roanoke City Public Schools

The editors would like to thank the authors for accepting the challenge of working on this handbook and for writing chapters rich with guidance and advice for mathematics specialists. We would also like to thank the members of the advisory board for their thoughtful reviews of the chapters and their personal stories, which enhance and underscore the ideas presented in each of the chapters in the handbook.

1

Setting the Stage

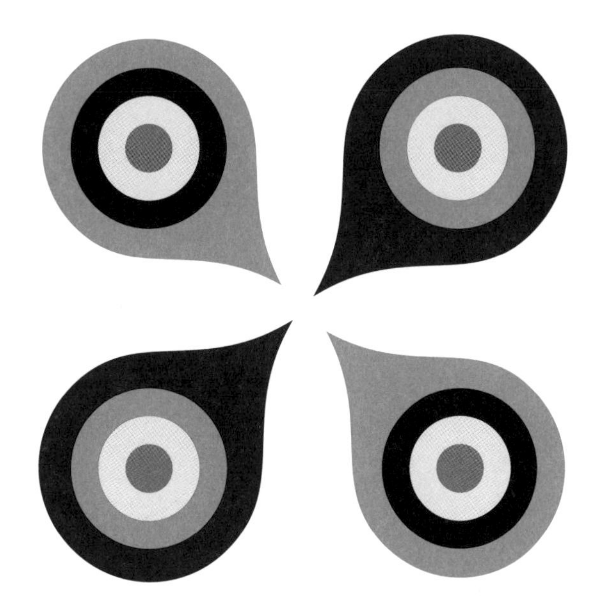

The Role of the Elementary Mathematics Specialist

Patricia F. Campbell

The following vignette, drawn from Doyle (2010), presents a cycle of interactions between an elementary mathematics specialist and a classroom teacher. The vignette can serve as a useful starting point for considering the role of the elementary mathematics specialist (the summary and interpretation are the author's and do not necessarily reflect Doyle's views).

Ms. Doyle is a mathematics specialist who works in an elementary school located in a midsize urban school district. She and Ms. Crane, one of the teachers in the school, had finally agreed to meet to discuss how Ms. Crane might teach an upcoming geometry strand, since three or four students in Ms. Crane's class did not seem to understand any mathematics lesson unless Ms. Crane subsequently pulled them aside for targeted instruction. Before the meeting, Ms. Doyle reviewed some of Ms. Crane's resources. Ms. Doyle reflected that she had been expected to do this sort of review in her coaching and leadership course and that she had continued to do it now while working in a school because "it provides a clearer picture of the prerequisite knowledge that the students need and gives me a better understanding of what true conceptual knowledge should look like" (Doyle 2010, p. 113).

At their meeting, after informing Ms. Doyle that she had only a 20-minute planning period, Ms. Crane shared her whole-class lesson plan. The lesson addressed congruence and the plan consisted of pages from the teacher's edition of a mathematics textbook emphasizing teacher modeling after a warm-up activity, with time for guided practice prior to students' independent completion of workbook pages. Looking at the plan, Ms. Doyle realized that she and Ms. Crane could do a great deal of work on this lesson to make it meet the needs of various students, but Ms. Doyle also knew that she "had to make sure that the beginning of our working relationship remained positive. I didn't want Ms. Crane to feel that I didn't see any value in her selection of a lesson plan" (Doyle 2010, p. 114). So Ms. Doyle focused her discussion with Ms. Crane on the meaning of congruence, since understanding congruence was the goal of the lesson, and on considering what prior knowledge, both strengths and weaknesses, Ms. Crane believed her students would bring to the lesson. When asked to show where the plan would confront the expected difficulties and how she could provide support, Ms. Crane noted that vocabulary would be a challenge for some students. At that point the available time for planning ran out. So, Ms. Doyle asked Ms. Crane to think more about how to support her students' learning through a non-textbook task, perhaps involving manipulative materials.

The next day, Ms. Doyle observed Ms. Crane as she followed the traditional textbook plan in her classroom. Ms. Doyle noticed that Ms. Crane had accurately identified which students would find the lesson challenging and that the other students seemed able to use the terminology "congruent," "non-congruent," and "similar." Although Ms. Doyle was glad that most of the students seemed to "gain as much understanding from the lesson as they possibly could," she wondered how she could "get teachers to understand that it is possible and valuable to teach for conceptual understanding and still have the students do well on assessments" (Doyle 2010, p. 115).

Ms. Crane told the class to complete the independent workbook pages at their seats while she and four students worked at a nearby table. Ms. Doyle assumed that Ms. Crane would simply walk the students through the completion of the practice problems. However, Ms. Crane presented the children with vocabulary picture-word cards and, after using those to review the meaning of the terms, she distributed cutout shapes and told the students that they would decide whether paired shapes were congruent, non-congruent, or similar. But then Ms. Crane led the group through the comparisons rather than permitting them to determine and share their own approaches. Further, Ms. Crane did not follow up when one child suggested a useful strategy, because she was focused on having the students follow her directives with the shapes and then complete the worksheet.

Ms. Doyle had many questions running through her mind. Did Ms. Crane know how to focus students' attention on conceptual meaning? Did Ms. Crane not recognize the teachable moment when the child suggested a useful strategy? Or did she not pursue the child's idea "because she didn't know what questions to ask" (Doyle 2010, p. 116)?

Ms. Crane sought out Ms. Doyle during lunch and was eager to talk about the lesson. They agreed to meet after school. Ms. Doyle began that post-observation conference by asking Ms. Crane how "she thought the lesson went" (Doyle 2010, p. 116). Ms. Crane replied that in her opinion the lesson was effective and the children in the small group had understood. When asked how she knew that, Ms. Crane described the responses of the four children in the small group, and she shared the workbook pages that all the children had successfully completed. Ms. Crane remarked that the vocabulary cards and cutout shapes were quite effective for the children in the small group. When asked what she thought about the strategy suggested by the one child, Ms. Crane replied that "she saw it, but that pursuing it would get the students off task" (p. 116). Besides, she explained, the students would not be able to use that strategy on the state assessments because they would not have cutout shapes. Ms. Doyle then suggested using tracing paper as another way to address congruence and similarity, and she offered to demonstrate its use in a lesson that would challenge students to come up with different strategies. After agreeing that Ms. Doyle could do that, Ms. Crane noted that she was running out of time and needed to leave.

Later Ms. Doyle reflected, "I thought we had just gotten started, but it was after school and we were on her personal time." But as Ms. Crane was leaving, Ms. Doyle asked her to think about a question: "Would the small group activity have been as effective if she'd used it with the whole class?" She also challenged Ms. Crane "to think about how the small group lesson may have been different had the students worked in pairs to discuss and categorize the shapes" (Doyle 2010, p. 116).

What the Vignette Does or Does Not Reveal about the Role of an Elementary Mathematics Specialist

The vignette about Ms. Doyle and Ms. Crane illustrates many of the daily responsibilities and challenges that elementary mathematics specialists encounter as they assume one of their roles—coaching teachers. It also suggests how an elementary mathematics specialist operates as an on-site facilitator who enables others to grow and change, rather than as a manager who directs and controls the actions of others. So who exactly is an elementary specialist, and what does the specialist do?

The elementary mathematics specialist is a leader in the school, but she assumes that role by earning the respect of the other teachers, by being approachable, by continuing to learn, and by using interpersonal skills that ultimately allow her to influence the instructional practice of her peers. Typically she has no supervisory responsibilities, but she challenges both early-career and veteran teachers to become more effective by supporting and fostering collaboration focused on mathematics teaching. She works to foster instructional change and promote teaching practices that could advance student learning, but she exercises influence somewhat informally, through suggestions and questions.

Allow time for teachers to change.

If I had been too aggressive with some of the teachers in my school, or if I had insisted on too much change at one time, I would not have been able to establish collaborative relationships, where teachers and I share ideas and look for ways to improve teaching practices.

—Advice from a mathematics specialist

The elementary mathematics specialist is comfortable with mathematics content and mathematics teaching and has the expertise to identify and interpret resources as needed, but he functions as a cautious, knowledgeable colleague. He is expected to bring about programmatic change, but he does not simply dispense advice. Rather, he listens to individual teachers and works patiently in partnerships determined by teachers' needs and willingness.

As the elementary mathematics specialist operates collaboratively in classrooms without challenging the authority of teachers, her presence defies the standard routine of isolated teachers working with students in classrooms. She typically comes from the ranks of teachers, and she remains a teacher. Yet, even when she is interacting with students in the classroom, she does so with the goal of advancing a teacher's understanding and professional growth.

Don't forget to reflect!

We need to model for the teachers whom we are coaching how important it is to take time to reflect. In the "plan-do-reflect" cycle, "reflect" holds the same weight as "plan" and "do." We all need to reflect on our work to move forward. Reflection is often an overlooked piece that needs emphasis right from the beginning of a mathematics specialist's career. As we reflect, we begin to learn more about ourselves and about the people we work with. Reflection allows us time to readjust and improve on the work that we do.

—Advice from a mathematics specialist

The vignette about Ms. Doyle illustrates one aspect of an elementary mathematics specialist's busy day—interacting with a single teacher about a single teaching episode. Although coaching individual teachers is not the only element in an elementary mathematics specialist's job description, it is an important one. When an elementary mathematics specialist and a teacher engage over an extended period in purposeful conversations about the teacher's students and teaching, their interaction can enhance the teacher's knowledge and foster a safe partnership that produces ideas and improved teaching. The changes that teachers incorporate in their practice may then positively affect student learning. But the elementary mathematics specialist is frequently expected to be more than a coach for individual teachers.

Elementary mathematics specialists typically meet regularly with small groups of teachers, often in grade-level teams, to plan for curricular pacing, highlight mathematical meaning and emphasis in an upcoming instructional unit, or solve a mathematics problem as an entry point for considering students' misconceptions or needs. Mathematics specialists are frequently engaged in conversations with teachers about how to interpret student work or results from standardized assessments. In many schools, elementary mathematics specialists are expected to work with their principals to effect schoolwide change across the mathematics program. This frequently means that a specialist will be expected to work with teachers on cross-grade mathematics education issues spanning curriculum and assessment. But one constant in all of these programmatic roles is that the elementary mathematics specialist serves as a school's ready resource for mathematics, providing on-site, collegial professional development while at the same time serving as the "community organizer" for mathematics in a school (Neufeld and Roper 2003).

Allow teachers to grow, just as teachers allow students to grow.

When we work with teachers, we are encouraging them to allow their students to grapple with mathematical ideas while working on rich tasks. We urge teachers to ask questions as they foster the growth of a mathematical environment where students are expected to offer their ideas, to explain their thinking, and to defend their responses, while providing wait time and not stepping in to tell the class the answer. But we as specialists must take this same approach when we work with teachers. We need to model this approach not only when we are working with their students in co-teaching or demonstration settings, but also when we are co-planning and debriefing with the teachers as we seek their thinking, foster their reflection, and raise questions about their ideas.

—Advice from a mathematics specialist

School-Based Professional Development

Year after year, top-down efforts to reform education and improve student achievement seem to blossom and fade. Although education policy frequently emphasizes the definition and alignment of curriculum standards and standardized assessments, compelling evidence also suggests that "teachers are crucial to students' opportunities to learn and to their learning of mathematics" (National Mathematics Advisory Panel 2008, p. 35). In other words, what and whether students learn are ultimately dependent on their daily classroom instruction. But teachers need continuing opportunities to improve their teaching practice and to increase their knowledge if they are to inspire and ignite learning in all their students over the course of their career.

Infrequent teacher workshops addressing unrelated topics do not foster professional growth. Instead, professional development occurs when teachers come together regularly, over an extended period of time, to examine their students' learning and engage in the work of planning for and discussing their own teaching. This type of collaboration allows teachers to learn from one another. This does not simply mean that teachers should come together periodically to share instructional activities that other teachers may or may not decide to add to their repertoire. Rather, effective professional development encourages teachers to examine their instructional practice, to consider the needs of their students, and to try a modified approach, returning again to repeat the cycle as they examine what did or did not work, in part by considering how and why the instructional approach supported or failed to support student learning.

This image of professional development sounds worthwhile, but how can it be carried out? Teachers are very busy people, and they cannot be regularly released from their classrooms to attend professional development sessions. Nor should they be expected to volunteer their personal time to attend sessions in their school district or at a local college.

One solution to this problem is to think of schools as places where not only students but also teachers learn (Hawley and Valli 1999). The elementary mathematics specialist enables this vision of job-embedded professional development within schools as she serves as the on-site resource for teachers. She is the approachable leader whom teachers can see as "being in this together with us."

At the same time, the elementary mathematics specialist brings both instructional expertise and a deep knowledge of mathematics and of students to his interactions with teachers. It is the specialist who works "to support change, to foster implementation, to promote reflection, to applaud efforts, and to challenge further growth" (Campbell 1996, p. 462). By doing so, the specialist assists teachers in their efforts to implement new approaches and enhance their teaching practice in the real environments of their classrooms.

A Knowledgeable Colleague Who Facilitates Job-Embedded Professional Learning

The vignette portraying the interaction between Ms. Doyle and Ms. Crane illustrates some aspects of coaching an individual teacher: The specialist met with the teacher in a pre-observation conference, observed instruction, and then conversed with the teacher in a post-observation debriefing. But this vignette reveals only the beginning of the relationship that Ms. Doyle and Ms. Crane established as their partnership evolved and matured.

Coaching individual teachers

As a specialist and a teacher work together on their shared goal of advancing student learning, their interactions during pre-observation conferences, lesson observations, and post-observation debriefings will deepen and become more focused. In addition, the elementary mathematics specialist's work with an individual teacher may also encompass the following:

- Modeling or demonstration teaching. The specialist may teach the students in a teacher's classroom while the teacher observes, or the specialist and a teacher may visit another teacher's classroom to observe skillful instruction that all three staff members can discuss at a later time.
- Co-planning. The specialist and the teacher may jointly design lessons, perhaps targeting specific instructional strategies or anticipated concerns about student learning.
- Co-teaching. The teacher and the specialist may simultaneously or sequentially implement a lesson that they have designed together.
- Reviewing student work. The specialist and the teacher may interpret the mathematical performance or understanding revealed in assessments or assignments completed by the teacher's students.
- Mentoring. The specialist and the teacher may address the teacher's mathematical understanding, consider aspects of the mathematics curriculum, discuss instructional approaches, or talk about change-related concerns.

- Learning. The specialist may freely admit to the teacher that she is not an expert with experience in or a deep understanding about teaching mathematics at all grade levels, while emphasizing a willingness to work together with the teacher to advance their shared understanding of mathematics content and curricular materials to support productive mathematics teaching and learning in the teacher's classroom.

Seize available moments.

Teachers do not have a lot of time. I have found that informal lunch discussions or a quick conversation in the hall can yield results because the teacher and I are able to talk while the information is still fresh. Teachers are so busy that they don't often take the time to reflect. Prompting teachers with reflective questions is a great way to keep them thinking about the mathematics and where they might go next.

—Advice from a mathematics specialist

When listed in this way, the performance expectations for an elementary mathematics specialist may appear intimidating, but no specialist completes all of these coaching activities every day with each individual teacher in the school. Rather, these are the varied approaches that an elementary mathematics specialist may engage in as he works with an individual teacher. Specialists and teachers decide what coaching activity to undertake and when to do so by talking with and listening to one another. The intent over time is for the specialist and the teacher to establish a trusting interaction within which the teacher feels safe enough to explain a rationale, contribute ideas, ask questions, provide information, admit frustration, offer alternatives, seek help, and discuss approaches—all with the aim of improving his instructional practice. In this way, the elementary mathematics specialist supports the professional development of the teacher with the intended effect of enhancing the mathematical understanding of the teacher's students.

A number of these coaching activities—modeling, observing, co-teaching—occur in a teacher's classroom. Teachers are more likely to come to accept their specialist as someone who understands the daily and cumulative challenges of teaching when they see that she conducts herself comfortably in their classrooms. Other coaching activities—co-planning, debriefing, reviewing student work—target the day-to-day professional demands and expectations of teaching. Teachers are more likely to accept their specialist as a knowledgeable and accessible resource when they see that the specialist can supply or locate information about mathematics content, curriculum, and instructional materials without threatening the teachers' standing. Similarly, teachers are more likely to accept their specialist as a valuable consultant when they see that she can recognize gaps in a lesson, think aloud about cause-and-effect relationships, and seek the teachers' opinions regarding possible instructional alternatives or student needs.

Coaching small groups or grade-level teams of teachers

In addition to working with individual teachers, elementary mathematics specialists often work with small groups of teachers. Frequently these are grade-level teams. All teachers who are responsible for teaching students the same grade-level curriculum in mathematics meet with the specialist to address curriculum and instruction. Particularly in large schools, this is an efficient way for the mathematics specialist to interact with teachers regarding curricular meaning, instructional materials, and assessment expectations. The advantage of the small-group format is that it allows teachers to learn from one another, as well as from their collective interactions with the specialist. The intent is for small groups of teachers to meet regularly with the specialist to address a shared agenda so that together they may establish a sense of community and gradually transform their understanding and their teaching practices in ways that yield benefits.

For this small-group approach to be beneficial, the elementary mathematics specialist and the teachers must first agree on what needs or instructional challenges to address and verify that they have some control over these within the mathematics program. Then their subsequent discussion and activities can focus directly on these needs and challenges. When working with a small group of teachers, the elementary mathematics specialist's role is to address needs and support the professional interaction of the teachers. It is the specialist who will guide the team in framing a common goal, despite differing perspectives. It is also the specialist who will help the members of the group establish norms for their meetings and determine who will facilitate positive discussion so that the group operates without stress or divisiveness. Many novice mathematics specialists find this area particularly challenging. For that reason, chapter 4, "Supporting Grade-Level Teams," and chapter 5, "Supporting Groups of Teachers across Grades," address ways of working with and supporting groups of teachers.

Teachers who come together in small groups vary in their focus, and, as a result, so do the groups' emphases. But typically the agenda reflects a shared commitment to addressing the teaching of mathematics in an effort to improve student learning. Thus, many times a small group of teachers will begin by examining curricular documents to identify learning targets for their students, as specified in mathematical objectives and standards. This permits the elementary mathematics specialist to focus the discussion on the meaning of the mathematics that the teachers are teaching, while considering mathematical connections that might lead teachers to deepen their understanding.

A grade-level team of teachers may work with the elementary mathematics specialist to consider not only the pacing and ordering of mathematics objectives over a unit or period of time, but also the mathematical emphasis. What are the critical big ideas in a particular unit or grade? What ideas do students commonly develop in relation to this mathematical content, and how can an awareness of these ideas help teachers when they plan, teach, and assess? What are typical misconceptions, incomplete understandings, or points of confusion that students often experience when considering these mathematical ideas? What are some instructional materials or approaches that a teacher might use to support students' consideration of the big ideas of mathematics addressed in this unit? How might these materials be used? What instructional strategies or key questions might focus or foster student discussion during this unit? How might a teacher informally assess student learning during instruction? By considering these questions, teachers are more likely to design and deliver instruction that supports the learning of all students.

Support collective learning.

When a mathematics specialist can bring a team of teachers together, even when perspectives differ, great things happen to mathematics thinking and learning. I love what happens when one teacher discusses a lesson and then the others join in, asking questions and sharing ideas. It's a chance for the mathematics specialist to sit back, facilitate discussion, and watch learning happen among the teachers.

—Reflections from a mathematics specialist

The elementary mathematics specialist serves as the catalyst in these small-group sessions. Frequently when working in planning teams, teachers come up with a teaching idea that all agree is worth pursuing, but no one has the time to develop a necessary component or to collect the required materials. When the specialist steps up and volunteers to do this, the potential for productive collaboration surges. But a specialist needs to do so with the understanding that a number of teachers in the group will then try the approach in their classrooms and that some of them will invite the specialist or others to observe the lesson. These final steps help establish the specialist as a partner, not a subordinate. After the teaching of the co-developed lesson has occurred, the entire group meets again for a debriefing. At this time, the teachers who taught or observed the lesson share their experiences and might share examples of student work, completed either during or as a result of the lesson. This is an opportunity for those teachers and the other teachers to ask questions and reflect on implications. This debriefing session allows the group to consider what worked or did not work in the lesson and how this information might inform future planning.

Small groups of teachers may also meet with the elementary mathematics specialist to review and interpret assessment results. Teachers receive and collect achievement data about their students every year, but often they do not know how to use these data reports. The elementary mathematics specialist can organize the data so that teachers can raise questions about their meaning as they discuss implications. This process in turn may create a demand to examine the data further. The specialist can then work with small groups of teachers, defined by grade-level teams or simply by interest, to interpret relevant data to gain a better understanding of what students have or have not learned. As the teachers and the specialist clarify what student-centered concerns the data indicate, they can prioritize problems, set goals, and make plans for addressing those concerns.

Advanced study-group options

After the elementary mathematics specialist has become established in a school, an atmosphere of trust and support can emerge. At this point, typically after a specialist has been working in a school for a year or two, some teachers may express an interest in doing more work with the specialist. These may be teachers who have always been very interested in teaching and learning mathematics. Other teachers, after working with the mathematics specialist to change their mathematics teaching, may find that now that they understand more about their students' learning, they want to know more. In either case, the specialist may address this need by leading an inquiry or lesson-study group.

These advanced study groups take many forms and define their own interest. A group may decide to develop and use common tasks and then analyze student work. When small groups of teachers do this with the specialist, they typically develop a shared interpretation of the mathematics that the tasks elicited from the students, which may or may not have been the mathematical applications that the teachers initially thought the tasks would prompt. Joint review of student work may also lead the teachers and the specialist to discuss their interpretations of the differing levels of student performance and understanding revealed in the work. The specialist and the teachers may also consider common misconceptions that students have and reflect on how their current instructional strategies may be influencing or related to student work.

Alternatively, a group of teachers may decide to form an inquiry group in which they read and discuss particular educational references or resources with the specialist. These teachers then take what they learned from their discussion and work together with the specialist to modify some aspect of their teaching. This may mean that they collaborate to change their assessment practices, modify their instructional routines, or change how they interpret curriculum standards to raise expectations for their students.

A group of teachers from different grades may decide to meet with the specialist to discuss the trajectory of mathematics learning across the grades for some mathematical topic, referring both to their curriculum and to educational references to extend their understanding of ways to support their students' learning of a big idea in mathematics. Some teachers may decide to form a lesson-study group with the elementary mathematics specialist.

Lesson study is a process through which teachers, often from differing grade levels, act together in a group to identify a mathematical skill or understanding that they want their students to develop. The mathematics specialist can bring information about the mathematics and research-based best practices to the group discussions. The teachers then define and investigate questions regarding how their students develop that knowledge and how their instruction might foster student understanding. The group then jointly develops a detailed lesson plan that targets that issue, and one teacher carries out the plan in her classroom while some of the others observe. The entire group of teachers then comes back together with the mathematics specialist to discuss observations and revise the lesson plan, repeating the cycle of observed teaching and discussion. On the basis of their experience, the group produces a report, referring back to their original questions and describing what they have learned.

Provide support for teachers' efforts to collaborate.

Mathematics specialists can work with teachers to plan a lesson and then teach a teacher's class so that the released teacher may observe another teacher teaching the co-planned lesson. This process may not have the impact of a full-scale lesson study, but I have teachers begging for this opportunity because it gives them a chance to collaborate and to discuss the mathematics and student learning.

—Advice from a mathematics specialist

Programmatic Responsibilities

Although working with teachers, either individually or in small groups, consumes large portions of an elementary mathematics specialist's day, specialists are also called on to provide programmatic leadership for mathematics in their schools. This is not a completely new phenomenon, since for many years particular teachers have served as informal leaders in their schools. Indeed, researchers (for example, Danielson [2006] and Killion and Harrison [2006]) have studied the roles that teacher leaders assume. They define a school's informal teacher leaders as those faculty members who take initiative, who act as liaisons between their faculty peers and their school administration, or who serve as instructional resources in their schools, mentoring other teachers about possible teaching practices. An elementary mathematics specialist fits each of these descriptors. But the specialist is assuming these roles as assigned responsibilities of the specialist's position.

If a group of elementary mathematics specialists compared their responsibilities for the mathematics programs in their assigned schools, they would quickly identify differences. These differences would reflect the fact that the programmatic responsibilities associated with this role are determined to some extent by the school district and to a large part by the plan of action established by a specialist and her principal.

School district expectations

Certainly, many factors affect the elementary mathematics specialist's work with teachers. These include district decisions regarding curriculum pacing and district expectations for local assessments or benchmarks for student progress. But the district also determines the limits and latitude within which a specialist will work. For example, school districts establish the duration of a specialist's workday and the length of her school-year contract. These decisions communicate expectations regarding when the specialist will be available to work with teachers and to meet with the principal. The central administration in a school district typically determines whether an elementary mathematics specialist will be assigned to work with one school or with a number of schools. School districts also set policy clarifying whether the elementary mathematics specialist has any role that could be perceived as encompassing teacher evaluation. Generally the elementary mathematics specialist is not viewed as a supervisor of teachers and therefore is not responsible for teacher evaluation. However, districts may expect specialists to provide their principals with information describing the focus of their work with identified teachers, without evaluating any teachers' progress toward change. This policy is in place in some districts so that when a principal observes teachers teaching, the principal does not "mistake fledgling attempts at change for poor teaching" (West and Staub 2003, p. 132).

Other key factors in the influence that school district policy has on the role of the elementary mathematics specialist are whether and how the district provides principals with professional development addressing the roles that a specialist is expected to assume and what approaches a principal might take to create a school climate that is supportive of the work of the specialist. When a principal understands the specialist's role and shares accountability for the implementation of that role, the principal and the elementary mathematics specialist have the basis for a collaboration that can advance a school's mathematics program. The role of the elementary mathematics specialist boils down to supporting schoolwide instructional change to facilitate increased student learning. When school district policies recognize the potential of elementary mathematics specialists and provide professional development for principals and specialists, specialists can fulfill the responsibilities of this role.

The elementary mathematics specialist serves as the liaison for mathematics between her school and the school district's curriculum or administrative offices. She attends update sessions at the district's central office. She is expected to know and clarify district-level policy regarding mathematics assessment, curricular focus and pacing, and commercial textbook adoption for both the teachers and the principal in her school.

In some school districts, the mathematics specialist is also part of a team that provides professional development for groups of teachers at the district level for the purpose of addressing particular curriculum needs. No matter what policies are set in place by a school district, the elementary mathematics specialist will be viewed as a member of the organizational structure of the district and must work within the system.

The local school's mathematics program

The principal is the accountable educational leader in a school. The principal's views about mathematics teaching and learning, priorities for improvement, goals for mathematics instruction, and preferences for communication and interaction all affect a specialist's work. Because of this, an elementary mathematics specialist's programmatic responsibilities for mathematics are negotiated and agreed on through conversations with the principal. Often, the principal and the specialist have conversations in which they discuss a vision for the school's mathematics program and the principal's thoughts about the role of an elementary mathematics specialist. This interaction allows them to set common goals, enabling them to work collaboratively to support the program. The principal will probably let the specialist know how often they should meet to discuss the specialist's work or whether and how often the principal expects to receive updates on the specialist's activities.

Be aware that the work of mathematics specialists will vary.

The mathematics specialist's role will be different across schools and school districts because no two schools have exactly the same needs. Focus on what your school's needs are, and don't worry about whether your schedule looks the same as that of another mathematics specialist.

—Advice from a mathematics specialist

The elementary mathematics specialist may be a member of a school's leadership or school-improvement team. Although the specialist naturally considers all administrative decisions in terms of their impact on the mathematics program in a school, he may need to step back at times. The elementary mathematics specialist must work with other school-level leaders as a member of the school's organizational structure, recognizing that mathematics may not always be the priority.

An elementary mathematics specialist's programmatic responsibilities take many forms. One common duty involves assisting both administrators and teachers in interpreting mathematics assessment data. Specialists often are expected to reorganize charts or tables of end-of-the-prior-year mathematics achievement data by topic, grade, and student demographics so that the data can provide information in a more accessible form. Specialists may be expected to serve on a school's leadership team, examining data and formulating plans for improvement. Specialists may be expected to lead grade-level teams or across-grade groups of teachers who are charged with designing or suggesting approaches that will target identified student needs in mathematics. To determine whether new and existing approaches are effective, the specialist should know how to use formative assessments during mathematics instruction and how to work with teachers so that formative assessments are not simply "more testing."

The principal may expect the elementary mathematics specialist to ensure that the curriculum delivered in the school is aligned with the intended curriculum distributed by the school district. To fulfill this expectation, the specialist must meet not only with grade-level teams, but also with across-grade teams to promote teachers' understanding of how the curriculum introduces and develops particular big ideas of mathematics across the grades. This work frequently expands to include work with teachers on collaborative long-term planning.

Another programmatic role that specialists frequently assume involves resource management. This includes the identification, organization, storage, and distribution of supplies for mathematics instruction, including both manipulative materials for students and instructional resources for teachers. Elementary mathematics specialists determine what instructional materials and resources are available for teachers to use to meet curricular demands in advance of their need, while also knowing what materials and resources will be needed. Further, the specialist must know how to offer a rationale for buying those supplies and how to organize all information that will ease the logistics related to purchasing so that the items can be secured. Before delivery of the materials and resources, the specialist needs to educate herself about their use and then outline possible activities linked to the curriculum. In this way, the specialist will be ready to work with teachers on techniques for using the new resources and materials when they arrive.

In a school, the elementary mathematics specialist is viewed as the go-to person for questions about mathematics and mathematics teaching from parents, teachers, and community leaders. She may work with parents and community leaders to foster continuing home-school-community partnerships focused on supporting students' learning of mathematics. For example, an elementary mathematics specialist may team with teachers to organize a math night—a setting that not only permits interaction between the parents, students, and teachers, but also introduces the mathematics specialist to the community.

Building Instructional Capacity

Recognize your impact while stepping back.

We are the ultimate diplomats. We will never have the spotlight, since our job is to make everyone else look good. So take time for yourself, and take time to interact with other mathematics specialists. Share stories with them—of both successes and challenges. They will understand and appreciate your perspective. And recognize that while the job sometimes seems thankless, nothing can beat the aha moment of a teacher starting to recognize and feel comfortable with her own instructional progress. Well, maybe that is topped by the joy she will later share about her students' mathematical successes.

—Advice from a mathematics specialist

The critical role that an elementary mathematics specialist assumes is contributing to the growth of instructional capacity—the instructional capacity of the teachers in a school and of a school's mathematics program. The position of an elementary mathematics specialist in a school will evolve over time as a direct result of the groundwork that a specialist lays by building relationships and respectfully interacting with coworkers and community members. The specialist will inevitably encounter temporary setbacks, but by staying positive, focusing on the goal of improved instruction, and working collaboratively with the instructional and administrative staff in her assigned school or schools, she and her colleagues will learn together as they take up the challenge to "emancipate, empower and transform both themselves and their students" (Ladson-Billings 1992, p. 109).

References

Campbell, Patricia F. "Empowering Children and Teachers in the Elementary Mathematics Classrooms of Urban Schools." *Urban Education* 30 (January 1996): 449–75.

Danielson, Charlotte. *Teacher Leadership That Strengthens Professional Practice*. Alexandria, Va.: Association for Supervision and Curriculum Development, 2006.

Doyle, C. B. "Coaching: One Mathematics Specialist's Story." *Journal of Mathematics and Science: Collaborative Explorations* 12 (2010): 111–17.

Hawley, Willis D., and Linda Valli. "The Essentials of Effective Professional Development: A New Consensus." In *Teaching as the Learning Profession: Handbook of Policy and Practice*, edited by Linda Darling-Hammond and Gary Sykes, pp. 127–50. San Francisco: Jossey-Bass, 1999.

Killion, Joellen, and Cindy Harrison. *Taking the Lead: New Roles for Teachers and School-Based Coaches.* Oxford, Ohio: National Staff Development Council, 2006.

Ladson-Billings, Gloria. "Culturally Relevant Teaching: The Key to Making Multicultural Education Work." In *Research and Multicultural Education: From the Margins to the Mainstream*, edited by Carl A. Grant, pp. 106–21. Bristol, Pa.: Falmer, 1992.

National Mathematics Advisory Panel. *Foundations for Success: The Final Report of the National Mathematics Advisory Panel.* Washington, D.C.: U.S. Department of Education, 2008.

Neufeld, Barbara, and Dana Roper. *Coaching: A Strategy for Developing Instructional Capacity.* Cambridge, Mass.: Education Matters, 2003. http://annenberginstitute.org/pdf/Coaching.pdf.

West, Lucy, and Fritz C. Staub. *Content-Focused Coaching: Transforming Mathematics Lessons.* Portsmouth, N.H.: Heinemann, 2003.

Research Findings

Patricia F. Campbell and Aimee J. Ellington

The position of mathematics specialist is a relatively new addition to schools, created in many school districts in response to pressure to raise students' mathematics achievement. In part, administrators are turning to specialists because educational research has shown that teachers' attendance at occasional, unrelated teacher workshops does not promote instructional change (Darling-Hammond and Richardson 2009; Knapp 2003). Effective professional development needs to be ongoing, providing a sustained opportunity for teachers to come together to collaborate and learn from one another (Yoon et al. 2007). Because the position of elementary mathematics specialist is new, only now is research being conducted to study the nature of the position and determine the impact of a specialist on teachers and students. Studies are also documenting the day-to-day work of specialists and the effect that they are having on student achievement. So, what does research say about the knowledge and skills that a mathematics specialist needs to be most effective in her job? What does this initial research tell us about how a mathematics specialist can encourage change in teachers' instructional practices? This chapter addresses these and other questions about elementary mathematics specialists and schooling.

Transition from Expert Teacher to Novice Mathematics Specialist

As described in chapter 1, a mathematics specialist must wear many hats in his school—instructional coach, resource coordinator for mathematics materials, and mathematics liaison to the school district, to name a few. Indeed, it is not unusual for a new mathematics specialist to feel as if the various aspects of this position are emerging and shifting as the school year unfolds, and that he is not always operating with a road map indicating where things are heading.

Keep in mind that making a change in career paths is both an exciting and difficult endeavor. The person making this particular career switch is quite often an experienced, effective classroom teacher (Chval et al. 2010), but even so she will need to draw on and develop new skills and understanding to be an effective coach of other teachers. Researchers who have studied the transition from teacher to coach maintain that a mathematics specialist must be more than just an effective classroom teacher who is interested in a career change (Poglinco and Bach 2004; West et al. 2007). Master teachers ready to move into the role of elementary mathematics specialist should keep in mind that extensive classroom experience is a necessary but not a sufficient prerequisite for the job.

Kathryn Chval and her colleagues (2010) have documented the unique set of challenges associated with the transition from classroom teacher to school-based mathematics specialist. One uncomfortable shift is from the familiar role of accomplished teacher, with particular, earned status in the school, to the unaccustomed position of novice, in a different and unfamiliar role. This can leave even the most confident teacher feeling uneasy because not only do the other teachers in the school view her as a novice, but she also sees herself in this way. Interpreting data gathered from fourteen first-year mathematics specialists, Chval and colleagues (2010) described four aspects of the "mathematics coach identity" (p. 210), each of which a specialist must navigate when beginning this new position. Each incorporates specific details of the specialist's relationship with members of the school community—teachers, students, administrators, and even the new specialist herself. More specifically, this study revealed that a new specialist's expectations are often different from the reality that she frequently encounters when establishing herself in a school. Each aspect of this new identity is described briefly below:

- Unanticipated obstacles. Anticipating his work with teachers, a new specialist frequently has the expectation that he will spend a considerable amount of time coaching teachers but quickly encounters obstacles to this goal. Some of the hindrances stem from requirements of the position, but others have to do with the teachers themselves. A specialist must deal with resistant teachers who are hesitant to work with him or who may go so far as to reject his offers of help. Other teachers may take advantage of having an extra person in the classroom and want the specialist only to help carry out a planned lesson as directed or to step in and teach a lesson while the teacher attends to other noninstructional demands, instead of engaging in coaching as a true learning experience.
- Unclear relationships with students. Having recently been a teacher but now not having a classroom of her own, a new specialist often struggles to make sense of or establish her relationship with students. Although her work with teachers as the school's mathematics coach also involves opportunities to work with students, she is not the final authority in another teacher's classroom.
- Ambiguous status as instructional staff member and administrative mathematics leader. A new specialist believes, and rightly so, that his primary role is to develop and implement the school's mathematics program in collaboration with other members of the administration. However, often other administrative duties are placed on him. As a result, he must find the appropriate balance for a team player who is both a member of the instructional staff and a mathematics leader in the building.
- Persistent need to be a learner. During the first year or so, a mathematics specialist will find that this position constantly requires her to assume the role of learner. If a teacher asks a question about mathematics content or about an instructional approach, the specialist may need time to look things up, study, or figure out an appropriate answer. She may spend time researching different curricular materials that she will then share with her teachers as they work together to determine what might be the most appropriate approach for addressing students' needs. In addition, the specialist must engage in her own professional development. This means that a specialist must build time into her schedule to expand her own knowledge and skills.

Each of these components of the position of elementary mathematics specialist requires a specialist to see himself with a new identity—as a coach, as a roaming teacher, as a program coordinator, and as a learner facing a multitude of demands. This means that the new specialist must negotiate and communicate as he learns how to balance his own expectations with the expectations of others. It is these negotiations that help the specialist form and adapt to this role in his school (Chval et al. 2010).

The Importance of Interpersonal Skills

Success in almost any job depends at least in part on social and interpersonal skills. These skills in turn depend on insight and perception about the environment, coupled with an ability to interact with others to convey information in ways that influence behavior to improve performance. The successful elementary mathematics specialist is attuned to the school environment and a talented communicator with highly developed interpersonal skills.

Social forces in a school building

A school is a dynamic social organization with diverse members and many complexities. The mathematics specialist is placed in a school to foster change in teachers' mathematics instruction with the overall goal of increasing students' mathematical knowledge and skills. The specialist is essentially in place to encourage instructional changes or educational reforms that will encompass all the mathematics teachers in the school. An early study of an effort to implement schoolwide change in mathematics instruction noted, "Instructional change is not easy; it is demanding, threatening, and risky. This risk is not taken by the principal or the teacher educator [the mathematics specialist]; it is taken by each individual teacher" (Campbell 1996, p. 449).

Research examining the implementation of educational reforms reveals that social pressure and other organizational factors influence the change process. All members of an organization do not embrace change at the same time. Each person makes a decision based on his own perspective on the effort that is under way as well as his personal reaction to the social forces within the organization (Frank, Zhao, and Borman 2004). In other words, a teacher's thoughts and ideas affect his willingness to try new things. But he can be influenced by others whom he views as knowledgeable about a particular reform effort. And social pressure can also help people move toward reform and change.

What does this mean for the mathematics specialist? She should attempt to use the social forces within the school to help teachers embrace the benefits of change. For example, initially the specialist should identify and work with teachers who are less resistant to trying different instructional techniques—who may actually be those teachers who have a reputation for having stronger mathematical and pedagogical skills—relying on them in turn to convey positive messages about the experience when they talk to more resistant teachers, thus encouraging them to participate in a coaching experience.

Communication and trust

To have a positive impact, a mathematics specialist must establish relationships built on mutual respect and trust with members of the school community—particularly the teachers whom he is encouraging to make changes in instructional practice (Feger, Woleck, and Hickman 2004; Obara 2010). A specialist's credibility is based on this trust, along with the pedagogical skills and mathematical knowledge that he has to share with his colleagues (Neufeld and Roper 2003). For coaching sessions to be beneficial, a collaborative, collegial relationship must exist between the specialist and the teacher (Obara 2010). The classroom teacher brings a wealth of knowledge about her students' mathematical understanding, skills, strengths, and abilities. She is also the authority figure for that group of students. A coach must provide open, honest feedback while being respectful of the teacher and sensitive to her concerns. He must also bolster a teacher's confidence, encouraging the teacher to try different methods of instruction while at the same time supporting and accepting a teacher's vulnerabilities (Neuberger 2011). School-based efforts that yield instructional change that supports student achievement in mathematics are not designed to have teachers unquestioningly adopt an instructional routine as promoted by an authority figure (Campbell and White, 1997; Campbell et al. 2003; Martin et al. 2011). Rather, the goal of these successful efforts is for teachers to "participate in ongoing, interactive, cumulative learning with their peers" (Campbell 1996, p. 453) with guidance from an on-site leader who can encourage reflection, support professional interaction, appreciate effort, serve as a mentor, and address concerns.

A mathematics specialist needs strong communication skills. She must be able to encourage a teacher to open up about his mathematical and pedagogical weaknesses (Neuberger 2011) and engage him in meaningful discussions to design a plan for improvement. In addition to communicating with teachers, specialists will also be viewed as representatives of the school's mathematics program by the school administration and other district personnel. The ability to communicate effectively is important in this aspect of the job as well. Specialists are called on to explain the successes, challenges, and concerns associated with the mathematics program in the interest of strengthening the learning environment for all members of the school (Feger, Woleck, and Hickman 2004).

Requisite Knowledge-Based Skills and Abilities

The position of mathematics specialist is quite unique. It requires a base of knowledge and skills that cover a wide variety of areas, including mathematical content knowledge, pedagogical content knowledge, coaching strategies, and assessment techniques. Even when a specialist thinks that he has all aspects of the job covered, he will encounter situations in which he must investigate and evaluate new advances in mathematics education so that he can back up recommendations or decisions that he is asked to make—itself yet another skill.

Mathematical content knowledge

Although it seems obvious that an elementary mathematics specialist must have a solid knowledge of the mathematics content addressed in the elementary grades (Feger, Woleck, and Hickman 2004; Obara 2010), this statement has more to it than you might suspect. Ball, Thames, and Phelps (2008) describe two different domains of mathematical content knowledge: (1) common content knowledge, which is the mathematical content and skills required for various aspects of work and everyday life, as opposed to classroom mathematics, and (2) specialized content knowledge, which is the mathematical content and skills that are peculiar to the teaching profession. Teachers are using their specialized content knowledge when they consider all the relevant mathematical concepts underlying a particular mathematics procedure or when they interpret the mathematical ideas that were either accurately or inaccurately applied within a student's work. The mathematics specialist must have a deep conceptual understanding of elementary mathematics and be familiar with the specialized content knowledge associated with all the mathematics taught in the grade levels with which she works (Association of Mathematics Teacher Educators et al. 2010).

The mathematics specialist's conceptual understanding must be broad as well as deep. A mathematical learning trajectory describes the mathematical milestones students must achieve and the skills that they must develop to understand various mathematical concepts fully (Daro, Mosher, and Corcoran 2011). A trajectory is the natural pathway through which learning is achieved. Depending on the concept, the learning trajectory may span several years of a child's educational timeline—through the elementary grades and beyond. Mathematics specialists must have a global view of these pathways and a detailed understanding of the time that children will take to reach different milestones. This flexibility with mathematics content is important to help teachers develop rich lessons that are accessible to their students (West et al. 2007).

Pedagogical content knowledge

Pedagogical content knowledge (PCK) is the knowledge that informs a teacher's decision to use specific instructional strategies to guide children in skill development and conceptual understanding. Ball, Thames, and Phelps (2008) describe two domains of PCK. Knowledge of content and students combines mathematical knowledge of a topic with an understanding of how students learn that particular topic. Knowledge of content and teaching is necessary to connect specific mathematics content with the design of instructional tasks that will help students develop their conceptual understanding of that mathematical content or build their mathematical skills. Specialists must draw from a "large repertoire" of PCK when working with teachers and their students (West et al. 2007, p. 31). They must be familiar with questioning strategies and with a collection of effective mathematical tasks and activities that help children develop mastery of various concepts (Feger, Woleck, and Hickman 2004). Additionally, specialists must be skilled in using a variety of instructional strategies, including cooperative grouping techniques and ways to incorporate technology and manipulatives in instruction. Most important, they must know when particular strategies are useful for enhancing student learning (Obara 2010) and be able to lead teachers in reflective discussions about the use of a particular strategy or approach (Anstey and Clarke 2010) as well as about student thinking or misconceptions.

Coaching strategies and skills

When a specialist coaches a teacher in her classroom, that teacher is more likely to make changes in her own instructional practice (Poglinco and Bach 2004) than is a teacher whose opportunities for professional development most often take place outside of the classroom, at the end of the school day, or in place of regular teaching-related duties. However, coaching teachers is difficult work. It requires questioning skills (Feger, Woleck, and Hickman 2004) and demonstration techniques (Poglinco and Bach 2004), along with interpersonal skills (Neufeld and Roper 2003) to maintain a comfortable, collaborative relationship with the teacher. Further, the effective specialist must make adjustments to her techniques as her familiarity with the teacher's level of mathematical understanding evolves (Neufeld and Roper 2003).

The ability to ask the right questions is central to conducting an effective coaching session. Feger, Woleck, and Hickman (2004) describe the various aspects of good questioning techniques for specialists:

- Questions should be based on student learning.
- Questions should encourage teachers to reflect on their practice.
- Questioners should not always expect an immediate answer but should be comfortable with the silence that often accompanies a thought-provoking question.
- Questions should be phrased so that they require more than one-word answers.
- Questioners should be able to gauge when to ask a question and when to wait for a more appropriate time or place.

At the same time, specialists must keep in mind that one goal of their work is to maintain a collaborative relationship with the teacher. So questioning will be ineffective and possibly damaging to the relationship if the teacher feels defensive (Feger, Woleck, and Hickman 2004).

A specialist engages in various coaching strategies, depending on the needs of teachers at different levels of mathematical understanding and instructional experience. Research studies (Feger, Woleck, and Hickman 2004; Neufeld and Roper 2003; Poglinco and Bach 2004) have outlined the techniques that a specialist will find useful when doing this kind of work. They include modeling or demonstrating a mathematics lesson for a teacher, planning lessons with a teacher, co-teaching a lesson with a teacher, and observing a teacher or a student in the classroom and providing feedback about the observation. Regardless of the strategy used, the specialist must remember that the goal of the activity is for the teacher to gain a better understanding of how students learn and to make meaningful changes in her instructional practice.

The specific strategy that a specialist decides to use will depend on the teacher's level of experience, the content covered, and many other factors. Nevertheless, research supplies some clues about what is necessary if the intent is to provide an effective coaching experience. First, the coaching session must have a specific purpose and address agreed-on goals for student learning (Feger, Woleck, and Hickman 2004). Before engaging in either demonstration teaching (modeling) or co-teaching, the specialist and the teacher must pre-plan and set up a time to carry out debriefing in addition to scheduling the actual lesson (Neufeld and Roper 2003). During either modeling or co-teaching, the teacher must have an active role in the instructional process (Feger, Woleck, and Hickman 2004). If the teacher is not participating in the instruction, then she should have an "assignment" to keep her engaged during the lesson. Taking notes, recording students' mathematical responses, or writing inferences interpreting students' mathematical understandings can be an enlightening experience for a teacher. The teacher's notes can then be the foundation for a meaningful discussion about the lesson during the debriefing. For either the new specialist or teachers new to the building, modeling lessons allows the specialist to establish his credibility as someone who can develop and present effective mathematical tasks (Anstey and Clarke 2010) and is willing to establish a collaborative working relationship (Feger, Woleck, and Hickman 2004).

Research (Feger, Wolek, and Hickman 2004; Neufeld and Roper 2003) strongly emphasizes the need for a follow-up discussion between the teacher and the coach after a modeling or co-teaching activity. Typically termed a "debriefing session," time devoted to this follow-up discussion is a great opportunity for collaborative learning. To be most effective, this session must happen shortly after the coaching session (Neufeld and Roper 2003), when time has not diminished or altered memories of what took place. The discussion should be directly connected to the lesson and should focus on the students' understanding (Neuberger 2010). It is an opportunity for the teacher to ask questions about areas of mathematical confusion (either for the students or the teacher) and for the coach to help the teacher reflect on the lesson and offer guidance for the next lesson.

Regardless of the coaching strategy that is used or the questioning that takes place during a conversation with a teacher, the specialist should look for opportunities to provide reinforcement. Coaching activities and related discussions must continue throughout the school year, giving a teacher multiple opportunities to practice what she has learned through these educational experiences (Poglinco and Bach 2004). Reinforcement allows the teacher to strengthen her understanding of the connections between rich mathematical tasks and student learning.

Knowledge of mathematics curricula

The mathematics curriculum is the foundation of a school's mathematics program. A specialist will need to conduct an in-depth study of the curriculum adopted by her school district, taking into account which content is covered at different grade levels and how the content is addressed and assessed. She must be familiar with the basic principles and underlying themes of the curriculum (Feger, Woleck, and Hickman 2004) so that she will be able to help teachers make the most effective use of the instructional materials and textbooks provided by the school or district. As Obara

(2010) explains, a specialist's knowledge of the curriculum is paramount since she is "expected to help teachers connect concepts within grade levels and between grade levels—important in planning and sequencing topics" (p. 244). At the district level, specialists are typically involved in the curriculum and textbook adoption process. They are often asked to provide feedback on available curricular materials. As a result, they must be familiar with the fundamental constructs on which different curricula are based (Obara 2010) and be aware of new commercial educational materials that become available. They also need to understand how the curricular objectives might be paced, ordered, and integrated. This is particularly important because the mathematics specialist and her teachers will need to collaborate and plan how to address all mathematics standards and objectives in a meaningful, timely, and coherent fashion, as influenced by the scheduling of standardized assessments.

Special populations of students

Mathematics specialists should be comfortable in addressing the needs of all students in the school building, including students with disabilities, English language learners, and accelerated or gifted students. Although students in these populations have some different educational needs (Obara 2010), they share many needs with their traditional counterparts. To work effectively with the teachers who provide instruction to these students in both mainstream and individualized classroom settings, specialists must be aware of ways to address the challenges and opportunities presented by these students (Neufeld and Roper 2003). Specialists will be asked for suggestions about appropriate instructional techniques for working with students who are below grade level. They will be also asked about strategies to keep accelerated students engaged in mathematics lessons (Obara 2010). The mathematics specialist will have opportunities to work as a coach with special education teachers (Obara 2010), either individually or in collaboration with classroom teachers. These teachers have many of the same mathematical and pedagogical weaknesses as regular classroom teachers and will benefit from participating in coaching-related experiences.

Assessment

The mathematics specialist is heavily involved in the school's assessment program. Specialists are often called on to conduct analyses of student achievement data from high-stakes tests and, in collaboration with the principal and other building leaders, they must use the results to suggest and lead efforts to make changes to the school's mathematics program (Neufeld and Roper 2003). However, this is not the only way in which specialists are involved in assessment. In fact, to be effective, specialists must be knowledgeable about both formative and summative assessments and the appropriate role of each in the learning process. Specialists must help teachers recognize the importance of using formative assessments to gather knowledge about student understanding and to use that information to modify their instructional strategies (Anstey and Clarke 2010; Neufeld and Roper 2003). Specialists should ensure that teachers consider mathematical learning trajectories (Association of Mathematics Teacher Educators et al. 2010) when they develop assessment instruments. Because assessment is such an important component of the educational process, specialists must keep up to date on the latest research addressing how to assess student learning most effectively and share that information with their teachers.

Research and resources

Because all the information that a specialist may be asked about covers such a wide range of topics, it just is not possible for him to be familiar with everything. So, an important aspect of the job is knowing where to look for interpretations or findings of mathematics education research and pedagogy, as well as knowing how to find additional teaching resources that will enable the specialist to do his work. In the area of coaching, the more the specialist knows about research on pedagogy and about new instructional materials, the easier it will be for him to answer teachers' questions and to develop rich mathematical tasks that will help teachers implement sound instructional strategies. When specialists are familiar with critical mathematics education research, both current and past, and can share it with classroom teachers, they establish their own credibility (Obara 2010). Specialists must have firsthand knowledge of professional development materials that are effective in developing their teachers' mathematical pedagogical and content knowledge (Feger, Woleck, and Hickman 2004). This knowledge is essential preparation for various aspects of their job, including conducting coaching sessions, participating in grade-level and vertical-team meetings, and designing professional development opportunities for teachers. Time devoted to reading research interpretations and findings can also be an opportunity for professional development for the mathematics specialist.

The Impact of Elementary Mathematics Specialists

When educational policymakers and school district administrators consider whether to place elementary mathematics specialists in their schools, they have one question: Will placing a mathematics specialist positively affect student achievement across a school? Recently, a collaborative research project involving four universities and five school districts in Virginia set out to answer that question (Campbell and Malkus 2011). It identified twelve sets of three schools, with each triple of schools having comparable student populations and similar past performance on state mathematics assessments. None of these schools had an elementary mathematics specialist at the start of the project. Two schools in each triple were randomly selected as the sites for new elementary mathematics specialists, who had just completed five mathematics courses and two leadership-coaching courses that were developed by the project. The remaining schools without specialists were the control sites. The courses were designed to deepen the soon-to-be specialists' understanding of mathematical concepts and skills, enhance their specialized content knowledge for teaching mathematics, and expand their pedagogical content knowledge for mathematics. The two leadership-coaching courses were designed to introduce the participants to current research on teaching and learning mathematics, develop their leadership and discussion skills, and support their emerging coaching skills.

Impact on student achievement

Using results from Virginia's state mathematics achievement test for grades 3, 4, and 5, researchers conducted a statistical analysis that compared three years of student scores from schools with a specialist with three years of student scores from control schools (Campbell and Malkus 2011). The analysis indicated a statistically significant difference in the achievement scores between the schools, with the students in the schools with mathematics specialists having significantly higher scores. Further analysis revealed that during a specialist's first year in a school, the difference in achievement was not statistically significant at any grade level. However, the pattern was an increase in scores favoring the schools with the specialists in the first year, followed by an even greater increase in scores in those schools in the second year, followed by a still greater increase in their scores in the third year. The size of the increases in scores in the second and third year of a specialist being in the school resulted in the statistically significant effect.

Although the schools with the specialists had significantly higher scores at all three grades, the impact was stronger in grades 4 and 5. This might mean that specialists can have more access to or influence on elementary teachers who are working with more abstract mathematics, or it might mean only that third-grade students find it difficult to convey what they understand on a paper-and-pencil, standardized assessment.

Impact on teachers' perspectives on mathematics teaching and learning

Elementary mathematics specialists are placed in schools to influence both teachers' knowledge and how they teach. But research indicates that teachers' ideas about teaching and learning mathematics interact with their instructional practice (Ross et al. 2003). In addition, the beliefs that teachers hold about teaching and learning may limit what they notice when they observe lessons being taught by others (Grant, Hiebert, and Wearne 1998). When teachers and mathematics specialists discuss and reflect on what happened during instruction, the process might influence teachers' beliefs. So, in the Virginia study, researchers also looked to see whether specialists had an effect on teachers' beliefs about mathematics teaching and learning (Campbell and Malkus 2010).

These researchers gave teachers a survey based on the work of John Ross and his colleagues (2003), asking teachers to indicate whether they agreed or disagreed with statements about mathematics curriculum and instruction and about students' mathematical needs and understandings. Some statements emphasized what has been termed "traditional teaching": the idea that the best way to teach students to solve mathematics problems is to model how to solve one kind of problem at a time. Other statements emphasized supporting student efforts to make sense of the mathematics: the notion that "I don't necessarily answer students' math questions but rather let them puzzle things out for themselves." Over time, the beliefs of the teachers in the control schools did not differ from the beliefs of the teachers in the schools with a mathematics specialist, unless the teachers frequently worked with the specialist. If a teacher was highly engaged with her specialist, then her beliefs changed significantly, becoming more in agreement with the "making sense" perspective and more at odds with the "traditional" perspective.

What Lessons Can Be Learned from Research on Mathematics Specialists?

Effective elementary mathematics specialists provide on-site professional development that offers teachers mathematics content combined with instructional strategies, while also considering students' understandings and explanations. But as specialists support schoolwide improvement in mathematics, they do more than just mentor teachers. They prepare instructional resources, interpret assessment data, organize curricular materials, work with administrators, and serve as a voice to parents. Given all these demands, what recommendations can research offer to specialists who are just getting started?

Take the time to build professional relationships

Findings from the Virginia study of elementary mathematics specialists (Campbell and Malkus 2011; Campbell and Malkus 2010) and a study of Reading First coaches (Bean et al. 2010) were similar. Although some coaches or specialists spent substantial time attending to non-coaching or non-mentoring demands, these patterns of activity seemed to reflect the culture or expectations in a particular school. That finding can be joined with the fact that the positive impact of the elementary mathematics specialists on student achievement in Virginia did not happen as soon as the specialists were placed in their schools. Instead, it emerged over time, as a knowledgeable mathematics specialist and the teachers and the principal in a school learned how to work together and then did the work together. If an elementary mathematics specialist is to foster instructional improvement and professional growth in teachers, she must have the time and inclination to build and maintain collaboration across her school. Furthermore, this collaboration needs to link with and foster the school's sense of community and professional identity (Frank, Zhao, and Borman 2004).

Work *with* your principal and your teachers

An elementary mathematics specialist typically reports to a school principal. Recent research suggests that a specialist will be most effective when his role and needs are understood and supported by both his local school principal and the district administrators who supervise principals (Neufeld and Roper 2003). A specialist and his principal must work together as instructional leaders in their school. But that collaboration must also include teachers. If teachers see that a specialist spends most of his time focused on administrative or organizational tasks, they will not consider him as someone who is willing or available to help them address instructional needs or concerns (Bean et al. 2010). Because coaching ultimately relies on building relationships, the effectiveness and value of the specialist will depend "on the quality of the relationship that a coach is able to establish with each individual teacher" (Biancarosa, Bryk, and Dexter 2010, p. 29).

Seek out professional development

Four seemingly contradictory research reports offer more insight into what might influence the potential effectiveness of a mathematics specialist or coach. A recent study of Reading First coaches in Florida middle schools found that coaches had an inconsistent impact on student achievement, since scores on the state reading tests increased in only two of the four schools in the study (Lockwood, McCombs, and Marsh 2010), and another study of literacy coaches found no effect on student achievement (Garet et al. 2008). However, a different study—a four-year study of seventeen Literacy Collaborative coaches—found a statistically significant positive impact (Biancarosa, Bryk, and Dexter 2010), similar to the impact measured in the Virginia study of elementary mathematics specialists (Campbell and Malkus 2011). A key reason for these differing results may lie in the differing qualifications and preparation of the specialists or coaches in these studies. The two studies that did not find a significant relationship between coaching and student achievement provided coaches with only three days of professional development addressing coaching prior to placement, with one of the studies providing another four days of in-service sessions over the school year. The two studies that found that specialists or coaches had a positive impact on student achievement required the coaches or specialists to enroll in graduate-level professional development targeting both coaching and the integrated study of content and pedagogy for at least one year prior to placement. The findings from these studies suggest that the content knowledge and pedagogical knowledge of specialists, as well as their understanding of the skills and demands inherent in supportive leadership and coaching, are critical to improved student achievement.

If your school district or local college offers professional development for mathematics education leaders or for coaches, take advantage of it (Virginia Mathematics and Science Coalition, 2007). Professional organizations such as the National Council of Teachers of Mathematics and the National Council of Supervisors of Mathematics offer coaching or leadership institutes. Finally, search for online courses, webinars, and references. You need not invent this position on your own. There are resources available.

References

Anstey, Leonie, and Barbara Clarke. "Leading and Supporting Mathematics Teacher Change: The Case of Teaching and Learning Coaches." *Mathematics Teacher Education and Development* 12 (2010): 5–31.

Association of Mathematics Teacher Educators (AMTE). *Standards for Elementary Mathematics Specialists: A Reference for Teacher Credentialing and Degree Programs.* San Diego: AMTE, 2010. http://www.amte.net/sites/all/themes/amte/resources/EMSStandards_Final_Mar2010.pdf.

Association of Mathematics Teacher Educators (AMTE), Association of State Supervisors of Mathematics (ASSM), National Council of Supervisors of Mathematics (NCSM), and National Council of Teachers of Mathematics (NCTM). *The Role of Elementary Mathematics Specialists in the Teaching and Learning of Mathematics.* Joint Position Statement. Reston, Va.: AMTE, ASSM, NCSM, and NCTM, 2010. http://www.nctm.org/about/content.aspx?id=26069.

Ball, Deborah Loewenberg, Mark H. Thames, and Geoffrey Phelps. "Content Knowledge for Teaching: What Makes It Special?" *Journal of Teacher Education* 59 (November/December 2008): 389–407.

Bean, Rita M., Jason A. Draper, Virginia Hall, Jill Vandermolen, and Naomi Zigmond. "Coaches and Coaching in Reading First Schools: A Reality Check." *Elementary School Journal* 111 (September 2010): 87–114.

Biancarosa, Gina, Anthony S. Bryk, and Emily R. Dexter. "Assessing the Value-Added Effects of Literacy Collaborative Professional Development on Student Learning." *Elementary School Journal* 111 (September 2010): 7–34.

Campbell, Patricia F. "Empowering Children and Teachers in the Elementary Mathematics Classrooms of Urban Schools." *Urban Education* 30 (January 1996): 449–75.

Campbell, Patricia, Andrea Bowden, Steve Kramer, and Mary Yakimowski. *Mathematics and Reasoning Skills: Final Report* (Revised). Grant No. ESI 9554186. College Park: University of Maryland, MARS Project, 2003.

Campbell, Patricia F., and Nathaniel N. Malkus. "The Impact of Elementary Mathematics Coaches on Student Achievement." *Elementary School Journal* 111 (March 2011): 430–54.

———. "The Impact of Elementary Mathematics Specialists." *Journal of Mathematics and Science: Collaborative Explorations* 12 (2010): 1–28.

Campbell, Patricia F., and Dorothy Y. White. "Project IMPACT: Influencing and Supporting Teacher Change in Predominantly Minority Schools." In *Mathematics Teachers in Transition*, edited by Elizabeth Fennema and Barbara Scott Nelson, pp. 309–55. Mahwah, N.J.: Lawrence Erlbaum, 1997.

Chval, Kathryn B., Fran Arbaugh, John K. Lannin, Delinda van Garderen, Liza Cummings, Anne T. Estapa, and Maryann E. Huey. "The Transition from Experienced Teacher to Mathematics Coach: Establishing a New Identity." *Elementary School Journal* 111 (September 2010): 191–216.

Darling-Hammond, Linda, and Nikole Richardson. "Teacher Learning: What Matters?" *Educational Leadership* 66 (February 2009): 46–53.

Daro, Phil, Frederick A. Mosher, and Tom Corcoran. *Learning Trajectories in Mathematics: A Foundation for Standards, Curriculum, Assessment, and Instruction.* Philadelphia: Consortium for Policy Research in Education, 2011.

Feger, Stephanie, Kristine Woleck, and Paul Hickman. "How to Develop a Coaching Eye." *Journal of Staff Development* 25 (Spring 2004): 14–18.

Frank, Kenneth A., Yong Zhao, and Kathryn Borman. "Social Capital and the Diffusion of Innovations within Organizations: The Case of Computer Technology in Schools." *Sociology of Education* 77 (April 2004): 148–71.

Garet, Michael S., Stephanie Cronen, Marian Eaton, Anja Kurki, Meredith Ludwig, Wehmah Jones, Kazuaki Uekawa, et al. *The Impact of Two Professional Development Interventions on Early Reading Instruction and Achievement.* NCEE 2008-4030. Washington, D.C.: National Center for Education Evaluation and Regional Assistance, Institute of Education Sciences, U.S. Department of Education, 2008.

Grant, Theresa J., James Hiebert, and Diana Wearne. "Observing and Teaching Reform-Minded Lessons: What Do Teachers See?" *Journal of Mathematics Teacher Education* 1 (1998): 217–36.

Knapp, Michael S. "Professional Development as a Policy Pathway." *Review of Research in Education* 27 (January 2003): 109–57.

Lockwood, J. R., Jennifer S. McCombs, and Julie Marsh. "Linking Reading Coaches and Student Achievement: Evidence from Florida Middle Schools." *Educational Evaluation and Policy Analysis* 32 (September 2010): 372–88.

Martin, W. Gary, Marilyn E. Strutchens, Stephen Stuckwisch, and Mohammed Qazi. "Transforming East Alabama Mathematics (TEAM-Math): Promoting Systemic Change in Schools and Universities." In *Disrupting Tradition: Research and Practice Pathways in Mathematics Education*, edited by William F. Tate, Karen D. King, and Celia Rousseau Anderson, pp. 105–18. Reston, Va.: National Council of Teachers of Mathematics, 2011.

Neuberger, Jim. "Benefits of a Teacher and Coach Collaboration: A Case Study." *Journal of Mathematical Behavior* 31 (January 2012): 290–311.

Neufeld, Barbara, and Dana Roper. *Coaching: A Strategy for Developing Instructional Capacity.* Cambridge, Mass.: Education Matters, 2003. http://www.annenberginstitute.org/Products/Coaching.php.

Obara, Samuel. "Mathematics Coaching: A New Kind of Professional Development." *Teacher Development* 14 (May 2010): 241–51.

Poglinco, Susan M., and Amy J. Bach. "The Heart of the Matter: Coaching as a Vehicle for Professional Development." *Phi Delta Kappan* 85 (January 2004): 398–400.

Ross, John A., Douglas McDougall, Ann Hogaboam-Gray, and Ann LeSage. "A Survey Measuring Elementary Teachers' Implementation of Standards-Based Mathematics Teaching." *Journal for Research in Mathematics Education* 34 (July 2003): 344–63.

Virginia Mathematics and Science Coalition (2007). *Virginia Mathematics and Science Coalition: Statewide Masters Programs.* http://www.math.vcu.edu/Statewide_Webpages/index.html.

West, Lucy, Ginger Hanlon, Phyllis Tam, and Milo Novelo. "Building Coaching Capacity through Lesson Study." *NCSM Journal of Mathematics Education Leadership* 9 (Winter 2007): 26–33.

Yoon, Kwang Suk, Teresa Duncan, Silvia Wen-Yu Lee, Beth Scarloss, and Kathy L. Shapley. *Reviewing the Evidence on How Teacher Professional Development Affects Student Achievement.* REL 2007–No. 033. Washington, D.C.: National Center for Education Evaluation and Regional Assistance, Institute of Education Sciences, U.S. Department of Education, 2007.

2

Supporting Teachers

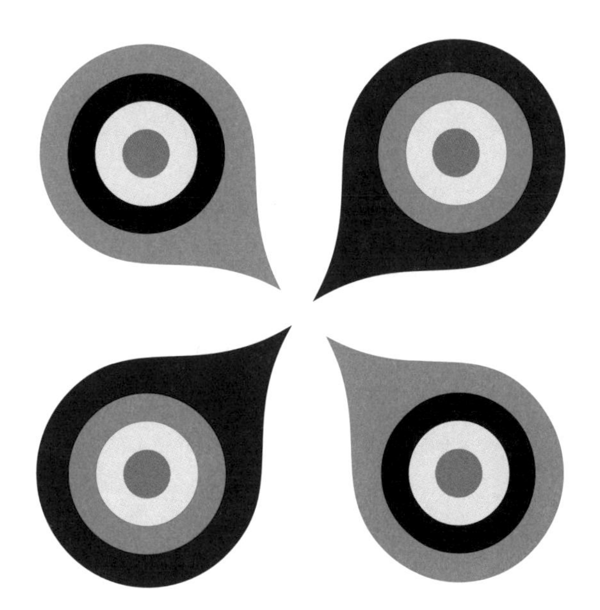

Coaching Individual Teachers

DeAnna Moreau and Joy W. Whitenack

One of the more important ways in which the elementary mathematics specialist serves teachers is as a coach, working with individual teachers in their own classrooms (Hall and Simeral 2008). As a coach, the mathematics specialist helps teachers to—

- develop a deeper understanding of the mathematical ideas framing the curriculum that they teach;
- teach content more effectively to support students' learning;
- become skilled in interpreting and assessing students thinking; and
- develop lesson plans that support students' learning. (West and Staub 2003)

Several important questions surround the elementary mathematics specialist's work as a coach:

- What does her coaching role entail?
- How does he begin his work with individual teachers?
- How does she gain the teacher's trust?
- How does he shift teachers' instructional decision-making process from focusing primarily on their own teaching to using students' work and needs as a basis for decisions?

This chapter addresses each of these issues. Because the focus throughout is the mathematics specialist's work as a coach, the chapter uses the word "coach" rather than "elementary mathematics specialist."

The Coaching Model

Coaches use many strategies. One critical approach is known as the "coaching model" (West and Staub 2003). The coaching model consists of a three-step process:

1. Planning a lesson with a teacher
2. Supporting the teacher when she teaches the planned lesson, either by observing or by co-teaching in her classroom
3. Debriefing the lesson with the teacher in a discussion analyzing the conduct of the lesson and the actions of, as well as the interactions between, students and the teacher

Each of these components of the coaching model is important. When working with individual teachers, a coach will implement each of these three components, although in varying degrees.

Planning, or more precisely, co-planning

Planning the lesson in advance with the teacher is the first step in the coaching model. As the coach and the teacher co-plan the lesson, they make a variety of critical decisions. They decide what student learning goals the lesson will focus on. Exactly what mathematical understandings will it target? After identifying the mathematical content, the coach and the teacher discuss how that content might be taught in the lesson. They decide what problem, activity, or activities they will use in the lesson to challenge and support students in working toward those goals. This decision requires them to think carefully about the mathematics behind the activities in the lesson. They may decide whether the teacher will make manipulative materials available or what representations the teacher could use to support student learning. They decide whether and when the students will work in groups, work independently, or be expected to engage in a whole-class discussion. They may discuss how particular students are likely to approach or complete the activities.

The teacher and the coach then consider how the lesson may play out in the classroom. They discuss how the lesson will begin, what ideas and skills the teacher will highlight, and what questions the teacher will ask. They might consider stumbling blocks that the students could encounter. Thinking about these challenges could shift the discussion to scaffolding questions that the teacher could ask. Scaffolding questions support students' efforts to make sense of the mathematics without doing the mathematics for the students.

The teacher and the coach discuss how the lesson will end. Will the students be expected to share and explain their work? What solutions might the students share? What questions might the teacher ask to probe their thinking?

Additionally, the coach and the teacher decide what their respective roles will be during the lesson. Who will teach the lesson? Or will they both teach at different times? When one person is teaching and the other person is observing, what will the observer focus on? Will the observer take notes about the methods used by different students, or will she focus on the instructional strategies?

Observing, modeling, or co-teaching

During the lesson, the coach takes whatever role that he and the teacher decided on when they planned the lesson. If the coach's role is to observe the lesson, he might act as a scribe, creating a written record of the lesson as it unfolds. Or he might take notes about how different students solve problems as they work in small groups. Or the teacher might ask him to focus on a particular aspect of her instructional practice. For example, the coach might keep a list of the teacher's questions and the students' responses. He might be positioned where he can see the classroom clock so that he can record how much wait time elapses from the moment when the teacher finishes asking a question to the moment when she calls on a student to answer. The coach might have a roster of the students' names and tally how often the teacher calls on particular students.

If a coach is co-teaching, or if she is actually teaching the lesson independently while the teacher observes, she and the teacher should have determined in advance what aspect of the co-planned lesson she will be responsible for and what teaching strategies she will demonstrate. For example, the coach may have an explicit role, such as introducing one of the activities or modeling the asking of good questions when monitoring students' small-group work. The coach may be leading a whole-class discussion in which students share their answers and describe their strategies. During this time, the coach may be modeling how to ask students questions about their explanations to promote justification and reasoning. If the coach has one of these more explicit roles, then she will need to prepare carefully and thoughtfully about how she will model best practices. Similarly, the teacher will need to understand his role during those segments of the lesson when the coach is teaching. If the teacher is observing, what should he look for or focus on? Should he take notes?

Debriefing

In the debriefing session, the coach guides the discussion so that he and the teacher can talk about whether they met the goals that they set out to accomplish:

- How did the students think about and complete the activities or solve the problems in the lesson?
- What, if any, difficulties did the students experience?
- How did the teacher focus the discussion on students' ideas?
- If they did not meet their goals for the lesson, what modifications in either the lesson plan or the organization of the class might have improved the outcome?
- What misunderstandings did the students have?

These are just a few of the many questions that the coach and teacher can explore in debriefing the lesson. Ideally, a debriefing session sets the groundwork for future planning. This, in turn, can restart the coaching model as the coach and the teacher consider next steps.

Vignette: Crazy Cakes for Two

The following vignette portrays the three stages of the coaching cycle: planning; observing, modeling, or co-teaching; and debriefing.

Ms. Doman is in her first year of working as a full-time mathematics specialist. Her school has three or four teachers at each grade level. At the beginning of the year, the principal asked Ms. Doman to work with teachers in their classrooms to help them develop best practices for mathematics instruction. With the principal's help, Ms. Doman began to schedule times to work with teachers at each grade level. When she introduced herself to Ms. Allen, one of the fourth-grade teachers, Ms. Allen was very interested in having Ms. Doman work with her and her students in the upcoming unit on understanding and representing rational numbers as fractions, decimals, and percentages.

When Ms. Doman prepared for her planning session with Ms. Allen, she noted that an early focus in the unit was on finding fractions of asymmetrical regions. Ms. Doman knew that one of the lessons cited in this unit, Crazy Cakes for Two (Tierney 2006), could be particularly effective. This lesson provides pictures of asymmetrical shapes that students are expected to split in ways that will make two equal parts.

First the mathematics, and then the plan

When Ms. Doman and Ms. Allen met the next day to plan, Ms. Allen admitted that she did not understand the mathematical intent behind the Crazy Cakes activity. Because she did not understand the rationale, she was unsure how to teach a lesson using it.

Ms. Doman decided that before writing a lesson plan, they should solve some of the Crazy Cakes problems together. This work would give them an opportunity to investigate the meaning of the mathematics. They could also anticipate and discuss issues that the students might encounter. As they worked, Ms. Allen had no trouble explaining how the shapes could be partitioned into two equal parts. As they talked about why the different parts were equally partitioned, Ms. Allen began to realize that this activity was a natural way for her students to work with halves.

After working through the activity, they talked about which problem they would use to introduce the activity, how long Ms. Allen would take to introduce the activity, and how long she might let the students explore several of the shapes. As they continued to talk about logistics, Ms. Allen suggested that they teach the Crazy Cakes lesson together since she had not taught it before. As they continued to plan, they agreed that Ms. Doman would introduce the lesson. Both teachers would walk around and talk to each of the small groups, taking notes and asking questions to probe the students' reasoning as they solved the problems. To end the lesson, Ms. Allen and Ms. Doman would both lead the discussion and ask questions as students shared what they had figured out in the small groups. Then Ms. Allen would ask the students to write a reflection in their journals about what they learned during the lesson.

Co-teaching: It's the amount, not the shape, of cake

To introduce the activity, Ms. Doman asked the students whether they had ever shared cake with a friend. She also asked whether they had thought about the need to share a cake fairly so that no one received a larger slice. They responded with several suggestions about cutting a cake in half so that each friend received the same amount of cake. Ms. Doman then introduced the Crazy Cakes for Two activity. The students quickly broke into their small groups and got started.

Many of the students wanted to cut each of the cakes in half by making one cut across the cake that would result in symmetric pieces. But they were discouraged when they realized that the cakes could not be easily cut into two congruent portions—portions matching in both size and shape. In planning the lesson, Ms. Doman and Ms. Allen had prepared some scaffolding questions, which each of them used now with a few groups of students. Other groups figured out independently that two fair shares of cake did not have to have the same shape, as long as "you got the same amount of cake to eat." Ms. Doman and Ms. Allen each took notes, recording which groups needed the scaffolding questions and how those students responded.

After students completed the activity, each group shared its solutions with the whole class. For example, students in one group explained how they shared the cake by removing a small triangular shape sticking out of one part of the cake (fig. 3.1 shows their solution on the left). They cut off the small triangular shape and moved it to the "other side," sliding it into a space adjacent to another triangular shape. Once they had moved this piece, they had a rectangle that they could split into two congruent parts. They explained that each friend would receive one-half of the "tall rectangle."

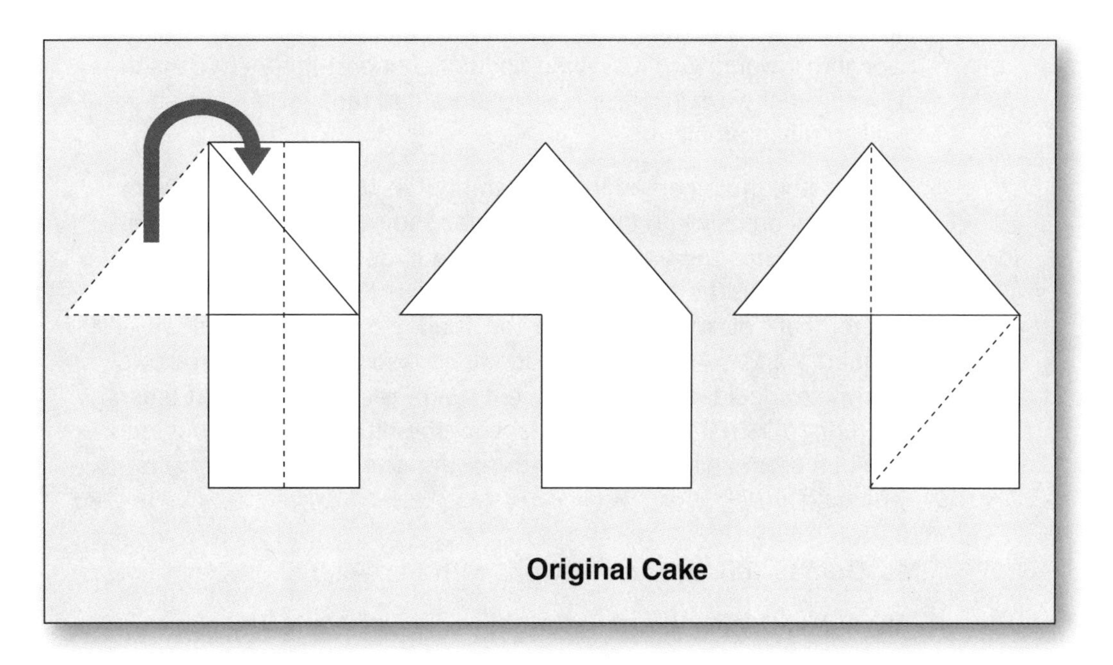

Fig. 3.1. A cake (shown in the center) and two ways to share it (shown on the left and right)

The students in another group explained that they lengthened the base line of the small triangle sticking out of the cake, extending that line to make a larger triangle and a rectangle (this work is shown on the right in fig. 3.1). Then they demonstrated how they divided the triangle and the rectangle into two congruent parts, forming triangles.

The class had a lively discussion about these students' claim that as long as each friend received two of their triangular pieces of cake, the sharing would be fair. This discussion was focused on the concern that if one friend got the two triangular shapes on top of the figure and the other friend got the two bottom triangular shapes, the shape of one friend's share would be a triangle and the shape of the other friend's share would be a square. The issue was whether their shares of cake could be fair if they were not the same shape.

After the students discussed their ideas, Ms. Allen asked them to write in their journals, explaining what they had learned during the lesson.

Debriefing: Much to talk about

During the debriefing session at recess, Ms. Allen had a chance to share her insights about the lesson. Ms. Allen began the discussion by telling Ms. Doman that she was excited about all of the connections that the students made during the lesson. She was surprised that the students made connections between the measure of area and halving. Ms. Doman then suggested that they look at the students' journals to see what they had written about these ideas. She made this suggestion for two reasons. First, it would give both Ms. Allen and her a better gauge of how much the students understood. Second, it would give Ms. Allen additional opportunities to consider the different ways in which her students had thought about and solved these problems.

All the students seemed to understand that they needed to divide the cakes equally into two equal parts. They also wrote about the fact that it was the measure of the area in each friend's share, typically called the "amount of cake," rather than the shape of the share, that determined whether the sharing of the cake was fair or "equal." As Ms. Allen and Ms. Doman looked at different students' work, they decided that the students were ready for the next lesson, featuring 10×10 grids. In this lesson, the students would begin to work on partitioning the grids into equal parts for halves, fourths, and eighths.

Ms. Doman reflects on her work with Ms. Allen

When Ms. Doman thought about her work with Ms. Allen, she realized they had begun to work comfortably and effectively together. They had a common goal of helping Ms. Allen's students develop meaningful understandings related to fractions, and they were on their way to accomplishing that goal. Ms. Doman thought about how important it was that they had begun their planning session by working through some of the same problems that Ms. Allen's students would solve. By solving various problems, Ms. Allen had the opportunity to understand the important ideas that the students could encounter as they engaged in the activity. Ms. Doman knew that it is crucial for a teacher to have a deep understanding of the mathematical ideas underlying the lessons and activities that she presents to her students. Otherwise, it is very difficult for her to understand her students' work or the problems that they encounter.

Ms. Doman recalled that she and Ms. Allen had spent a fair amount of time planning many of the details of this lesson together, including deciding what each other's role would be during the lesson. But now that the lesson was over, Ms. Doman reflected that planning the logistics of the lesson with such precision had made Ms. Allen much more comfortable.

Ms. Doman also thought about the different roles that she and Ms. Allen had played as they followed the plan that they had developed together. Each took the lead for different parts of the lesson. Ms. Doman had introduced it, modeling how a teacher might set up a problem or activity with students, discuss intent, and raise ideas without solving the problem for the students. Then Ms. Allen had joined with Ms. Doman to monitor the small-group work, questioning students about their ideas. Ms. Doman decided that when she and Ms. Allen planned their next lesson, she would ask Ms. Allen if she wanted to introduce the lesson.

Capitalizing on Opportunities to Coach Individual Teachers

The vignette about Ms. Doman and Ms. Allen illustrates the distinct components of the coaching model. But before a coach can coach a teacher, she has to gain access to her. A coach may have many different opportunities for working with individual teachers.

Finding times to meet with teachers

A coaching interaction can begin through a variety of approaches. The coach may first observe a teacher teaching a lesson, talking briefly with the teacher before or after he observes this lesson. Alternatively, he and a teacher may agree to meet to plan a lesson outside the regular school day or during the teacher's planning period. There is no ideal time or arrangement for meeting. The coach and the teacher may meet to plan a single lesson, a series of lessons, or an entire unit. They can make different arrangements of time and commitment as they begin working together. What is important is that the coach and teacher find the time to meet before any lesson that will be observed or co-taught and that they also find the time to discuss the lesson after it is taught.

Which teacher should the coach work with first?

One of the ways for the coach to determine which teacher to work with first is by making ten- to fifteen-minute "drop-in visits" to classrooms at the beginning of the school year. During these visits, the coach can gather some initial information about each teacher's mathematics instruction. By observing for this brief period of time, the coach can take notes on how the teacher and students work together, for example, or whether students have opportunities to explain and justify their answers, or what types of questions the teacher asks. As the coach makes these visits, she can begin to plan which teachers she might work with first. In some cases, she will identify teachers to approach because they need additional instructional support. In other cases, as was the case with Ms. Allen, a teacher may request a time when she and the coach could work together.

In another approach, the coach may work first with teachers who are new to teaching or who are new to teaching mathematics at a particular grade level. He can come by a classroom and introduce himself to the teacher, invite the teacher to co-plan a lesson, or help the teacher set up his classroom. Possible advantages of working with a new teacher include a greater willingness to accept help, to follow up on suggestions, and to plan lessons. A potential disadvantage is spending more time helping the teacher manage the classroom or become familiar with general instructional practices, rather than thinking deeply about teaching for mathematical understanding. So working with new teachers involves trade-offs.

Sometimes working with teachers can be challenging

Some teachers do not realize that they might benefit from working with a coach who could help support their teaching and their students' learning. They may be comfortable with their current teaching practices, and possibly they have received feedback that they believe justifies that satisfaction. Or they may be uncomfortable with teaching mathematics, but they do not want others to know of their insecurity. In either case, they are not at the point of making a change, whether it is working toward a more sophisticated goal such as aligning assessments more closely with their teaching practices or finding a way to teach a topic differently (Hall and Simeral 2008). No matter why a teacher is reluctant to work with a coach, the coach must take particular care when approaching and working with him. Chapter 12, "Turning Challenges into Opportunities," provides more detail about how a coach might meet different challenges when working with individual teachers.

Enhancing Teachers' Mathematical Understanding

Sometimes the coach may be surprised to realize that a teacher does not completely understand the mathematical concepts that she is responsible for teaching (National Research Council 2001). This situation gives the coach a wonderful opportunity to support that teacher's continued learning. If the teacher, for instance, does not understand why a procedure makes sense, she and the coach can talk about this idea when they meet together. Suppose, for example, that a teacher cannot explain why the following shortcut works:

When multiplying by 10, just put a zero at the end of the number.

The teacher and the coach can work through problems to explore how multiplying by 10 affects the place value of each of the digits in a number, with the value associated with each digit becoming ten times as large as the digit shifts to the left. Discussions such as these between the coach and a teacher are important because they provide opportunities for the teacher to expand her understanding of the different concepts that are addressed in the curriculum.

Another important way for the coach to support a teacher's continued learning is to explore how similar mathematical ideas are addressed in the curriculum. As the teacher begins a new unit, the coach can ask questions such as the following:

- "What concepts did the students learn about this topic last year?"
- "What representations or manipulatives did the students use last year to explore these ideas?"
- "How do the concepts that the students learned last year connect with the ones that you will be teaching in this unit?"
- "Do any other topics that you have already taught this year connect with this unit?"

By asking these kinds of questions, the coach creates an opportunity for the teacher to consider connections among relevant mathematical ideas. Through this conversation, the teacher may also realize an important fact: instruction planned for the upcoming unit must not only address the mathematical expectations in the unit, but also help students recall prior learning and connect mathematical ideas.

Teachers and coach have many other opportunities to continue learning about the content that they teach. For instance, the coach and a teacher can talk about and explore mathematical ideas as they co-plan an upcoming lesson or debrief a just-completed lesson. Teachers can also continue to learn about the content that they teach as they make long-range curricular plans with the coach.

Daily co-planning and debriefing

When planning a lesson, the coach and a teacher might anticipate how different students will solve different problems. As they engage in this discussion, the coach might ask key questions such as the following to highlight the mathematics that is addressed in the lesson:

- "How might the students represent their ideas?"
- "How might students use their current understandings to solve this problem?"
- "What important ideas will the students work with as they solve this problem?"
- "How are the important mathematical ideas related to other concepts that the students either have learned or will learn?"

When a coach and a teacher debrief a lesson, the coach can continue to focus attention on the big ideas that the students are grappling with. For instance, as Ms. Doman and Ms. Allen discussed what happened during their co-taught lesson, they talked about the different ways in which the students solved the Crazy Cakes problems. When the coach and a teacher talk about the mathematical strategies that the students used or the reasoning that particular students explained during a lesson, the teacher has another opportunity to consider the mathematical meaning of the different ideas addressed in the lesson.

Talk with teachers about their students' thinking.

I was observing a third-grade class that was using pattern blocks to investigate fractions. I noticed that most of the third graders did not understand that if they were to show how an outlined area (such as that formed by two adjacent hexagons) could be separated into six equal parts, then in each of the six parts, the union of shapes needed to have the same area. So, after class, I met with the teacher to talk about the students' thinking and, at the same time, to revisit ideas about area and unit fractions that underpinned the curriculum.

We planned a lesson for the next day. We decided that the teacher would use all six available pattern-block shapes to make a configuration and that she would call it a "funky cookie." She would ask the students to talk about whether it would be fair to share the funky cookie among six friends by giving each friend one of the six pattern blocks in the cookie. We anticipated that the students could explain that it would not be fair to give each student a different pattern block because each pattern block was a different size. We planned questions that the teacher would ask to prompt students' explanations about how they could share the cookie fairly and to challenge students to explain how they could verify that the shares were fair. The lesson then had students return to using the pattern blocks to separate shapes into equal pieces.

—Reflections from a mathematics specialist

During debriefing sessions the coach and teacher can also use student work to examine and make connections among mathematical ideas. For instance, as they review the students' written work, they can look for examples that the teacher might ask students to share during the next class to focus class discussion designed to extend key big ideas. This conversation can also lead the coach and the teacher to explore other examples or consider how other ideas are related to one student's work. In some cases, the coach may also have an opportunity to recognize mathematical connections that are new to her. If so, she should use that occasion to make her own learning, and her excitement about that learning, transparent to the teacher.

Long-term planning

Another way in which the coach can help the teacher make connections among mathematical ideas is to explore the curricular content within or across grade levels. Or he and the teacher may talk about how mathematical ideas are connected across several lessons. In planning for a series of lessons in a unit, for instance, Ms. Doman and Ms. Allen would have opportunities to consider how students might continue to use ideas about area and division as they continued to explore fractions:

- How might the students use their ideas about finding halves to find fourths and eighths?
- If the students used the 10 × 10 grids to find halves, fourths and eighths, would they make connections between these representations of fractions and both decimal and percent equivalences?
- How is the 10 × 10 grid similar to the model used in the Crazy Cakes activity? How is it different?
- What other mathematical ideas would the students explore if they used the grid?
- When the students shaded 40 squares in the grid, would they recognize this shaded region as 40%, $40/100$ (40 of the 100 squares), $4/10$ (4 of the 10 groups of 10 squares), and $2/5$ (2 groups out of 5 groups of 20 squares) of the grid?

These are the kinds of ideas that the coach and the teacher might explore as they continue to work together developing lessons addressing fractions, as well as other lessons in a rational numbers unit connecting fractions with decimal and percent representations.

One of the challenges that a coach faces during these planning sessions is helping the teacher understand that although the school, school district, or state may have a particular curriculum map outlining how many days to spend on a particular topic, students develop understanding of concepts over time. For instance, students may not have mastered all the skills or understood all the mathematical concepts addressed in fourth grade by the time they begin fifth grade. So, how should the fifth-grade teacher take this issue into account when planning? Or how can the second-grade teacher plan instruction for students who are still developing number sense related to the range of numbers that they studied in first grade? When planning with the teacher, one of the coach's goals is to help the teacher understand that the curriculum map is a guide illuminating how the students' understandings fit with school-district goals for mathematics instruction. By helping the teacher think about students' learning of mathematics as a fluid state, the coach can help the teacher consider curricular planning for students in a realistic way. With the coach's support, the teacher can see her students as continually developing and building on ideas, including those introduced in an earlier grade.

Fostering Change in a Teacher's Instructional Practice

A teacher naturally makes changes in his practices as he learns about teaching and about teaching mathematics more effectively. The key is for the coach to work with him collaboratively. It is the collaboration that encourages the teacher to persist in learning about and attempting to carry out what will be, to him, new but possibly more effective ways of teaching mathematics.

Fostering change through modeling

Modeling lessons for teachers can be very helpful. Sometimes teachers cannot imagine how they might teach a concept or introduce an activity differently without seeing how another teacher might teach it. Teachers may need to see what good teaching looks like. When the coach models a lesson, she provides an opportunity for the teacher to step outside of her usual role and reflect on different aspects of her practice. For instance, the teacher may ask the coach to model a lesson that addresses a particular concept that she does not fully understand how to teach. Or she may ask the coach to model part of a lesson that she has not taught before. The coach's aim is to provide opportunities that allow the teacher to see, reflect on, and develop an understanding of different instructional strategies that she might use to support her students' learning more effectively. Recall that in the vignette, Ms. Doman offered to teach the Crazy Cakes lesson so that Ms. Allen could observe how she could use these types of activities to help her students learn about fractions.

Give teachers time to observe students.

As a coach, when I model a lesson, I provide opportunities for the teacher to carefully attend to what the students are doing during the lesson. Often a teacher is so focused on her teaching and what will be her next move that she doesn't have the opportunity to observe different students at work. As the teacher observes her students, she can notice the different solution methods that they use or the understandings that they have. This is an opportunity not only for the teacher to observe teaching, but also for her to take time to learn more about her students.

—Advice from a mathematics specialist

To help the teacher focus on a strategy or issue during the lesson, the coach and the teacher need to discuss the role that the teacher will have during the lesson. The importance of giving the teacher a specific task was highlighted earlier. He might focus on how a group of students solves a problem, or the coach might ask him to jot down the questions that she asks during the whole-class discussion. The teacher could also note whether the questions that the coach asks seem to prompt a useful discussion. The teacher can focus on and learn about many different strategies as he observes the coach teach lessons that they have planned together. And sometime in the future, the coach will expect the teacher to co-teach or teach the entire lesson that they have planned together.

Remember that modeling requires the active involvement of the classroom teacher.

One of my teachers asked me to model a lesson in her mathematics class on the next Friday, and so we met to co-plan the lesson. Then, on that Friday morning, the teacher sent me an e-mail message saying that she would not be in the classroom during mathematics instruction. Because the purpose of modeling the lesson was for the teacher and me to work together, I asked the teacher to reschedule our time together for a different day. I also offered to be in the classroom to assist the substitute teacher if the substitute needed "another pair of hands," but I explained that I would not be able to teach the mathematics lesson since the teacher would not be present. Modeling is not serving as a substitute teacher.

—Reflections from a mathematics specialist

Fostering change through co-teaching

When the coach and the teacher are planning the lesson that they will co-teach, the coach must consider what parts of the lesson he thinks the teacher is ready to teach. Will the teacher feel comfortable leading the whole-class discussion after the students have completed the primary activity in the lesson? Would the teacher prefer that both she and the coach orchestrate this part of the lesson? The coach might encourage the teacher to step outside her "comfort zone," noting that if she has any difficulty at different points during the lesson, he will be ready to help. He might suggest that the teacher give him a cue if she would like him to join the discussion. For example, the teacher might say, "What do you think about this idea, Mr. Kane?"

During the lesson, the coach and teacher may confer while the students work, comparing notes about what they are noticing or how they think they might change their plan, perhaps because the students have not finished their assignment. These situations are opportunities for the teacher to learn about and possibly make changes in his practice. By talking through possible courses of action that he or the coach might take, he can explore new and alternative ways to implement a lesson.

Co-teaching is not simply an opportunity for the students to learn from two teachers, but an opportunity for the teacher to learn about teaching. The coach and the teacher should agree on their co-teaching goal prior to instruction. What about teaching will they make their focus? Asking good questions? Trying out a different way to record or highlight students' work during the whole-class discussion? As they focus on particular instructional practices, the teacher will have opportunities to use strategies that she has not used before. The coach can help support the teacher's learning during co-teaching by assisting when the teacher is leading the class, although such participation needs to be agreed on in advance. For example, the coach may ask students follow-up questions during a whole-class discussion. Another supportive co-teaching technique that the coach might use is to cue the teacher quietly about the implication of a particular student's method that the coach has noticed when monitoring small-group work. This prepares the teacher not only to ask that student to explain the method during the whole-class discussion but also to probe the student's reasoning.

Fostering change through debriefing

Every conversation between the coach and the teacher can be important. Debriefing after co-teaching allows them to reflect on their shared experiences. The intent is for the teacher to learn to reflect on his teaching, considering not only the skill with which he implemented particular instructional strategies, but also the degree and depth of his students' mathematical understandings. For this reason, during debriefing, the coach and the teacher may talk about the fact that the students' ideas or reasoning are still tenuous. Although the students may have been successful when solving particular problems, they may not be ready to apply the new ideas to solve a broad range of problems. Students may not be ready to give up particular recording methods if they rely on those methods to keep track of their thinking. As the coach and the teacher discuss plans for upcoming lessons, in addition to considering the instructional approaches that the teacher might want to attempt, they can talk about the supports or challenges that particular students may need.

In debriefing the lesson, the coach can create opportunities for the teacher to reflect on her own teaching practice as coach and teacher analyze students' work together. They might organize the students' work in stacks that represent those who are developing ideas addressed in the lesson, those who have mastered those ideas, and those who have misunderstandings about the ideas. As the coach and the teacher talk about why different students' work might fit particular categories, the teacher can develop a better understanding of the mathematics that her students are grappling with. The coach can also use this information to help the teacher consider how she will address the students' instructional needs when she plans subsequent lessons.

Fostering change through planning

When planning a lesson with the teacher, the coach needs to be careful not to take over the planning session. He needs to plan *with* rather than *for* the teacher. Although the teacher might draw a blank on how to proceed, the coach must be patient and try to elicit the teacher's ideas. By asking questions during the planning session, the coach communicates that he expects the teacher to play an important role in the planning session.

A coach may also need to discuss and model how to consider which activities or problems will help the students learn the content. She and the teacher may talk about how activities are related to one another and how, or if, particular activities might help students explore and make connections among ideas. In some instances, the teacher may suggest an activity that does not actually relate to the mathematical ideas that he needs to address. In such cases, the coach should ask the teacher how this activity would help the students learn the content that they hoped to address. She might walk through the activity with the teacher and record exactly what the students might need to do to complete it successfully. In so doing, the coach and the teacher together can rule out activities that would not help the students build new ideas or refine current ones. As they do so, the teacher can reflect on the importance of thinking carefully about the mathematical activities that he uses with his students.

The coach and teacher might use a simple three-column planning format, filling in information as they make their plan. In the first column, they would include the date and record one or two big ideas or strands that the lesson addresses. They could also include "I wonder" questions that the teacher might use to introduce the activity. In the second column, they would give a brief description of the activity that they plan to use. In the third column, they would write questions that they could ask to assess the students' understanding of those ideas. By guiding the planning process in this way, the coach can help the teacher reflect on the important components of planning process. At the same time, the coach is helping the teacher to organize and consider the complexities of her craft, learn about her students, delve into the mathematics that she teaches, and reflect on her instructional practices.

Building Trust and Supporting Change

Coaching is a challenge. The intent is for the coach to build trust with a teacher while encouraging him to confront and make changes in his practice. In addition to having a deep understanding of mathematics content and pedagogy, the coach must have a range of "soft" skills to work effectively with adult learners. These skills enable the coach to do the following:

- Nudge or shift teachers beyond their comfort zone without pushing them too far
- Communicate a genuine concern for both the teachers' and their students' best interests
- Answer challenging questions about why teachers need to make changes even when their students have outstanding state test scores
- Recognize that since elementary teachers teach all subjects, they may not have a thorough understanding of, or a desire to fully grasp, how mathematical ideas are connected across different grade levels

This list is not exhaustive, but it does highlight some additional issues that shape a coach's work. Building a teacher's trust as he supports her efforts to change requires a coach to have a range of affective skills and understandings.

Choose activities carefully and purposefully

One of the ways in which the coach can build trust and support change is by carefully selecting activities and resources that she will use during her meetings with the teacher. Thoughtfully selecting activities is very different from grabbing every worksheet on a particular topic. Rather than employing the "grab and go" tactic, a coach should think deeply about the teacher's abilities, interests, and strengths—as well as about the needs of her students. The coach may decide to make a few key activities or resources available, selecting materials that address the mathematical concepts that the teacher will cover in the next several lessons. As they consider these activities, the coach and the teacher can solve the problems together, talk about the important ideas, and discuss how students might address these ideas.

The coach often needs to use different approaches with different teachers. One teacher may be quite comfortable introducing a new activity—one that he has never used with his students before—whereas another teacher may not be at ease and may ask the coach to model how to introduce the activity. For instance, if a teacher is not familiar with using mathematical games, the coach can model ways of using a game to introduce a mathematical concept or review mathematical skills. While the students play the game, the coach can demonstrate different questioning techniques to help students explain their thinking. When the students reconvene for the whole-class discussion, he can also demonstrate how to highlight the important ideas that the students grappled with as they played the game. By modeling in class and later talking with the teacher about the lesson outside class, the coach can engage the teacher in a discussion of ways to use these types of activities to help his students learn.

Work collaboratively

The coach needs to be willing to teach and plan activities together with the teacher. This is not simply a matter of suggesting a teaching idea or providing materials. For example, when co-teaching, the teacher may need support if the students are stymied during a problem-solving task and she doesn't want simply to tell them what to do, but she doesn't know what else to do. The coach may step in and ask the students a question that will prompt them to reconsider or refocus their ideas, resetting their thinking and allowing the lesson to move forward. But when providing this support, the coach must do so without appearing to take over the lesson.

When planning together, the coach and the teacher should also discuss their differing ideas and then decide how to support the learning of the students in the teacher's classroom. This means that sometimes their co-planned lesson may involve an approach preferred by the teacher, even if it is not the approach that the coach would prefer. Regardless of the activities in which the coach and teacher engage, as they work together they need take the view that they are in a mutually beneficial partnership (Knight 2011).

Co-plan with care, without taking over.

Sometimes, I unintentionally derail a teacher's lesson during a planning session. I am simply so eager to share my expertise that I take a plan in a direction that the teacher wasn't expecting to go. I think it's important for a coach to recognize that when a teacher has planned a lesson (and the teacher is trying to describe how he envisions teaching the lesson in the way he planned), a coach should not take over. By taking over, the coach may alienate a teacher and make the working relationship ineffective.

—Advice from a mathematics specialist

Work respectfully

The coach needs to recognize that the teacher often has ideas that are grounded in tradition. This means that it is important for the coach to listen carefully when the teacher shares his ideas. If the coach needs to make suggestions, then she should try to make those suggestions fit with the teacher's ideas. If the teacher's idea does not align with good instructional or mathematical practices, the coach needs to respond carefully and respectfully, but also directly. Although it is important for the coach to be direct and to the point, it is also just as important for her to be able to explain her thinking and state why she has a concern that an approach may not help students understand the concept.

Use student needs to justify an approach.

When I was co-planning a lesson about estimating, one of my teachers shared a "trick" for rounding: "Look next door, 5 or more, go 1 more." I knew that this trick was not mathematically sound, and so I needed to respond. But I also needed to be careful to respect the teacher's ideas. So I said, "Instead of using a trick, why don't we use a number line to emphasize the distance that the number being rounded is from the boundary number?" Then I honestly explained that the rounding trick might confuse some of the students. But if the students could visualize the distances between their numbers and the different benchmarks (multiples of 10) by using the number line, that might help them understand the reasoning behind the procedure for making estimates or rounding. By addressing the teacher's suggestion, I acknowledged the teacher's idea and, at the same time, helped her understand why another approach might give better support to her students' understanding.

—*Reflections from a mathematics specialist*

Work honestly

Coaches must be genuine when providing feedback to teachers. Teachers want to learn and grow. But unless the coach gives honest feedback, the teacher cannot reflect on and refine her practice. It is equally important for the coach to be honest when he does not know the answer to a question. Whether it is a mathematics question, or a question about pacing or state standards, it is important for the coach to say that he will find out the answer to the teacher's question and get back to her. Being honest shows the teacher that the coach is also a learner and recognizes that he does not have all the answers.

Be genuinely interested

It is important for the coach to be genuinely interested in the teacher's opinions, ideas, reflections, and suggestions. Some teachers have many years of teaching experience; others have a deep understanding of child development. The coach will need to help the seasoned teacher make connections between her experiences and best practices. To do this, the coach must listen to the teacher as she shares her experiences and then draw on those experiences as they work together. Being genuinely interested in what the teacher shares, whether it is prior knowledge, experiences, or student concerns, will help give the coach entry points for moving her practice forward.

Help the teacher understand that teaching is about learning

When the coach and teacher plan a lesson that neither of them has taught before, they predict what could happen during the lesson. But "the only thing that is predictable in teaching is that classroom activities will not go as predicted" (Simon 1995, p. 133). Nevertheless, they can learn from each other as they anticipate how the lesson might play out, what challenges the students might encounter, and what, if any, adjustments they might need to make as they move through the lesson. By having these types of conversations, the teacher will become more comfortable as he realizes that he and the coach are "in this together," working to become more effective at teaching concepts by using new materials or new approaches. Even if the coach and the teacher have taught the lesson before, they may not always be able to anticipate what will happen in the lesson with this year's students. Teaching is unpredictable. But, through the coaching model, the coach and the teacher can work together to think about and to improve their instructional practice.

Be directive as a last resort

Occasionally, when the coach works in a teacher's classroom, she may observe a teacher teach something incorrectly, which in turn, causes the students to be confused. In these situations, the coach needs to intervene. But rather than correcting the teacher by labeling the teacher's statement as an error or mistake, the coach can speak to the students in statements such as, "Did you understand what Ms. [insert teacher's name] is saying? She is saying that [insert correction]."

Suppose, for example, that a coach and a teacher are co-teaching a lesson addressing division with remainders and the teacher states that the number that is the remainder can always be rewritten as a decimal with the same digits. For example, suppose that she says, "A remainder of 2 can be written as the decimal 0.2, and that would be equivalent." Then the coach might intervene and say, "Did you understand what Ms. Johnson is saying? She is saying that when you have a divisor of 10—when the number you are dividing by is 10—and you get a remainder of 2, then that remainder is the same as the decimal 0.2." Then the coach might say to the students, "Think of a division problem for which the remainder and its decimal equivalent are not that number of tenths. Think of a division problem where, for example, the remainder is 4 or 5 and the decimal equivalent is not 0.4 or 0.5." As the students give examples, Ms. Johnson might record their ideas before proceeding with her lesson. This example illustrates that the coach can intervene directly without stating that the teacher's ideas are wrong while still rectifying a mathematical error.

Recognize that timing is everything when correcting teachers' mistakes.

I was mortified when a teacher told her students something that was mathematically incorrect when she was teaching. I didn't want to embarrass or interrupt the teacher during the lesson, and I didn't want to alienate her so soon in the year! So I stayed quiet and waited until later in the day to discuss this issue with her. Luckily, she took the information graciously, and then asked me to give her a sign at any time during the lesson to let her know when she was incorrect. She also shared the information that she was not very comfortable teaching mathematics at this grade level—it was her first year teaching at this grade level. Although it is important for me to address a teacher's misconceptions directly, I know that I must be sure to do so in a way that saves face for the teacher. I believe that this teacher and I have a very productive working relationship because of how I handled these types of situations early in the school year.

—Reflections from a mathematics specialist

Work first with more receptive teachers

Felux and Snowdy (2006) recommend that a coach work with teachers "who are interested, curious and open to change" (p. 5). Some teachers are eager to work with the coach, especially if they do not understand how to use new curricular materials or if they are feeling challenged by teaching particular mathematics content. Other teachers are simply interested in learning more about their teaching and welcome collaborating with the coach. In either case, the coach has the opportunity to work with teachers who are willing to collaborate. This work, in turn, may help build new mathematics leaders in the school. So the coach should work with teachers who wish to work with him. As he works with these teachers, he can build a culture of professional learning that is contagious (Felux and Snowdy 2006). The hope is that other teachers who are more resistant will become curious and more open to engaging in the good work that the coach promotes.

Questioning strategies

The questions that the teacher asks during the lesson can provide students with opportunities to make connections, clarify their thinking, and build or refine understanding. A teacher's questioning techniques are an important part of his work.

The coach plays an important role in helping the teacher develop more effective questioning strategies. One way in which the coach can do this is to observe a teacher's lesson as it unfolds and record each of the questions that the teacher asks students. Once the coach has created this script of questions, she and the teacher can use it to identify the types of questions that the teacher asks. For instance, the coach might ask the teacher to consider specific aspects or effects of the questions:

- "How open-ended is this question?"
- "When you asked this question, what were you hoping to find out?"
- "Which of these questions helped you understand the students' thinking?"

Further, the coach may revisit instances when the students did not answer the teacher's questions, opening a discussion with the teacher about these questions:

- "Why didn't the students answer this question?"
- "Did the students not know the answer?"
- "Are there reasons why they might not have understood the question?"

In each of these situations, the coach can help the teacher view these instances as opportunities to ask more specific questions or to ask the same question differently.

As the coach and the teacher have these important discussions, the teacher is learning both how to ask questions and how to question his students' answers. This provides the teacher with an opportunity to learn as he reflects on and makes changes in how he conducts and supports mathematical discussions. This means he is learning to change his teaching—making changes that can provide more learning opportunities for his students.

Building teachers' trust provides the backdrop for the coach to support teachers as they change or refine their practice. Gaining each teacher's trust is key to the successes that the coach may have. He must communicate that he has both the teachers' and their students' best interests in mind. He also must convey a genuine interest in the teacher's work. A coach must be knowledgeable about mathematics and mathematics teaching, but those skills and understandings must be accompanied by other attributes. Teachers must see him as working honestly, truthfully, respectfully, and with good intentions. If the coach can successfully communicate that he wants to support the teachers' continued learning about their craft in the service of their students' learning, he is likely to be very successful in his daily work.

Some Final Thoughts about Coaching Individual Teachers

Working with individual teachers is complex. It is primarily through coaching that an elementary mathematics specialist engages in the work of supporting each teacher's professional learning. A number of coaching arrangements and techniques may be applied to support the teacher's work. But what they have in common, and what is most important to them all, is that a coach and a teacher are co-learners, working together as they decide how to provide the best support for students' needs.

References

Felux, Carolyn, and Paula Snowdy. *The Math Coach Field Guide: Charting Your Course.* Sausalito, Calif.: Math Solutions Publications, 2006.

Hall, Pete, and Alisa Simeral. *Building Teachers' Capacity for Success: A Collaborative Approach for Coaches and School Leaders.* Alexandria, Va.: Association for Supervision and Curriculum Development, 2008.

Knight, Jim. "What Good Coaches Do." *Educational Leadership* 69 (October 2011): 18–22.

National Research Council. *Adding It Up: Helping Children Learn Mathematics.* Mathematics Learning Study Committee, Jeremy Kilpatrick, Jane Swafford, and Bradford Findell, eds. Center for Education, Division of Behavioral and Social Sciences and Education. Washington, D.C.: National Academy Press, 2001.

Simon, Martin A. "Reconstructing Mathematics Pedagogy from a Constructivist Perspective." *Journal for Research in Mathematics Education* 26 (March 1995): 114–45.

Tierney, Cornelia C. "Different Shapes, Equal Pieces: Fractions and Area." *Investigations in Number, Data, and Space, Grade 4.* Glenview, Ill: Pearson Scott Foresman, 2006.

West, Lucy, and Fritz C. Staub. *Content-Focused Coaching: Transforming Mathematics Lessons.* Portsmouth, N.H.: Heinemann, 2003.

Supporting Grade-Level Teams

Carolyn Doyle and Candace Standley

Working with grade-level teams provides mathematics specialists with the opportunity to get inside the dynamics of a school's mathematics program and develop an understanding of the teaching practices of each teacher. Once a mathematics specialist has this insight, she can plan meetings and suggest activities that will help each grade-level team become more cohesive and focused on understanding and teaching the mathematical objectives and concepts in the curriculum and meeting the needs of the students.

Supporting Teams of Teachers: An Overview

Mathematics specialists should organize regular grade-level team meetings with a planned agenda. The agenda does not have to be typed and presented to the team, but the mathematics specialist should have specific goals and objectives for each meeting. Otherwise, the meeting can easily get off course. In addition, teachers will be more willing to attend future meetings if they feel the time spent was productive. For mathematics specialists, nothing is more important than talking about mathematics teaching and learning, but for elementary teachers, mathematics is just one piece of the work they do in a day. The mathematics specialist should be sensitive to the needs of the teachers and flexible when scheduling meetings. For some teams, a meeting before school might work best. For others, meetings during a team-planning period or after school might be better.

Encouraging teachers to "do the math"

Mathematics specialists should plan meetings that allow teachers opportunities to construct an understanding of what is presented, rather than simply telling teachers what they should do. In this regard, working with teachers is very similar to working with a class of students. Teachers need time to process new information and make connections with what they already know. It is best to provide opportunities for teachers to discover the power of a lesson or activity instead of simply telling them what to do. Mathematics specialists want to encourage and inspire teachers to also be learners.

See teachers as learners.

I started my fourth-grade planning meeting by admitting that the partial products method we used last year to teach multiplication had turned out to be just another rote procedure for some students. We had hoped it would help the children develop a deeper understanding of multiplication, but frequently that wasn't the case. Some fifth graders were writing out equations for each partial product. For example, one child solved 17 × 10 by writing and solving the separate partial products for 0 × 7, 0 × 10, 10 × 7, and 10 × 10, and then adding the four numbers, which included two zeros. Clearly, we would need to refine our approach this year. So I asked the teachers to think about how to build understanding before making the transition to a related algorithm. I also provided a couple of articles from *Teaching Children Mathematics.*

By the time we met again, the teachers had warmed up to the idea of teaching multi-digit multiplication differently. But they still had concerns. I said, "OK, you are my students. I want you to solve 18 × 14. I'd like to see an array, the traditional method, and a partial-products method, and I'd like you to write a word problem to match 18 × 14." What happened was amazing! The room was initially silent as the teachers tried to connect what they knew with what was new and unfamiliar. Then they looked to one another for guidance, asking questions as they went along. Once they finished, they shared their word problem as well as their thoughts about what misconceptions the children might have. They discussed the connections among the models. I was able to remind them that this is what we want our students to experience—making sense. We were now ready to become more specific about our ideas for teaching.

—*Reflections from a mathematics specialist*

Mathematics specialists should engage teachers in doing the mathematics themselves in ways that connect with understanding students' perceptions and developing instructional strategies. It is important for mathematics specialists to create a safe learning environment for teachers, allowing them to experience both the disequilibrium that comes from learning something new and the pleasure that comes from finally understanding.

Planning lessons, doing the mathematics, and sharing resources are good ways to involve teachers in the mathematics that they are teaching. Before a meeting, the mathematics specialist should refer to the school district's curriculum to find out what concepts teachers of that grade will be teaching in the coming weeks and what related concepts either have been previously addressed or will be taught. If the school district does not provide a curriculum, then the specialist can refer to the state curriculum, after determining what major mathematical topic a grade-level team has decided to address next. After evaluating the curriculum, the mathematics specialist should identify activities and manipulatives to share with the team.

In the team meeting, it is important to allow time for teachers to solve some mathematics problems and use some manipulatives. This hands-on work helps teachers develop a better understanding of how mathematical concepts are connected. Teachers often have the mathematical knowledge to complete a task, but they need time to explore how students will develop that understanding and to consider common misconceptions or confusion that students may reveal. Taking time to "do the math" also gives teachers an opportunity to construct an understanding without having to be brave enough to say, "I don't get it!"

Let teachers construct their own knowledge.

Today's activity really reinforced for me how important it is for teachers to have the opportunity to construct their own learning. Sometimes we assume that a teacher truly understands a concept, but he may not. Many teachers feel uncomfortable admitting that they don't know or understand how to do something that is in their grade-level standards. Today while working with a team of teachers on an activity that required them to model division of fractions by using manipulatives, drawings, and number lines, I was able to see the need for further exploration in this area. As teachers worked through the problems, they shared ideas, and it became easier for them to ask for help and clarification. If I had just given them the materials and gone over the changes in the standard, I would never have known how much they didn't understand about the concept.

—Reflections from a mathematics specialist

Blending mathematical ideas

Consider the different ways that the third-grade teachers in one team believe that multiplication should be taught. Mr. Mac has been teaching third grade for 30 years. He starts teaching multiplication in November, and he expects that all students will memorize the multiplication facts before moving on. He presents a 90-fact worksheet each day. Once students have mastered the facts with quick recall, he teaches arrays and problem solving. Miss Brown, another third-grade teacher at the school, starts with an exploration of multiplication. Her students write and solve story problems. They model multiplication on the number line. They build and draw arrays. She develops automaticity once her students have a thorough understanding of the concept of multiplication. Miss See is a brand-new third-grade teacher on the team. She remembers memorizing her multiplication facts and thinks her students should do that, but she also believes that her students should have a deeper understanding of multiplication than she did as a child.

Faced with a grade-level team like this one, the mathematics specialist can help the teachers blend their ideas so that all students are successful. This does not mean that all three teachers must teach in exactly the same way. But as the specialist works with each grade-level team, an important goal is to address each teacher's understanding of why it is important and how to support their students' efforts not just to remember but to make sense of the mathematics.

One way to accomplish this goal is to model a lesson for each teacher. A better way is to facilitate a modified lesson study so that the teachers can see how the children respond to a particular lesson. Another technique is for the team to co-plan a lesson for the teachers to teach in their classrooms. Then each teacher can bring samples of student work from this lesson to the next grade-level team meeting. The resulting discussion of students' work can permit a conversation spanning mathematical meaning, students' thinking, and implications for future instruction.

Providing research on best practices and then trying to apply an idea from that work in an actual lesson plan also helps teachers. If teachers are willing, talking about an article that everyone has read or conducting a book study can promote reflection and learning through discussion. Focusing on research-based best practices helps to keep teachers from feeling as though their instructional practices are under scrutiny or that their competence is being questioned.

Promoting the Mathematics

One of the best ways to help teachers see the connections among mathematical concepts is to co-plan a lesson and then have the teachers list the mathematics concepts covered in it. A variation on this process can also be a good activity for students: at the end of a mathematics lesson, students can identify all the mathematical concepts that they have used in it. For example, suppose that a lesson engages students in designing a floor plan for a house with 1000 square units of living space and asks the students to note the area and perimeter for each room. In the activity, students count, add, multiply, develop an understanding of area and perimeter, decompose and recompose 1000, and possibly subtract and divide. They may also discuss shapes and use fractions. The teacher's learning objective for the lesson should be clear; however, providing learning experiences that allow students to use mathematics in various situations will support their understanding as each concept is studied in depth.

The mathematics specialist can also engage teachers in planning lessons that connect mathematical concepts by making a suggestion and then letting the team develop the activity. In this case, the specialist serves as a knowledgeable resource as teachers devise potential activities.

A mathematics specialist may also support a team simply by supplying a handout and offering a few ideas. After offering teachers an idea or suggestion, the specialist facilitates team interaction as the learning unfolds. He needs to understand that although he may not get immediate rewards for his work, his impact is much more far-reaching in the school. The mathematics specialist's reward comes from working with teachers and watching as they and their students develop a love for and a deeper understanding of the mathematics.

Consider developing a grade-level mathematics field trip.

During a third-grade planning meeting, I shared a handout that I had found online for comparing the prices of brand-name and generic grocery items. The team of teachers brainstormed about ways that this handout could be used in the classroom. I asked if the team would be interested in a field trip to a local grocery store so that students could experience this mathematics in a real-world setting. Someone suggested contacting the local transit system to see whether the trolley could be made available. At that point, the teachers were buzzing about what the children could learn on this field trip. Students would need to understand paying a fare. Elapsed time could be factored in as well as keeping on a schedule. At the grocery store, students would have to understand the difference between brand-name and generic products. They would have to locate the prices, learn about unit pricing, and then decide how to compare costs. Seeing how grocery items are sorted and learning how items and brands are positioned in the store provided a social studies connection.

—Reflections from a mathematics specialist

Curriculum and Student Growth

In most situations, the state and school district provide a curriculum map that outlines what mathematics teachers are expected to teach in a school year to prepare students for future mathematics learning. The challenge for the mathematics specialist is to ensure that teachers teach *students* and not just curriculum! Using data to inform instruction and then planning differentiated lessons is a challenge for teachers. Teachers might say they do not have time for a problem-solving lesson or a lesson in which students are investigating the meaning of a concept. The reality is otherwise: we waste time by not providing this type of learning, because mathematics instruction that emphasizes teacher demonstration of mathematical approaches or solutions often results in reteaching or repeating a lesson. Such teaching also sets up the need to work with many students who "don't get it" and to plan how to reteach those students while simultaneously continuing to move the class forward through the curriculum. This situation presents a serious challenge for all teachers. Mathematics specialists can support grade-level teams as they address how to plan lessons that take the time to emphasize mathematical reasoning and support students' sense making, potentially eliminating the need to schedule future reteaching.

Pedagogy and Vision of Mathematics Instruction

The goal of building teachers' pedagogical knowledge is embedded in all the work of a mathematics specialist. Supporting teachers as they work in the interest of improving their mathematics instruction requires that the specialist tailor her professional development, co-teaching, co-planning, and modeling to meet the needs of the teacher. To do so, the specialist must gauge each teacher's understanding of mathematics content, as well as his knowledge of instructional practices, to identify his strengths and weaknesses and then provide the needed professional development.

One strategy that the mathematics specialist can use to identify and build on teachers' instructional strengths is to focus attention on a particular curriculum standard or objective or pose a question or problem to the group. Then the specialist should ask the teachers to verbalize their ideas about how to teach or introduce that concept to students. This discussion will often expand as the teachers share their perspectives on how students might learn a particular mathematical idea, or as they exchange insights into how students might solve a mathematics problem.

A grade-level team meeting can be a venue for sharing and building on each teacher's pedagogical knowledge. As each strategy is shared, each teacher should have the opportunity to articulate and clarify his understanding. The mathematics specialist can relate each teacher's contribution to another idea that a different teacher shared or elaborated on previously, thus giving additional perspective on the ideas. This venue can offer prime opportunities for the specialist to build on each teacher's pedagogical knowledge and provide encouragement for new strategies.

Talk with teachers about the mathematics.

Before the grade-level meeting, I asked the teachers in the third-grade team to be prepared to share their responses to the questions, "How do students develop fraction sense?" and "What understandings about fractions are third graders expected to develop?" I also asked them to bring samples of activities that they had used when teaching the concept of fractions. During the meeting, I gave each teacher an opportunity to share her thinking and understanding. I was surprised that all three teachers concentrated their comments on parts of a region, even though the curriculum builds to the understanding "a fraction is a number," with emphasis on the number line model. Although I had prepared a number of activities, I decided to share only a number line activity, in which rectangular strips of the same length are aligned with a number line. I didn't want the teachers to feel overwhelmed with many different models. Introducing one new model at a time and spending time developing a deep understanding of that model is much better than leaving teachers with a superficial understanding of a lot of models.

—Reflections from a mathematics specialist

During the team's discussion, as the teachers share their perspectives on how students develop an understanding of a particular mathematical concept, the specialist can pose additional questions to gain a clearer picture of the teachers' pedagogical knowledge. In determining where the teachers are in their thinking, the specialist should lead teachers to respond to key questions that will invite them to verbalize it, opening up a reflective discussion. For example, the specialist might ask the following:

- "What are the different levels of student understanding or thinking that you typically see?"
- "What are some student misconceptions that you might need to address?"
- "Do your materials offer a variety of cognitively demanding tasks or strategies?"
- "Are your approaches or tasks addressing student needs?"
- "How do you represent, model, or illustrate the concepts?"
- "How do you explain the concept?"
- "What types of examples do you use?"
- "What resources do you use to support the teaching?"
- "Which manipulatives do you think are best for teaching different aspects of the concepts?"

These are questions that the teacher with strong pedagogical knowledge of a concept will address and show evidence of as she plans a lesson.

By posing these questions to individual teachers and to the group as a whole in a grade-level team setting, the specialist creates a format that allows everyone to see and hear the same message. The ensuing discussion can bring the group to share and agree on a common mathematical language and vision for instruction that will improve student learning. At the same time, this discussion may include specific strategies and approaches that teachers can use when teaching the concept.

Remember, your questions matter most—not your answers.

It's the questions asked of the teachers, not the answers supplied by the specialist, which matter the most.

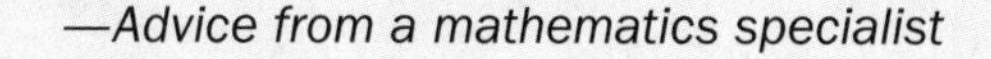

—Advice from a mathematics specialist

The mathematics specialist will have many opportunities in the course of his work to identify and build on the strengths and weaknesses of teachers' pedagogical knowledge. As the specialist co-plans and co-teaches with teachers, he can encourage teachers to share their thinking, and then he can follow up with suggestions or questions that will move the teacher to think about specific strategies and approaches, different levels of student understanding, common misconceptions that students develop, and appropriate cognitively demanding tasks, as well as possibilities for using different representations, manipulatives, or illustrations of concepts.

Supporting Growth in Content Knowledge

Lesson study is a wonderful way for teachers to promote one another's content and pedagogical growth. However, a drawback is that lesson study requires teachers to be out of their classrooms as they plan, observe, and debrief a lesson. Securing release time from the classroom can be problematic. Nevertheless, the mathematics specialist can make it happen by working with teachers to plan a modified lesson study.

Consider implementing a modified lesson study.

At a grade-level meeting, one of my teachers mentioned how much she enjoyed teaching a particular lesson to her second-grade class. We have a new teacher on the team, and she was interested in learning more about the lesson. So after the two teachers had briefly discussed the lesson and where to find a resource for it, I volunteered to teach the new teacher's class so that she could observe the lesson being taught by the veteran teacher. Once the observation had occurred, the two teachers discussed the lesson over lunch. This conversation led to a discussion of how the lesson could be changed to promote deeper understanding. To allow them to use their modified plan, I taught the veteran teacher's class the next day, so that she could observe use of the modified plan in the beginner's classroom. The benefit of this exchange went far beyond the original lesson. It promoted discussion about the mathematics, and it built camaraderie between the teachers so that they were more willing to discuss future mathematics lessons.

—Reflections from a mathematics specialist

Another strategy that a specialist can use to lead teachers to support one another's mathematical understanding and pedagogical growth is to include a mathematics problem as part of the agenda when grade-level teams meet. For example, a fifth-grade team was given the problem $47 \times 26 = ?$ and asked to solve it by using two different strategies. Figure 4.1 presents a sample of the strategies that the teachers shared.

During the team meeting, the specialist allowed each teacher to share her strategies. Two teachers were able to show two different ways to solve the problem, and the other two teachers were able to show only the traditional method for multiplication. Because the team members were encouraged to share their methods, the teachers were able to help and support one another in understanding the different strategies. In addition, this problem led to a discussion of the prior understandings and skills that each method relied on and the implications of this in the classroom, with the teachers discussing which of their students might experience more success with particular nontraditional multiplication algorithms.

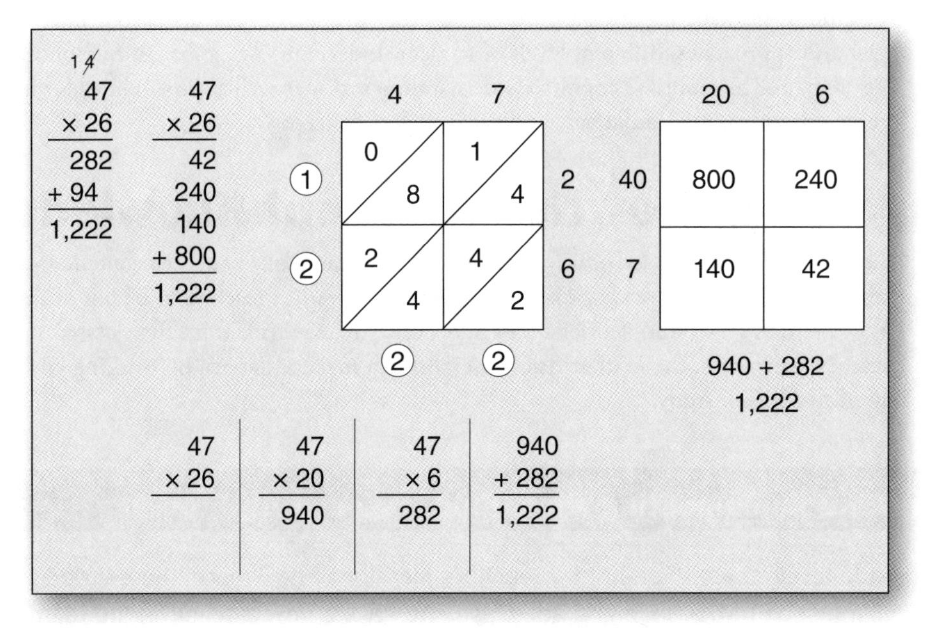

Fig. 4.1. Different ways of computing 47 × 26

By beginning with a problem in grade-level meetings, the specialist redirects the teaching and learning back to the teachers themselves. Each teacher has the opportunity to gain or offer support. The mathematics specialist is there to facilitate and guide this process as well as to offer her expertise at the appropriate time.

Another way to lead teachers to support one another's mathematical understanding and growth is by encouraging teachers to attend conferences, workshops, and school district–sponsored professional development as a group. When attending these events together, the teachers have the opportunity to share and discuss both mathematical content and instructional ideas among themselves. In the excitement generated by the professional development, many teachers find that they are comfortable discussing mathematical strategies as well as different ways of teaching concepts. In this environment, a teacher may feel safe in saying, "I don't understand."

The mathematics specialist can make these opportunities easier for teachers by talking to the principal about available funds, making arrangements for substitute teachers, and completing the necessary paperwork. Once teachers have attended a mathematics professional development activity, the mathematics specialist can be instrumental in making sure that they effectively use and share their new knowledge.

Regroup if necessary after a reality check of the dynamics of a grade-level team.

The dynamics of a grade-level team can be complex, and the issues may have nothing to do with how the teachers approach math instruction. Sometimes it is not possible to work successfully with an entire grade-level team because of personality conflicts. If the negatives are outweighing the positives, the specialist may need to reevaluate the situation. It may be necessary for the mathematics specialist to change the configuration for planning meetings. If one teacher is the source of dissension, then it might be necessary to work with that teacher individually. If there are two distinct "camps" within the grade level, perhaps meeting with the two groups separately might work better for everyone.

—Advice from a mathematics specialist

Mathematical Trajectory and Coherent Mathematics Programs

A coherent school mathematics program requires that all teachers understand the mathematical connections across the grade levels as well as the trajectory of student learning. To achieve a coherent and shared mathematics program, the mathematics specialist should facilitate professional development and structured discussions about the mathematics being taught, about expectations for student learning at each grade level, and about the district's curriculum.

Investigating a curriculum trajectory

The elementary mathematics specialist should provide opportunities for teachers to investigate the mathematics curriculum from kindergarten through the middle school. It is difficult for a school to reflect a coherent, shared mathematics program unless all teachers know and understand what students are expected to learn and when they are expected to learn it. This means that teachers need an understanding not only of when and what mathematical skills and concepts should be taught, according to the curriculum, but also of what the prerequisite skills and understandings are for each concept. It is generally accepted that each teacher needs to understand how and what she is teaching to her students. But in mathematics, it is just as important for each teacher to understand how what she is teaching will be instrumental to the students' learning of the next set of grade-level concepts or objectives.

The specialist who tries to cover all the concepts or objectives for all grade levels in one or two sessions will find this to be a daunting task. Addressing one mathematical topic at a time, as a part of the discussions of lesson planning for that topic, may be more effective. One method might be to select a key mathematical concept or objective and trace it first back to kindergarten and then up to grade 6, so that teachers can consider how students learn a concept and what content they are expected to address in relation to that content before leaving elementary school. The chart in figure 4.2 was developed during a third-grade team meeting in which teachers tracked standards in the Common Core State Standards for Mathematics across the clusters that addressed reasoning with shapes and their attributes in the domain of geometry.

In the vignette that begins on page 61, the mathematics specialist shares her reflections on the professional development session in which this chart was developed.

Kindergarten	First Grade	Second Grade	Third Grade	Fourth Grade	Fifth Grade	Sixth Grade
CCSS.Math. Content.K.G.2 Correctly name shapes regardless of their orientations or overall size. **CCSS.Math. Content.K.G.4** Analyze and compare two- and three-dimensional shapes, in different sizes and orientations, using informal language to describe their similarities, differences, parts (e.g., number of sides and vertices/"corners") and other attributes (e.g., having sides of equal length).	**CCSS.Math. Content.1.G.1** Distinguish between defining attributes (e.g., triangles are closed and three-sided) versus non-defining attributes (e.g., color, orientation, overall size) ; build and draw shapes to possess defining attributes. **CCSS.Math. Content.1.G.2** Compose two-dimensional shapes (rectangles, squares, trapezoids, triangles, half-circles, and quarter-circles) or three-dimensional shapes (cubes, right rectangular prisms, right circular cones, and right circular cylinders) to create a composite shape, and compose new shapes from the composite shape.	**CCSS.Math. Content.2.G.1** Recognize and draw shapes having specified attributes, such as a given number of angles or a given number of equal faces. Identify triangles, quadrilaterals, pentagons, hexagons, and cubes.	**CCSS.Math. Content.3.G.1** Understand that shapes in different categories (e.g., rhombuses, rectangles, and others) may share attributes (e.g., having four sides), and that the shared attributes can define a larger category (e.g., quadrilaterals). Recognize rhombuses, rectangles, and squares as examples of quadrilaterals, and draw examples of quadrilaterals that do not belong to any of these subcategories.	**CCSS.Math. Content.4.G.2** Classify two-dimensional figures based on the presence or absence of parallel or perpendicular lines, or the presence or absence of angles of a specified size. Recognize right triangles as a category, and identify right triangles.	**CCSS.Math. Content.5.G.3** Understand that attributes belonging to a category of two-dimensional figures also belong to all subcategories of that category. *For example, all rectangles have four right angles and squares are rectangles, so all squares have four right angles.* **CCSS.Math. Content.5.G.4** Classify two-dimensional figures in a hierarchy based on properties.	**CCSS.Math. Content.6.G.3** Draw polygons in the coordinate plane given coordinates for the vertices; use coordinates to find the length of a side joining points with the same first coordinate or the same second coordinate. Apply these techniques in the context of solving real-world and mathematical problems. **CCSS.Math. Content.6.G.4** Represent three-dimensional figures using nets made up of rectangles and triangles, and use the nets to find the surface area of these figures. Apply these techniques in the context of solving real-world and mathematical problems.

Fig. 4.2. Tracking grade 3 objectives back to kindergarten and ahead to grade 6 in the Common Core State Standards for Mathematics (National Governors Association Center for Best Practices and Council of Chief State School Officers 2010)

One day while I was standing on bus duty, two of the fourth-grade teachers walked by discussing the fact that many of their students knew only the four basic shapes and could describe the shapes only in terms of sides. Then the whispering began about what the third-grade teachers were teaching. That very same day, the second-grade team had an informal meeting around the copy machine. Once again the topic was geometric figures. These teachers were wondering what the first-grade teachers were teaching. They were taken aback about the lack of prior knowledge that the students had.

Hearing similar conversations from two different grade-level teams about the learning expectations of the previous grade level caused me to reflect on whether I was doing all that I should to create a coherent mathematics program in the school. How could we have a coherent program if teachers at every grade level didn't know what teachers in the other grades were teaching? Did the teachers really know how important it is for students to master the content or skill expected by each standard to be ready to build on it next year? Did they realize how what they were teaching now would affect the students' learning at the next grade? I really thought my school had a coherent program that the teachers and staff understood. However, it was as though they had tunnel vision when it came to teaching mathematics. As it turned out, teachers at each grade level knew what they had to teach, and that was their focus. They didn't look back at the prior grade-level standards and expectations, and they didn't look ahead, either.

I came up with a plan. I wanted the entire school to come together and track all the standards from kindergarten through sixth grade. I thought this would give the teachers an opportunity to see the prior knowledge that students should have when they come to a new grade and the skills that the next grade-level teacher is expecting them to have when they move on. Unfortunately, time was not available for this massive professional development undertaking. But I knew that something had to be done. We couldn't move forward as a school if we didn't all have the same vision of our mathematics program. My next plan of action was to do mini–professional development sessions with each grade level during our mathematics meeting time.

I met with the third-grade team first, since we had not had our weekly meeting yet. I began the professional development by giving the teachers a sorting activity with plane figures. They had to sort the plane figures into three groups and describe the categories that they made. After they had shared their groupings, I asked them if they felt that this was an appropriate task for their students. Then I asked the group to tell me the prerequisite knowledge that the students would need to have about plane figures to master this standard. One of the teachers, Ms. Wade, replied that they should already know the shapes and shouldn't need a lot of instruction to do the activity. She also stated that shapes were a "kindergarten thing." This was the perfect opening for me to move the group to see and understand that the objectives or concepts that we teach are not discrete entities. There is a connection across the grade levels.

My next question was, "What shapes do you think students learn at the kindergarten level?" They all agreed that these were the square, circle, triangle, and rectangle. Then I asked, "What do they learn in first grade?" One teacher said that they learned how to draw them. Then I asked about second grade. Another teacher commented that they talk about sides and then do something with 3-D shapes. I didn't comment on any of the responses. I just listened.

I suggested that we go on a field trip. Of course they had a look of surprise. Then I said, "Let's take a field trip through the standards. Let's see where our students have been on their journey through geometry and where they are going."

I gave the teachers a blank chart with seven sections. I had them label the sections kindergarten through sixth grade. Using the standards, I asked them to read and write the third-grade objective for geometric shapes, not addressing fractional parts, in the fourth section. I posed the question: "What instruction should the students have had so far to give them the prerequisite skills needed to address this third-grade objective?" I wrote their comments on a large chart. "At which grade level do you think this instruction was provided?" The teachers came up with a good list of prerequisite understandings, but they weren't sure when the students learned those ideas. We then took a "walk" through the standards. The teachers filled in their chart with all the previous grade-level objectives related to plane and solid figures. We discussed the trajectory of expectations across the grade levels and related these to their listing of prerequisite understandings. We also discussed some of the difficulties that students may have with a given grade-level objective if they have not mastered the previous grade-level objective.

A comment from Ms. Wade made a smooth transition to my next point. She said, "The K, 1, and 2 teachers really need to teach those shapes so that when we get their students, they will be ready to move right along." So I asked, "How does your instruction to meet this objective connect with the students' future learning? Are students finished with plane and solid figures?" No one knew. None of the teachers on this team had taught other grades, so I asked them to fill in the chart with the standards for plane and solid figures for grades 4 and 5. We had a discussion similar to our earlier one. Then I asked them to think about the following questions but not to answer aloud: "Are there standards that you know that your students are weak in grasping when they leave your classroom? What are some of the causes for this? Do you ever skip standards because you don't feel comfortable in teaching them?"

At the end of the activity, I asked for thoughts from the group. Most of the comments were very enlightening and indicated that many of the teachers had become reflective about their own instruction. Mr. Manuel responded that everyone will always be playing catch-up if anyone doesn't teach the expected standards. But Ms. Greene summed up the session best. She said, "It's not just about us and our grade level. It's about the grades before us and the grades after us. We're like a train that is connected. If one railroad car or part of the train comes off the track, that one car affects the whole train. So, if one teacher or grade level doesn't do its part, the resulting deficiency in learning continues to affect the student in future grades."

As I reflected on this session after the teachers had left, I realized that this format of working with just one grade level at a time was probably more beneficial than working with the whole faculty at once. The teachers had time to share and time to take a moment to pause and reflect. I plan to follow the same format with the other grades next week. I hope they will be as reflective as this group. I believe that these professional development sessions will move us in the right direction. We need our school to have a coherent mathematics program that is clear and understood by everyone.

In addition to creating a chart tracking a trajectory of standards as described in the vignette, the specialist might have examples of what activities to meet a mathematical expectation might look like in each grade. Giving teachers problems to solve that mirror student learning expectations can provide a window of opportunity for increasing teachers' conceptual understanding.

Shared instructional strategies build coherence

A first step in developing a shared understanding of mathematics is recognizing the mathematical connections across grades. But a shared vocabulary bank is also important. As students move from grade to grade, the cohesiveness of the mathematics program should be evident in the vocabulary used by teachers and students. The specialist can facilitate the development of this vocabulary by exploring the curriculum with the grade-level teams and having all the teams discuss and agree on the vocabulary and terminology that will be used by everyone.

Another effective technique to build understanding across the grade levels is for the mathematics specialist to facilitate meetings in which two or three grade-level teams gather to share their instructional strategies or emphases. If this technique is used, it is very important that the specialist have specific goals in place for the meeting. The specialist will need to ensure that the meeting addresses the continuum of student learning and understandings and does not become an arena for blame or personal attacks. Questions or topics may include the following:

- "What instructional strategies are teachers across different grade levels using?"
- "How might we develop a shared bank of strategies for use across grade levels?"
- "What concepts do you think may need more teaching time?"
- "Do you have enough materials to teach the concepts effectively? What do you need?"
- "What strengths or weaknesses are the students bringing to the grade level?"

Consider the following short vignette in which Ms. Stafford, the mathematics specialist, is working with teachers to address student weaknesses in rounding and estimating.

After reviewing test data, Ms. Stafford realized that rounding and estimation scores were low from third grade right through fifth grade. During team planning meetings, Ms. Stafford asked teachers to share their methods for teaching rounding. In the sharing session, Ms. Stafford quickly realized that the concepts of rounding and estimation were being lost in all the different "fun" approaches that teachers were using to try to help students master a skill in an engaging way (see fig 4.3). Further, an important idea was missing—the notion of using estimation and rounding to decide whether an answer obtained by applying a particular mathematical procedure or model made sense. Students were not learning that estimation was a tool that would help them identify possible errors.

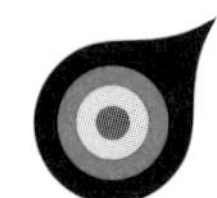

A situation such as Ms. Stafford encountered presents a particularly difficult problem for the mathematics specialist. This specialist needed to figure out how to guide her teachers to an understanding of the concept of rounding and estimation without appearing to be critical of their current instructional strategies, of which the teachers were particularly proud. When Ms. Stafford realized what was happening, she had a conversation with each grade-level team. What she found was that instruction related to rounding varied within each grade level as well as across grades. She asked teachers to consider situations in which someone might round numbers: what real-life scenarios would require rounding or estimation? She also asked teachers to consider how their various strategies did or did not support the place-value concepts that students were learning. What might students stand to gain if rounding and estimation focused on developing number sense and not just mastery of an isolated skill? She had the teachers brainstorm about a single strategy for rounding numbers to implement across the grades to help students develop a deep understanding of rounding and estimation.

The mathematics specialist must provide opportunities for teachers to construct mathematical understandings. If Ms. Stafford had been judgmental of her third- through fifth-grade teachers' strategies, she might have lost the respect not only of these teachers but also of other teachers in the school. Teachers want to do what is best for students, but their vantage point is restricted. The mathematics specialist can help teachers understand how what students are learning in one grade connects with what they will learn in the next.

- In Miss Ryu's third-grade class, students learned about "rounding hills." They put the 10s on the base of the hills and labeled the hills with all the numbers in between, with 15, 25, 35, … at the top. Miss Ryu asked the students to imagine that a car is traveling up a hill. If it runs out of gas, it will fall back down to the previous multiple of 10. If it is traveling down a hill and runs out of gas, it will fall to the next multiple of 10. Miss Ryu's students also imagined that gas stations are at the bases of the hills. If a car runs out of gas right at the top of the hill, the nearest gas stations are equal distances away, but the driver of the car "wants to go to the gas station that is farther along on the trip"—at the next multiple of 10.
- In Miss Smith's fourth-grade class, students used a strategy called "UZA," with U for underline, Z for zero, and A for arrow. For example, rounding 7,835,210 to the nearest ten thousand by using UZA would involve three steps:

  Step 1: Underline the digit in the ten thousands place: 7,8$\underline{3}$5,210

  Step 2: Replace all the digits to the right of the underlined digit by zero: 7,8$\underline{3}$0,000

  The students learn to do this when they are rounding because no matter the result of their rounding, these digits will turn into zeros.

  Step 3: Draw an arrow from the digit directly to the right of the place value to which you are rounding to that place value: 7,8$\underline{3}$5,210. Then decide if the digit where the arrow is starts is a "puny" number (less than 5) or a "muscular" number (5 or greater). In the case of this problem, the number is a "muscular" number; therefore, the 3 would change to a 4. The end result is 7,840,000.

  If students are unsuccessful with UZA, Miss Smith uses a chant that reinforces the terms "puny numbers" and "big, strong muscular numbers" with her students.
- In Mrs. Barker's fifth-grade classroom, students underline the digit in the place value they are rounding to and then rewrite the original number. But "poof!" (like magic), the digits to the right of the underlined digit change to zeros. Next, students place the "poofed" number on the left side of a number line. Then they add 1 to the underlined digit in the "poofed" number, and place it on the right side of the number line. Finally, students circle the digit in the original number that is "next door" to the right of the underlined digit. If that number is ≥ 5, they select the larger "poofed" number on the right; if it is < 5, they select the smaller "poofed" value on the left.

Fig. 4.3. Rounding methods taught in grades 3–5 in Ms. Stafford's school

Using Assessments and Data to Inform Instruction

The mathematics specialist, as the facilitator of improved instruction by grade-level teams of teachers, can engage teachers in learning how to create effective common assessments. Through productive questioning, the mathematics specialist can motivate teachers to think about a variety of aspects of their work. Such questions might include the following:

- "What do we want students to learn?"
- "How will we know whether they have learned it?"
- "What is the next step if they did not learn it?"
- "What is the next step if they already know it?"

As teachers reflect on these questions and collaborate to create common assessments, they are increasing the probability that all the students at a particular grade level will be taught and assessed on the same skills, with the same intensity and rigor.

As the specialist leads the grade-level team to reflect on what student learning should be, the focus should be on the district's curriculum and the mathematics program. To create an effective common assessment, a shared, coherent mathematics program must be in place and understood by all. The specialist may need to devote specific time to making sure that all the teachers understand the curriculum. Once the specialist and teachers have decided what the students should be learning, they must reflect further on the type of assessment that they will need.

The most effective questions for a common assessment are those that meet the purpose and the criteria that the group has agreed on collaboratively. Many questions may be interesting, and the students' responses to them may also be interesting, but the purpose of the assessment should be paramount in composing or selecting questions. Once it is clear what the students should be learning, then further discussion should focus on determining the type of assessment questions that is most appropriate. Would open-ended questions, in response to which students show their work, provide the best measure of this aspect of student learning? Or would short-answer questions or multiple-choice items be better? Or would some combination of the two formats be best?

Discuss and evaluate assessment items.

The fourth-grade teachers brought in an assessment that they had made the previous year. Our goal was to review the assessment to determine whether it was aligned with the current curriculum. One question caused a lot of debate. It was an interesting question, but it was not aligned with the curriculum. Then a teacher said, "Let's keep it on the test anyway. It will let us see how well the students can solve problems and analyze new concepts." I invited the group to reflect:

- "Is the question aligned?"
- "Does this question assess what will be taught?"
- "How will being assessed on brand-new material affect the confidence of the students?"
- "Will this question address our purpose for the assessment?"

—*Reflections from a mathematics specialist*

Looking at data

After administering and scoring a common assessment, the next step is to interpret the collected data. This step is just as important as creating the common assessment. The mathematics specialist will first need to categorize the students' scores and responses. Then he should create charts and graphs to organize the data. The specialist should then engage grade-level teams in discussions of how they can use these new data to inform practice. The teachers may have questions about how groups of students or individual students responded to particular items or the entire assessment. The specialist may recategorize, or disaggregate, the data to answer these questions for teachers, or he may work with the teachers to do so. Sometimes the data may be readily accessible in computer-generated disaggregated formats.

Although the data should be reviewed and considered through several lenses, it is most important to analyze them with the focus on the students. The specialist and teachers should examine individual students' strengths and weaknesses, as well as classroom and grade-level strengths and weaknesses.

Ways to look at and explore data abound, but the focus should be on ways to improve instruction. Teachers might want to discuss a student's work habits, his inability to pay attention, or his lack of home support in an effort to explain away the data. The mathematics specialist must help teachers see value in the data beyond what a student does or does not do. One way to explore data is to present a team with the pass rates for each question from each class. Teachers should celebrate their own and their students' accomplishments in areas where students were successful and reflect on the work that remains to be done in areas that need improvement. If the pass rate for a concept was high in one class and low in another, the discrepancy provides an opportunity for teachers to share instructional strategies. A concept that had a low pass rate across the grade level gives the team a chance to discuss how that mathematics concept was taught and what strategies team members can use to improve their students' understanding. Figure 4.4 shows a table that was developed during a third-grade data meeting. The specialist and grade-level teachers reviewed the data and made a list of students needing additional instruction within each of the assessed concepts.

Identify the place value through 1000s	Round whole numbers to nearest 10 or 100	Compare two whole numbers (3 or 4 digits)
Arianand	Arianand	Marie
Minh	Minh	Tyshawn
Lakar	Lakar	Victor
Marie	Marie	
Tyshawn	Tyshawn	
Estevan	Patrick	
Devontay	Kimberly	
	Dennis	
	Estevan	
	Devontay	

Fig. 4.4. A table made by a mathematics specialist and a grade-level team to identify students' remediation needs

Once data are disaggregated, the team needs to decide on the next step. If the majority of the students need additional instruction on a concept, an instructional or curricular issue may exist. A large number of students failing to master a concept may indicate that the instructional strategies or the curricular materials were not effective. If that is the conclusion, the mathematics specialist will need to provide professional development for the teachers to strengthen their approach to the concept. If the data show that only a few students failed to master a concept, then the teachers will need to provide a new approach or additional instruction only to those students. The specialist, however, will need to make sure that the teachers have a battery of strategies to remediate the students' understanding effectively.

Moving between Team Meetings and Teachers' Classrooms

When a specialist is working with a grade-level team, she is not only developing a relationship with a group of teachers, but also coming to know the individual teachers on the team. Her growing knowledge should help her identify possible ways of working both within grade-level teams and with individual teachers. But if a specialist is going to work as a coach with a teacher, she will first need to gain entry into that teacher's classroom.

Gaining access to teachers' classrooms is an important task for the mathematics specialist; however, it can be somewhat daunting. Choosing a technique for gaining entry and developing and implementing it require a degree of finesse. In one sense, the elementary mathematics specialist is maneuvering his way into what has previously been exclusively the classroom teacher's territory or domain. So it is important for the mathematics specialist to use techniques that will result in a teacher wanting him to work in his classroom, or at least seeing a need for the specialist to do so.

One strategy that the mathematics specialist can use is to be helpful to the classroom teacher whenever possible, even in ways that are not related to teaching mathematics. The specialist should be cautious, however, not to offer to do too much. Small tasks that take very little time are the best. Tasks that involve being inside the classroom are also good choices since they provide a way to gain informal entry into the classroom.

Be ready to share a quick, impromptu activity with students.

I noticed that a recurring topic of conversation during the grade-level meetings was the boisterous behavior of students as they were arriving and getting settled each morning. What I began to do was patrol the hallways during the morning announcements to assist the late students in getting to class. It is my habit to have a mathematics-related game, manipulative, or flashcards with me at all times. On one occasion, I was walking down the fourth-grade hall. Mr. Burton was having a discussion with a student in the hallway. His class was getting noisy. I asked Mr. Burton if I could assist him. He quickly said, "Yes, could you watch my class while I handle this?"

First, I managed to get the class quiet. Then, since on that day I was carrying number cards, I showed them the number 16. I gave them the task of showing as many ways of making 16 as they could in two minutes while working independently, and then I gave them two minutes to work in small groups. Afterward, we shared as a group. While we were in the middle of the activity, Mr. Burton returned. I asked him if I could have a few more minutes. He agreed, and we concluded the activity. On the way out, Mr. Burton thanked me for helping out. Just about the time I got to the door, Mr. Burton said, "I liked that activity, and the students seemed to enjoy it. Do you have any more like that?" I responded, "Yes, I will bring some with me to our grade-level meeting this afternoon."

—Reflections from a mathematics specialist

Providing short-term assistance to teachers at a time when they need it can provide an entry into the classroom. Sometimes simply respectfully demonstrating an awareness of the teacher's need and offering assistance can help the specialist and the teacher continue building their relationship. If the specialist volunteers on the spot to take the teacher's place while the teacher completes an unexpected task outside the classroom, the teacher may return to the classroom in time to see just enough of the specialist's activity with his students to pique his interest. The mathematics specialist can then bring the activity to the grade-level meeting, giving the whole team a chance to see the teacher's enthusiasm about the activity and the mathematics specialist's visit. It is very important for the mathematics specialist to share in such a way that no judgment or stigma is attached, enabling other teachers in the group to ask the specialist to come to their classrooms to model an activity.

A great way for a mathematics specialist to gain access to a teacher's classroom is for her to ask to practice a strategy that she has seen or read about. By making this request, the mathematics specialist sets up the situation as a learning opportunity for herself. This puts the main focus on the mathematics specialist as the learner—the one with the need—as opposed to the teacher. Although this is an indirect way of gaining entry into a teacher's classroom, the grade-level team will benefit from the feedback and insights of the observing teacher as well those of the mathematics specialist. Not only does the mathematics specialist gain access to the classroom, but an atmosphere of camaraderie develops as the specialist and the teachers adapt and modify the strategy to make it more effective.

Another technique that the mathematics specialist can implement is to ask to observe a strategy that the teacher is already using. When the mathematics specialist uses this approach, he not only gains more knowledge about how a teacher is using the strategy, but also about how the strategy is being received by students in a particular classroom. Once the mathematics specialist is in the classroom, he will find that additional coaching opportunities will become available. However, the mathematics specialist has to be very strategic in gaining access. The initial visit must be positive and nonthreatening for future collaboration to be effective.

Offer to share an idea in the classroom.

I am so excited! I met with the fourth-grade team today. I was trying to think of a way to help them teach students to measure to the nearest half, fourth, and eighth. It has been so hard to find a way to get into their rooms. There have been so many roadblocks. Today I found my "in"! I asked if I could try out a measurement strategy that I had read about. I said that sometimes these strategies look good on paper, but that you just don't know until you try it out. The funny thing is, I really do need to get comfortable with this measurement strategy. But now, at the same time, I have two instant volunteers!

—Reflections from a mathematics specialist

In some situations, a mathematics specialist is assigned to, or embedded in, a particular grade level for an entire school year. In such a case, the mathematics specialist works closely with the team and each day co-teaches with one of the teachers, either rotating through a team's classrooms on a schedule or always working in the same classroom each day. In these co-teaching settings, the teacher shares her pedagogical expertise, and the mathematics specialist shares her mathematical expertise. This is an excellent form of professional development for both. Being in classrooms daily gives the mathematics specialist a frame of reference for the progress students are making. It also provides her with the opportunity to see how students react to the mathematics and the lessons.

Teachers in this working relationship often try new ideas that they can share with the team, making adjustments to enhance student learning when needed. With two teachers in the room, it's easy to try new lesson ideas because while one teacher is teaching, the other can be monitoring how well children understand the mathematics. The next year, the teachers who worked closely with the mathematics specialist become the experts on their team, sharing ideas during planning and helping the team gather the necessary resources for lessons. Team meetings can center on discussions of lessons, and in some cases the mathematics specialist or the classroom teacher with expertise can visit another class to teach or observe a lesson. Although the mathematics specialist is focused on that grade level during the year, he will also need to share ideas with other grade levels.

Effecting Change

It is evident that the work done by the mathematics specialist and grade-level teams is invaluable in bringing about change in the way that mathematics instruction is delivered in our schools. From meetings about mathematics to idea-sharing moments in the classroom, the interactions of a teacher and a mathematics specialist make the two of them a powerful duo in providing students with access to mathematics. It is important to remember that the mathematics specialist is an integral part of every grade-level team. The changes that happen in mathematics instruction evolve over time as a result of the work done by the mathematics specialist as she builds trusting relationships and relates respectfully and professionally to all teachers. Staying positive and focused on the goal of improving instruction and student learning is the cornerstone of the specialist's success.

Reference

National Governors Association Center for Best Practices and Council of Chief State School Officers (NGA Center and CCSSO). *Common Core State Standards for Mathematics. Common Core State Standards (College- and Career-Readiness Standards and K–12 Standards in English Language Arts and Math).* Washington, D.C.: NGA Center and CCSSO, 2010. http://www.corestandards.org/assets/CCSSI_Math Standards.pdf.

Supporting Groups of Teachers across Grades

Laura S. Domalik, Vandivere P. Hodges, and Linda K. Jaeger

Working with one teacher can be challenging, working with a grade-level team can be more challenging, and working with a mix of teachers from varying grade levels can be most challenging. Each person, grade level, and group of teachers comes to the table with an agenda and wants or needs. But working with teachers from varying grade levels can also be a rewarding and illuminating experience. The mix of ideas, contrasting opinions, and distinctive bases of knowledge promotes the best reflection, the liveliest discussion, and, in the end, the most meaningful changes for students, teachers, and schools.

Working with teachers from different grades is not easy, and the mathematics specialist should not be haphazard about this work. All her efforts should be well planned, organized, and executed with a specific goal in mind: continued success and increased achievement of the students. Specialists must know the individual teachers in their schools. They must understand the wants and needs of teachers at different grade levels. And they must bring all participants together in a relationship that is cultivated to bring about change.

This chapter looks at the role that a mathematics specialist plays in supporting various groups of teachers as they collaborate to gain a deeper understanding of mathematics and a clearer picture of their students' mathematical development. The size and makeup of these groups of teachers will vary. The specialist may work with a small group of teachers who share a common interest or with a vertical team of all teachers within a grade band (for example, K–grade 2 or grades 3–5). He may involve all teachers in a school in schoolwide professional development, or he may even be asked to conduct a workshop drawing teachers from across his school district. As the size and focus of these groups change, so too will the specialist's role.

Working with Small Groups of Teachers

Collaborative work with individual teachers and small groups of teachers is a critical component of a specialist's work. This interaction builds the foundation for teachers to learn and change the way they teach. For many new specialists, initial work focuses on coaching individual teachers. Chapter 3, "Coaching Individual Teachers," addresses that work. From early in her school placement, however, the mathematics specialist will also support the work of grade-level teams. Chapter 4, "Supporting Grade-Level Teams," considers that work. Teachers develop a shared sense of purpose and deepen their understanding of mathematics content and teaching strategies in their grade-level teams. But once that work is under way, a specialist may decide she is ready to widen her involvement in and impact on her school's mathematics program.

One way to do this is to work with self-defined, small groups of teachers across the school. Teachers may voluntarily join together with the goal of improving their teaching practice in relation to an area of common interest. For example, a teacher whose classroom has students at different academic levels or from different nations may welcome the opportunity to join a small group of teachers addressing mathematics instruction for gifted and talented students, special needs students, or English language learners. The mathematics specialist can support this group of teachers by identifying a book or resource related to their interests and by participating in their conversations.

For example, in one school a group of teachers from different grades wanted to strengthen their questioning techniques. So the mathematics specialist suggested that they come together periodically and share their thoughts on the book *Good Questions for Math Teaching: Why Ask Them and What to Ask (K–6)* (Sullivan and Lilburn 2002). Over the school year, as differing mathematical topics were emphasized in the curriculum guide, the specialist suggested particular chapters to read. As the group discussed a chapter, teachers typically agreed to use suggested questions in their classrooms and then to come together later to share what happened. During these sessions, the specialist was ready with related stories drawn from his own experiences, lending credibility and showing empathy and understanding for teachers' concerns. In this setting, teachers saw the mathematics specialist as a fellow learner as well as a leader, helping to build a bridge of mutual respect and understanding.

Conduct a needs survey.

Whatever is needed is what the specialist offers. In the past, I have put a "needs survey" in teachers' mailboxes as a way to prompt them to reflect and call on me anonymously to assist with something specific.

—Advice from a mathematics specialist

Meeting with Vertical Teams to Help Develop a Plan of Instruction

In many schools, near the end of the school year, teachers are asked to reflect on their mathematics teaching. They are to do two things: first, make a list of what went well, and second, identify areas where they and their students struggled. The following vignette tells how one mathematics specialist used such a list as an entry for working with a vertical team of teachers.

For several years, many of the third-grade teachers at Elk Ridge Elementary School listed basic facts for addition and subtraction as an area in need of attention. Ms. Geller, the mathematics specialist, saw this as an opportunity to look at and in turn improve on instruction. She decided that she wanted to gather the K–2 teachers together, but she knew she could not question their instruction or point fingers and place blame. That would only make them defensive. Instead, she thought about how she could use their vested interest in the success of their students as the starting point for working together toward a common goal. Ms. Geller knew that she would have to play an important role in this process, since she was outside the classroom and could see the situation through a different lens. She was in a position to ask tough questions and guide the teachers to think deeply about their instruction, their common teaching practices, and the overall goal of student achievement. So began a yearlong journey for teachers, administrators, parents, and students who were interested in improving the children's knowledge and recall of basic facts.

Ms. Geller started by having a conversation with the principal about basic facts knowledge, since this topic allowed for a "big picture" focus. As she outlined the potential for working with the K–2 teachers on this shared goal, the principal quickly envisioned how this work could, in time, affect not only the K–2 classrooms but all the students in the school. By talking with the principal first and getting him on board, Ms. Geller drew his attention to a valid mathematical concern, gave him insight into why the problem might have developed, and began to brainstorm with him about possible solutions. This ongoing dialogue between the principal and Ms. Geller helped to form a relationship that was essential.

Starting with the principal

Having the principal's support is crucial before a specialist undertakes a schoolwide exploration. The principal can offer many incentives for the work of a vertical team. These can range from offering words of encouragement and praise to teachers to providing managerial support by establishing open times for meetings and discussions. When the principal conveys support in any form, the message is a validation of the work of the specialist and the team.

The mathematics specialist is in a key position to play an important role as the voice of the school, speaking not only for one grade but for all the teachers and students. She can see beyond an individual teacher's worries, move beyond grade-level complaints, and focus on what should be done in the interest of the school and its student population. The mathematics specialist wears a variety of hats. She is proficient in the mathematics, an expert on best instructional practices, an investigator, an analyst, and a team player. It isn't her role to step in and fix what is considered to be broken but rather to facilitate the interactions of a group of teachers so that they will come to recognize an issue that needs changing and then work together with them to find a way to accomplish the change.

Creating interest and enthusiasm in the teachers

After reaching out to the principal, a specialist must move to the front line, engaging the teachers. They are the ones who will implement the changes, so it is important to get them actively involved from the very beginning. Ms. Geller proceeded by approaching her teachers.

Ms. Geller called a meeting with the K–2 teachers. She shared the concern coming from higher grade levels and asked the teachers to respond. The teachers' responses were both positive and negative. They were concerned that the teachers from the upper grades were pointing fingers, but they also saw a need for further conversation about how they were teaching the children to understand and recall the basic facts for addition and subtraction. Ms. Geller stepped in and helped draw attention to the positive aspects of focusing on this challenge while steering clear of the blame game. As a group, the teachers needed this focus, and Ms. Geller was there to provide it.

At this stage, Ms. Geller's most important task was to listen and collect information about how individual teachers were teaching the addition and subtraction facts. This was a time for teachers to celebrate successes and also to inform one another about the instruction that was already taking place. It turned out that the K–2 teachers were also concerned that some students did not know basic facts, and they worried about its long-term impact on their ability to learn mathematics.

Working together toward a targeted goal in a cross-grade effort

Good teachers know that children don't learn their addition and subtraction facts, or reach any mathematical understanding, overnight. Research also tells us that facts are best learned over time through meaningful activities, that children benefit from naming and sharing or discussing strategies to recall facts, and that meaningful, focused, distributed practice is more effective than isolated flashcard drill and memorization (Van de Walle, Karp, and Bay-Williams 2010). Fact building is a journey—a process that takes time to develop, as Ms. Geller's group of K–2 teachers began to understand.

Guided by Ms. Geller, the group of K–2 teachers set the stage for the group's work. They began by asking themselves a number of questions:

- "How do children learn their facts best?"

- "What can we do as a team to foster this development?"
- "How will these strategies develop over time or grade levels?"

The K–2 group was committed to looking carefully at how they taught basic facts and to begin the process of making improvements. These classroom teachers were excited about this open dialogue. Ms. Geller again took on the role of the facilitator. She allowed teachers from each grade level to share what was already taking place and encouraged strong teachers to explain or highlight some of their best practices. Ms. Geller also shared some research-into-practice recommendations that helped to validate the team's work.

This role of facilitation is very important. It is a fine balance between listening and telling. Note that Ms. Geller's role wasn't to tell the teachers what to do but instead to guide and lead the teachers toward growth and improvement.

Ms. Geller continued to ask probing questions:

- "What's the mathematical objective?"
- "How do children learn this mathematics best?"
- "What questions can we ask to get students to focus on the mathematics?"
- "Why do we teach it that way?"
- "Is there a different way to look at it?"

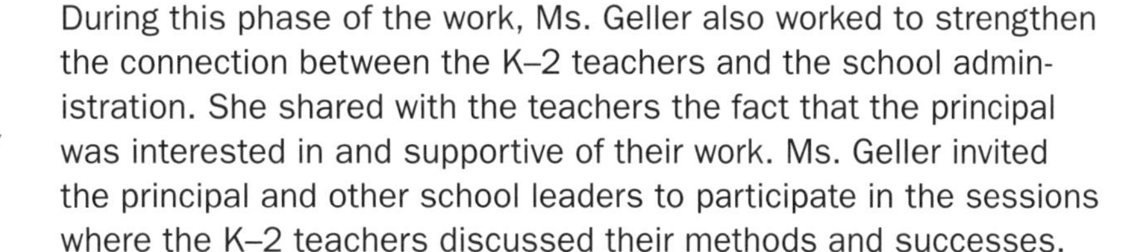

During this phase of the work, Ms. Geller also worked to strengthen the connection between the K–2 teachers and the school administration. She shared with the teachers the fact that the principal was interested in and supportive of their work. Ms. Geller invited the principal and other school leaders to participate in the sessions where the K–2 teachers discussed their methods and successes.

Teachers need to feel that their time, ideas, and commitment to their students are valued. This is an area where Ms. Geller helped to strengthen relationships—relationships among the teachers themselves and relationships between the teachers and the school administrators.

Developing content and pedagogy knowledge together

Now that the key players were all in place, the group had to establish some common beliefs and understandings.

Ms. Geller and the teachers started by listing the basic facts and talking about the different strategies that students typically used for successful recall of basic facts. Ms. Geller became the scribe and the cheerleader. She carefully recorded information in an organized fashion so that everyone had a clear picture of what was being discussed. She asked questions about what had been written down to check that all the teachers in the discussion group were in agreement. She recognized that consensus can be hard to attain when working within a group of teachers responsible for teaching students at a single grade level, but it can be even more difficult as the range of grade levels grows. Ms. Geller realized that it was her job to help the entire K–2 team come together to build a common understanding about children's learning of basic facts before the team members could move forward to address instructional approaches.

Together, the group labeled note cards, each listing one of seven common strategies for generating basic facts. The idea of looking at strategies was familiar to some of the teachers and new to others. Ms. Geller's responsibility was to build each teacher's familiarity with and understanding of basic fact strategies for a base of shared common knowledge for future work. Next, the group considered connections among the basic fact strategies and ordered the strategy cards as they discussed which strategies students might generate more easily and which presumed greater understanding. By asking questions, Ms. Geller helped the teachers consider how understanding advanced from one strategy to another.

The group quickly realized that the children at each level, from kindergarten to first and then to second grade, would be bringing different ideas and skills to their learning. Ms. Geller had to pose questions to guide teachers toward seeing how their work at a specific grade level supported the work of the whole team. Some of the kindergarten teachers were concerned that their students were not ready to work on recalling basic facts. So Ms. Geller pointed to the work they do in recognizing numbers and numerals, sequencing numbers, and building number relationships in terms of parts and totals. She pointed out that this work is foundational and crucial to the work that first- and second-grade teachers do. Without this foundation, the students in the upper grades would be at a loss. As Ms. Geller made these connections, other teachers in the group began suggesting additional ones.

Unlike in the past, when teachers working with students at different grade levels stayed confined and isolated from one another, mathematics specialists working with vertical teams encourage cross-grade-level dialogue and trust. Ms. Geller's teachers were building connections between what was going on in their own classrooms and the work that was under way in other grades. As their work together was building their individual and shared content and pedagogical knowledge, the teachers were coming together as a stronger, more focused team.

If these productive conversations are to take place, a relationship has to be fostered. Teachers must know and believe that they are free to share their thoughts, ideas, and feelings without risk. A level of trust has to be established. None of this develops overnight or without effort. A mathematics specialist has to make this sense of safety, respect, and support her goal and focus. For real growth and change in a school mathematics program and the teachers who deliver it, a specialist needs time—time to listen and watch teachers in action, to ask questions, to model best practices, to collect ideas and research, and to encourage all members of the group to believe in the potential of their shared effort and to take ownership of it.

This work across grade levels allows teachers to hear what their colleagues in other grade levels are doing and to see the connections with their own work. To decide how instruction at one grade level can grow out of the work of a previous grade level and then to connect this instruction with the work of the next grade level can be an eye-opening experience for all. Mathematics specialists help to bridge ideas and point out connections. This conversation facilitates a sense of being united for a common good or goal. For example, it was relatively easy for Ms. Geller and the teachers to stand together and take responsibility for the addition and subtraction basic-fact development of all K–2 students in their school because they saw how connected their work had become.

Make time to meet across grade levels.

In my school, we schedule vertical team meetings, K–2 and 3–5 once a month after school. One month, I meet with the K–2 teachers while the reading specialist meets with the 3–5 teachers. The next month, we switch groups.

—Advice from a mathematics specialist

Putting their work into action

Once a team has the mathematics ideas well organized, they need to decide how to make it happen in their school. This can provoke a lot of questions, as in fact it did for Ms. Geller's teachers.

As the teachers in Ms. Geller's vertical K–2 team decided how to put their work into action, they considered a number of strategic questions:

- "What would fact practice look like?"
- "When would it take place?"
- "Would instruction be only at school, or would it also have home connections?"
- "How could parents help?"

For each fact strategy, Ms. Geller helped the team members realize that they needed the following:

- A common language and visual cues
- Common tools, mini-assessments, activities, and games
- Extensions for stragglers and advanced learners
- Schoolwide activities and parent workshops

Ms. Geller set up a template with these entries for the teachers to complete for each fact strategy. She asked the entire group to work on the first fact strategy ("neighbor" facts, such as 8 + 1, 8 – 1) so that they would have a common experience, and then she had the teachers work independently before coming together again to share, organize, and connect ideas. Ms. Geller also completed the template on her own. She collected her ideas prior to the group meeting so that she could support others and have ideas ready to share. Her role was as a resource, with activities, ideas, and questions to share.

Ms. Geller's teachers decided that what it meant to "practice the basic facts" could look different at different grade levels and in different classrooms. They created a menu that each teacher could choose from to instruct students. All teachers were to use the fact focus for the month, the common language, and the common tools, but when and how they would offer the instruction was up to individual teachers.

After creating the first menu about neighbor facts, the teachers decided that trios of teachers, one from each grade level, would form mini-groups with responsibility for investigating the next strategy. Teachers are always battling time, and this was a way to use everyone's time effectively. Each trio would then come back to the group and share its findings. The whole team would then add to or clarify any details before a menu was published. Each month, ideas about a new strategy were shared, developed, and discussed. The team was building a fact notebook one strategy at a time. Because this journey began in the late spring, the first three or four strategies were ready before school began the following year. The team then met on a monthly basis to stay ahead and keep generating the next fact strategy menu.

Ms. Geller was an active member of the team, sharing ideas and encouraging others to share theirs as well. She was also the secretary, organizing and typing the notes and getting feedback about their clarity. Ms. Geller created notebooks for each team member and ran copies of games, "check-ins," and necessary materials. Because a mathematics specialist doesn't have students with her all day, she can provide this important service to teachers. It is sometimes these small details that encourage others to participate and commit to an idea. Teachers would leave their notebooks out, and Ms. Geller would add the next strategy and necessary materials.

Having these ideas well organized and easily accessible was key to keeping the teachers engaged and motivated.

Ms. Geller was also given the task of informing and educating other stakeholders. She was to inform the principal, the other specialists in the school, and the parents about the fact focus for the month. She created a newsletter that contained ideas for connecting these fact strategies to other content areas. The K–2 teachers decided that parent workshops should be offered so that parents could help support students at home. Ms. Geller offered monthly workshops that included a fact overview, a game to play with students, and specific flashcards that focused on the strategy of the month, as well as insights into the language that was being used at school.

This journey was a huge success in many ways. But, in the end, teachers were responsible for implementing these new ideas in their classrooms. Yet, Ms. Geller was always on call to support them. Different teachers looked for different means of support. Some teachers needed to bounce ideas around with a colleague; others needed more explanation of a strategy or clearer directions on playing a game with the students. Some teachers needed Ms. Geller to co-plan and help them organize their time, and others needed her to model a game or a whole-class discussion with the students. Whatever support an individual teacher needed—that was what Ms. Geller offered.

Not only did Ms. Geller's school see measureable results in students' basic fact knowledge, but the teachers also grew in their relationships with one another. Grade-level teams were stronger professionally, and mixed groups of teachers were now having more mathematical dialogue. Ms. Geller had provided meaningful yearlong professional development addressing a common instructional challenge, encouraging teachers to work as a team and to share the responsibility of instruction across the grade levels.

Open doors, letting teachers see beyond their own classrooms.

I have many roles at my school. Sometimes I am the listener, sometimes I am the facilitator, and sometimes I am the peacekeeper. Teachers can get stuck in their own bubble. Some are unable to see beyond their own classroom and consider another point of view. I consistently look for and point out the good teaching and positive experiences happening all around the school. Sometimes my teachers need a gentle nudge to appreciate the great work that their colleagues are doing.

—Reflections from a mathematics specialist

Leading Lesson Studies

Inviting teachers to work together to address a common challenge is just one approach that a specialist can use to support teachers from different grades. Another approach to providing ongoing professional development to a group of teachers is to lead them through a lesson study. Lesson study is a Japanese model of teacher-driven professional development, and it can serve as a continuing program to enhance the professional culture within the school. In a lesson study, teachers work collaboratively and reflectively as they create, implement, and evaluate a shared lesson plan. The goal of lesson study is to improve classroom instruction by advancing the knowledge of teachers and creating more effective lessons. Teachers do this by working together with a knowledgeable colleague.

What happens during lesson study?

The first step in lesson study is to determine a goal for mathematics instruction, related to a mathematical topic that students have consistently had difficulty in understanding. Next, a group of teachers organizes an entire unit of instruction on that topic, identifying content objectives and possible instructional emphases, before beginning to plan a specific lesson that the entire group will observe. When mapping out this unit, teachers think about the sequence of instruction as well as possible learning activities. They consider student thinking and common student misunderstandings. The teachers then create a detailed lesson plan together, with their collaboration giving them a common background, a shared responsibility, and a focused understanding of the lesson that will be observed and taught.

One teacher then teaches the students with the co-developed lesson plan. As she does this, the other members of the study group observe, documenting student engagement and thinking. Then the teachers meet to share the data collected and evaluate and reflect on the effectiveness of the lesson (Takahashi 2005). This discussion is focused on interpreting what students did or did not understand, what instructional steps worked or did not work in the lesson, why the lesson may have played out as it did, and how it could be modified to strengthen student learning. Next, the teachers work together to make revisions to the lesson on the basis of the data from the observations. Afterward, a different teacher in the study group teaches the modified lesson, or, depending on time and resources, multiple teachers in the study group may teach the revised lesson to their classes. The teachers again evaluate and reflect on the revised lesson (Taylor et al. 2005). They summarize data and observations from the lessons and compile a final report containing a polished lesson.

Most professional development opportunities are one-time events, where an "expert" comes and shares his ideas with teachers. Teachers may resent the time required to attend this session or to implement the changes recommended in the professional development. Reluctant teachers frequently say, "That won't work with our students because ...," and very little is achieved. In contrast, lesson study brings validity and ownership to professional development because teachers conduct a form of action research as they collect data in their own classrooms. New as well as seasoned teachers can work as teams to bring a deeper understanding to the mathematics. A number of American schools are adapting a form of this Japanese model of professional development to fit the needs of their particular schools, teachers, and students.

Planning

The mathematics specialist must have a clear vision of what a lesson study might look like within his school before taking on this work. Ideally, a specialist would have participated in a lesson study before facilitating one. As a first step, he should work with teachers to consider what the focus of the lesson study will be. This means that the teachers need to agree on a desired outcome. Will the emphasis be on trying out a particular teaching strategy? Do data show a weakness in specific content knowledge in the school? Because of the unique role of the mathematics specialist, he is able to understand the school culture. He knows teachers as individuals from one-on-one interactions and knows how they work as teams. He should also know the teachers' instructional preferences, how they choose to learn, and how comfortable they are with change.

Before presenting a formal request to conduct a lesson study to the principal, the mathematics specialist should work with a school-year calendar to map out time intervals when the team will conduct the lesson study to ensure that it will not be interrupted by school holidays or other district commitments. Another consideration is the standardized testing schedule, since teachers are less likely to want to commit to lesson study during that time.

A mathematics specialist who is new to a school may want to wait until after her first year of placement at a school to initiate a lesson study, giving herself time to build an understanding of teacher and student needs. She must develop relationships and trust, proving that she is part of the school "team." School climate is very important to the success of lesson study; a mathematics specialist should not expect to be able to lead a lesson study at every grade level or every year.

One final aspect of the specialist's preliminary planning for a lesson study is the identification of a person who will act as a "knowledgeable other" for the lesson study. This person might be another mathematics specialist, a university professor, or the school district's curriculum specialist. This knowledgeable colleague joins the team to provide fresh eyes to observe the process and to give suggestions to help enrich the lesson.

Talking with the principal

The support of the principal is vitally important to the success of lesson study. The principal must be willing to help provide uninterrupted time for the teachers to work on the lesson study, as well as to provide release time and substitutes for teachers' classrooms when they are observing the co-planned lesson. He may also be able to award professional development points for teachers, providing a further incentive for their participation.

When meeting with the principal, the mathematics specialist will probably first need to share in a clear fashion what lesson study is. It is important that the principal understand that lesson study is a process for developing teachers' content knowledge and examining student thinking, not a way to show teachers how to write effective lesson plans. Then, using school achievement data, the specialist and the principal might discuss which grade levels could benefit from the lesson study. They should also discuss the principal's role and participation throughout the lesson study process. Because many school districts are trying to find ways to cut their budgets, principals may appreciate this relatively inexpensive way to provide powerful professional development for teachers.

Inviting teachers

Once the specialist has completed the organizational planning with the principal, she will be ready to invite teachers to join the lesson study team. Because the focus of lesson study is students' mathematical thinking, seasoned teachers and novices can work together to gain insights. Some important qualifications of any teacher working on a lesson study team are a willingness to learn, a commitment to the team, and a desire to gain a deeper understanding of student thinking.

The lesson study team can be either a grade-level or a vertical team. The specialist can invite and welcome reluctant teachers into a lesson study group but should never force them to join. The interest and enthusiasm of the other teachers in the group may inspire more hesitant teachers to take an active part in the study. However, if a teacher chooses to drop out, the specialist should not see it as a negative evaluation but simply proceed with a more focused group.

One final consideration is scheduling meetings. Although it would be ideal if the principal could provide time during the school day, the likelihood is that the teachers and the specialist will need to meet before or after school. This means that the specialist will need to manage the group's time carefully, setting a clear agenda and keeping the group on task.

Choosing topics

Many lesson study teams determine their topic by examining school achievement data. The specialist can bring these data reports to the team, and the team can then decide what mathematical topic they want to address. For example, the data may show a weakness in student achievement with fractions, and the team may choose to study a lesson on equivalent fractions. Each of the teachers in the group will need to examine professional literature addressing the learning and teaching of the chosen topic and then be ready to share findings with the team.

Decide on the best way to share research.

I have found that providing a one-page synopsis sometimes works better than asking everyone to analyze and synthesize a lengthy research article. Be sure that the synopsis covers all the important and relevant ideas about the subject at hand.

—Advice from a mathematics specialist

Planning the lesson

The specialist serves as the facilitator in the lesson study process. Some of his responsibilities are to prepare copies of materials, schedule meetings, make arrangements for classroom coverage, and invite the knowledgeable other and the principal to the meetings.

During the planning meetings, the mathematics specialist should lead a discussion about rich mathematical tasks. This discussion will help ensure that the lesson being developed has a strong focus on the mathematics and not on "cute activities." This discussion can help teachers build a deeper understanding of the mathematical content and bring to light some common misunderstandings on the part of either the teachers or students. The mathematics specialist should help the team recognize that they do not have to come up with a new task but can rewrite an existing problem or redesign an existing activity to increase its rigor. For example, one lesson study team modified a story problem:

Billy has 1 dime and 1 nickel. He wants to buy a pencil for 25¢. Does he have enough money?

They changed the problem to the following:

Ms. Jones wanted a soda that cost 75¢. She has two quarters, a nickel, and a penny. Does she have enough money? If not, how much more money does she need?

This revised problem provided a task that allowed the team to consider the different strategies that second graders might use.

Next, the team works collaboratively to write a complete lesson plan. Their prior review of student thinking will help team members define teacher questions, anticipate student responses, and plan for teacher follow-up or response. The final lesson plan should identify the goal, connections to mathematics standards (including connections to mathematics standards at other grade levels), the activity to be used to launch the lesson, teacher questions, anticipated student responses, anticipated teacher follow-up to those responses, materials, and types of evidence to be collected.

Observing the lesson

During the observed lesson, all members of the team, including the mathematics specialist, are positioned around the room and assigned specific students to observe. All observers take notes, documenting how students react during the lesson. Exactly what do the observed students do, say, or ask during the lesson? Because the observers are trying to gather data documenting the students' understanding of the lesson, they should have minimal interaction with the students.

Debriefing the lesson

Immediately after the lesson, the lesson study team should discuss observations. If possible, the knowledgeable other facilitates this discussion. If no one is available to take this role, the mathematics specialist assumes this responsibility. The discussion should center on the students' demonstrated understanding of the mathematics content, including surprising or unanticipated student responses. In the case of the problem about how much more money Ms. Jones needed to buy a soda, the "correct" answer is 19 cents, but one student wrote that she needed two dimes. The lesson study team discussed children's knowledge of vending machines, which do not accept pennies. The team decided that in the context of vending machines, the answer of two dimes was acceptable.

At this point, the team should discuss what questions or what alternate materials or representations could have been used to help clarify students' thinking about the task. The team then revises the lesson for the rest of the team to teach.

Reteaching the lesson

In the original model of Japanese lesson study, the revised lesson is taught and then revised additional times, with the members of the team observing and documenting the impact of the revisions on student learning. However, depending on time and resources, different members of the team may teach the revised lesson to their classes with or without an observer present, noting any additional changes that they make while teaching it and any significant understandings or misunderstandings that they observe in their students. The mathematics specialist may observe the teaching of revised lessons or may teach a class for the teacher who taught the original lesson, allowing her to have the opportunity to observe another class.

Reporting on the lesson

When all members of the team have had the opportunity to teach the revised lesson, the team reconvenes to write a final report. The mathematics specialist facilitates the team discussion and compiles this report. It should include background information, long- and short-term student goals, teacher questions, observation notes, student responses, lesson modifications, and a summary of what the team learned about the students' mathematical thinking.

Ending and beginning again

The goal of lesson study is not to develop a library of picture-perfect lesson plans but to deepen teachers' understanding of how students think about mathematical concepts. Many times the end of a lesson study cycle will find the team with more questions to examine in the future. The mathematics specialist has the advantage of participating in and collecting feedback from multiple lesson study teams. This allows her to connect the questions raised by one team with those of another. These questions can help teachers think about their own teaching practices, thus becoming better teachers.

Schoolwide Professional Development

School leaders have a vision for their school's academic program. This vision may drive schoolwide professional development sessions, or these sessions may be determined by external factors, such as a change in state standards or district assessments. Whatever the rationale, time and funds for professional development are extremely limited. As a result, the mathematics specialist may find herself helping teachers recognize and appreciate the purpose of collaborative professional development work. But the mathematics specialist must make sure that any professional development that is offered in mathematics is worthwhile and consistent with the work that she is doing with individual teachers and in small-group settings.

Model good practices for teachers.

My principal lets me begin some of our faculty meetings with a challenging mathematics problem. This "opener" gets teachers talking about mathematics and sharing their own strategies. I use this type of activity to model a way that teachers can work with their students to create a rich environment for learning mathematics. Having experienced this process in several meetings, some teachers are catching on to the idea and using it in their own classrooms.

—Advice from a mathematics specialist

Setting Goals Schoolwide

When the specialist turns her attention to schoolwide professional development, coordination with the principal and the school leadership team becomes mandatory. The school leadership team will identify needs, set priorities, and develop a list of goals for the year. Team members will examine data sources such as student achievement scores and teacher requests, while also considering the demands associated with implementing new initiatives, new textbooks, and new technology. Once identified, the goals for mathematics have to be prioritized and weighed along with the goals for other content areas. Time and resources will need to be negotiated. Being an advocate for mathematics instruction is important, but the specialist must also be a team player and understand the overall school needs. Making the most of whatever time she is given to work with teachers is the key.

Develop a few concrete, doable goals for the year.

Developing a list of goals for the year is crucial. I remember during my first year, I was stretched in many different directions, dabbling in this and that with different teachers and grade-level groups. I wish someone had told me to pick one or two areas to focus on. Giving teachers opportunities to look at student data and guiding them toward a common need is something I wish I had done in my first year as a specialist.

—Advice from a mathematics specialist

Logistics and planning

An ideal way to support schoolwide professional development for mathematics is through a sequence of connected workshops spread out across the school year. This approach allows the specialist to offer engaging and meaningful learning opportunities within sessions and then to assign independent or small-group tasks to be completed between sessions. These assignments might include reading relevant articles, trying new strategies with students, collecting student work on a common task, videotaping a lesson, or observing a colleague. When results of these experiences are shared in follow-up sessions, all the teachers become responsible for the learning of the group. If a school's or a district's model for professional development has traditionally been one-day workshops, each with a different focus, then it may take time to move to a sequence of connected workshops. If so, the mathematics specialist may need to start on a small scale, with a few related events, and document outcomes to share with the principal.

Setting up ongoing professional development sessions requires coordination early in the school year, or possibly even the summer before, when the school calendar is being established. Sometimes the time and topics for professional development days are preset at the district level. So if more time is needed at the school level, the mathematics specialist will need to negotiate with the principal and the school leadership team for additional time to bring teachers together.

Establishing the purpose of a workshop

Sometimes the mathematics specialist identifies goals for a workshop. Sometimes the principal sets the goals on the basis of her perceptions. At other times, data from district benchmark assessments or statewide assessments determine the focus. When school achievement scores are low, the principal will naturally turn to the mathematics specialist for help and advice about ways to improve student performance. In all these cases, the principal and the specialist come to a collaborative agreement about the work to be done at the school.

When leading a professional development workshop, the mathematics specialist must set out the need for or purpose of the work early in the session. Teachers are more likely to buy into the work if they see clear connections with their students and their needs (Guskey 2002). If at all possible, the specialist should share relevant data with the teachers, allowing them some time to explore the information. Providing data in a variety of ways, such as charts, graphs, and written summaries, may be helpful (Love 2009). Having the teachers work in teams to identify trends and student issues in the data allows them to identify the same goals for the workshop as those that the specialist has outlined. Teachers will then be more likely to take ownership of the investigation of approaches for addressing the identified needs.

Demonstrate a willingness to be a team player.

The mathematics specialist must be a team player and understand the needs of the other members of the school team. The specialist should not have tunnel vision when it comes to mathematics but must consider the school as a whole when making decisions. For example, the specialist may want to have a professional development meeting totally devoted to mathematics, but data and time constraints may warrant creatively combining mathematics with reading or science.

—Advice from a mathematics specialist

Careful workshop planning is like careful lesson planning

In many ways, planning a good workshop is similar to creating a good lesson plan: Identify the goal and work backward from it, keeping in mind the hoped-for outcomes (see fig. 5.1). The mathematics specialist may be the sole facilitator of the workshop, or she may decide to enlist the aid of several well-regarded teachers in the school. Including others on the presentation team shows respect for them and secures their support, as well as building their leadership capacity. The goals of the workshop should be clearly stated early in the session and posted along with the agenda so that participants have a sense of how the time will be allocated. Group norms should also be established early in the workshop to ensure that everyone understands what is expected in participation and social courtesy. Being respectful while others are talking and stepping out in the hall to use a cell phone may seem obvious, but it is helpful for the group to list their expectations and to agree explicitly on the norms for easy reference later, if necessary.

Organization of the space is another issue that the specialist should consider ahead of time. Part of his planning should include considering such practical questions as the following:

- "How do I want the tables to be arranged?"
- "Where should the projector and computer sit?"
- "Do I need a table for handouts and materials?"

If the specialist expects the teachers to interact and have discussions, tables are a good choice; they are likely to be more conducive to engagement than individual desks. It is also important to decide how teachers will be grouped for each activity. Workshop activities should vary, and, depending on the desired outcomes, the groups might be reconstituted in the session, possibly with the tables needing to be rearranged. The specialist should estimate a time frame for each activity and determine an order that will allow a progression of connected ideas. If the workshop has multiple facilitators, the specialist should identify who will do each part. Access to any needed materials, from scissors to tape, should be easy, and all technology equipment should be set up and tested on-site ahead of time.

What's Your Vision? (Part 1)			
Time	**Focus**	**Leader**	**Organizational materials/notes**
1:00	Do we currently have a school-level mathematics vision? Is the vision articulated in writing and distributed so that everyone knows about it? (The following activity will allow us to think about what is important to our school in creating an environment where students are learning with understanding.)	Pat	Decide: How are teachers grouped? Are grade levels seated together? Will there be group handouts or reference materials?
1:15	Each group creates a chart. Emphasize that a group must really spend time thinking about what students are doing or saying or how they are engaging with the mathematics in the "ideal" mathematics classroom. Consider the following: • What are students doing? • What do teachers have to do to enable students to engage in that way? • What does the mathematics specialist need to do with teachers for them to have the knowledge or skills to do this?	All	Charts, markers
1:45	Post and share. Conduct a gallery walk. Use Post-it notes to allow others (not in a group) to post their questions/comments, adding to the chart for the benefit of the group.	All	Tape, charts, Post-it notes, wall space for posting
2:00	These charts can help us to identify a particular focus for our work. Note that there are many things that could be worked on. Ask the group, "How will we determine the greatest need at this point?"	Pat	

Fig. 5.1. A facilitator's guide for a workshop addressing a school's vision of mathematics

The specialist should keep in mind the overall workshop goals as she determines what focus questions to pose for each activity and lists the responses that she expects. She should think about how she will react to each possible response. What controversies may arise? Is she prepared to handle them? By anticipating teacher responses, the mathematics specialist can facilitate discussions more effectively and adjust as needed when surprises occur. Faced with an unexpected response, the specialist has a choice. She may follow the path generated by that comment or place that idea in the "parking lot" (particularly if the group norms included a decision about a way to post ideas for later consideration). In thinking about her time frame, the specialist must be sure to leave sufficient time for a meaningful closure activity and should develop a set of exit questions that will provide feedback to her and her co-facilitators. This will help in future planning, as the specialist incorporates the group's questions and concerns in future sessions.

As the school's knowledgeable mathematics resource, the specialist will be expected to lead during the workshop, but she must also be more than a good listener. She must be an enthusiastic learner who encourages everyone to contribute knowledge for the good of the cause. The sample facilitator's guide in figure 5.1 illustrates some details that can lead to a more meaningful workshop discussion. The guide is not meant to be a script to be followed during the workshop. Rather, it is intended as an example of a guide that can be referred to easily during a workshop.

Integrating new resources

Specialists are often asked to organize schoolwide workshops exploring how to incorporate newly purchased materials into teaching practice. These materials may include textbooks, manipulatives, and technology. If the material is new to a school, the mathematics specialist may need to practice using it to learn its advantages and limitations. He should not be shy about asking for help. Another teacher in the school may be able to provide assistance, or at times outside help may be required. Being willing to seek help and advice sets a good example for others. The important thing is for the mathematics specialist to show teachers that he is doing all that he can to offer support and is willing to learn new things. For example, when SMART Boards were purchased at one school, the mathematics specialist asked a colleague if he could teach a unit on fractions in the teacher's classroom, integrating the hands-on use of pattern blocks and the SMART Board virtual manipulative. This allowed the specialist to gain experience with the materials and to think about the appropriate way to blend the use of concrete materials with the computer-assisted option. It also sent a message to his colleagues that he was not only comfortable in exploring new ideas but excited about working with students and learning something new.

Working beyond Your School

So far, all the examples in this chapter have focused on how a mathematics specialist works within her school, with colleagues that she sees on a daily and weekly basis. However, mathematics specialists may also be called on at the school district level to work across schools, with different groups of teachers. In many ways, working across schools is similar to working within a school. Mathematics specialists focus on addressing good mathematics, working to improve student achievement, using data to identify specific needs, engaging teachers, and being well prepared. But working at the district level is also different in important ways.

Unlike working in his own school, working at the district level may move a specialist outside his comfort zone. Within a school, the mathematics specialist knows his teachers. He becomes familiar with their instructional approaches, their strengths, and their beliefs about mathematics. When conducting a workshop with teachers across the district, he may not be as comfortable with his audience. So he needs to plan in-session opportunities for learning about his audience. He must allow time to ask participants to identify their grade-level placements. He must offer an opportunity for the participants to state what they are presently doing in their classrooms and to indicate how they think about mathematics teaching, as related to the topic of the workshop. This information might emerge as participants solve problems together, as the specialist changes the composition of small groups throughout the session, or as he provides opportunities for participants to share what's happening at their schools. After they share some of these thoughts, the specialist can introduce ideas to stretch each participant's thinking. Knowing the audience is essential to making the workshop meaningful for all.

When presenting a district-level workshop, a mathematics specialist may not have the same credibility that she has within her own school. Teachers assigned to the specialist's building know her; she has worked with them and supported them on a daily basis in a variety of ways. The teachers attending a district-level workshop may not know what she can offer. This means that it is very important for a mathematics specialist to be prepared and well organized, having thought through possible questions that might arise, as well as her responses. The specialist must also be ready to share personal anecdotes and meaningful stories about the students and teachers with whom she works. The participants must feel that she is a real person, and these examples can help them build connections with what is happening in their own schools. Again, the specialist must provide opportunities for the teachers to share experiences and build connections with one another. Children in the same grade tend to behave similarly across a school district, and real stories help to build unity among workshop participants. The intent is to motivate the teachers to talk with one another.

Finally, it is most important for the specialist to focus on the mathematics and mathematics teaching. To specialists organizing a workshop across schools, we offer a few simple pieces of advice:

- Bring strong examples to share.
- Solve mathematics problems together.
- Examine student thinking.
- Pose good questions.
- Look at student work.
- Encourage teachers to collaborate and share their ideas.

Most important, step out of your comfort zone, and enjoy the ride!

References

Guskey, Thomas R. "Professional Development and Teacher Change." *Teachers and Teaching: Theory and Practice* 8 (August 2002): 381–91.

Love, Nancy, ed. *Using Data to Improve Learning for All: A Collaborative Inquiry Approach*. Thousand Oaks, Calif.: Corwin Press, 2009.

Sullivan, Peter, and Pat Lilburn. *Good Questions for Math Teaching: Why Ask Them and What to Ask (K–6)*. Sausalito, Calif.: Mathematics Solutions, 2002.

Takahashi, Akihiko. "For Teachers: Planning and Writing a Research Lesson." In *Building Our Understanding of Lesson Study*, edited by Patsy Wang-Iverson and Makoto Yoshida, pp. 31–38. Philadelphia: Research for Better Schools, 2005.

Taylor, Anne R., Shari Anderson, Karen Meyer, Mary Kay Watner, and Christine West. "Lesson Study: A Professional Development Model for Mathematics Reform." *Rural Educator* 26 (Winter 2005): 17–22.

Van de Walle, John A., Karen S. Karp, and Jennifer M. Bay-Williams. *Elementary and Middle School Mathematics: Teaching Developmentally*. 7th ed. Boston: Allyn and Bacon, 2010.

Working with Resource Teachers

Karen Mirkovich, Patricia A. Robertson, and Jason A. Scherm

What exactly is a "resource teacher"? A review of job descriptions from various school districts, as well as the authors' experiences, suggests that the definitions and roles of resource teachers vary widely across different settings in rural, suburban, and metropolitan school districts. Generally speaking, in this chapter, a resource teacher, including a mathematics specialist, is assumed to be a teacher who has special competencies and assists with instruction by working with both teachers and students. The specific role varies from site to site. An initial task for the mathematics specialist, then, is to assess the scope and role of the various resource teachers in her school and understand how their methods compare and contrast with her own. For example, in many school districts, resource teachers in non-mathematics subject areas often pull students out of the classroom for individualized or small-group instruction. In contrast, when the mathematics specialist works in the classroom, she is typically modeling lessons, co-teaching or providing targeted differentiation with the classroom teacher, observing students and teachers during instruction, and playing other instructional roles within the classroom.

Understanding these contrasts between mathematics specialists and other resource teachers will help the specialist navigate collegial professional relationships with both classroom teachers and other resource teachers. Indeed, over time, a mathematics specialist inevitably interacts with a school's reading specialists and special education resource teachers, as well as teachers who work with English language learners (ELLs). In addition, a mathematics specialist may work with instructional technology specialists, teachers who work with gifted students, media specialists, and possibly other resource teachers, depending on the specific positions in each school system. Although the responsibilities assumed by resource teachers may differ, the benefits for students increase if all resource teachers in a school understand one another's roles. The mathematics specialist can leverage his impact on classroom instruction in his school if he begins by establishing professional and productive partnerships with other resource teachers. However, before forming those partnerships, he must first understand the different roles and responsibilities of each resource teacher and plan strategically for integrating his support with theirs.

Understanding the Expectations of Resource Teachers

Developing professional partnerships is challenging, since a school district's central office may have rules, routines, and vision statements for resource teachers, and these may not coincide with a mathematics specialist's vision. The mathematics specialist should learn about different resource teachers' professional cultures and understand their professional goals, as well as the expectations and assumptions established by their school or district-level supervisors. Respecting one another's job responsibilities promotes mutual trust and willingness to establish relationships; without these, working collaboratively is difficult.

Fostering respectful communication

When a newly placed elementary mathematics specialist invests the time to learn about the other resource teachers' responsibilities and expectations early in her placement, she facilitates communication that will help her and the other resource teachers learn how to work together productively. Examining each other's job descriptions and discussing commonalities can be an important first step for a specialist and a resource teacher toward developing a collaborative relationship. Through conversations about job responsibilities, each resource teacher will also become more familiar with the individual perspectives and working styles of colleagues. It is productive to begin the year by considering the varying methods of providing leadership and communication that are evident in the daily work of different resource teachers. When all resource teachers understand and respect one another's individual styles of communication and leadership, their partnership is strengthened.

Focusing on common priorities

If resource teachers are going to work together, they need to identify common ground. What are their priorities? What are their beliefs or assumptions about how students learn? Establishing common priorities may occur quickly if the specialist and the resource teachers have worked together before on special projects, taken courses together, or taught together on a team. The mathematics specialist may have been a classroom teacher on the staff and may have already established a rapport with resource teachers. In other circumstances, the resource teachers and the elementary mathematics specialist may be forming new relationships and may require time to develop shared beliefs and experiences before determining priorities.

It is important that resource teachers and the mathematics specialist, as school leaders, work as a team addressing common goals. This teamwork may include discussing data to determine the next instructional steps, identifying and providing school-based professional growth experiences, and working with parents to support children. Discussing data includes having conversations about students, their work, and their test scores. Keeping the conversations focused on the evidence of student learning allows all parties an opportunity to share their knowledge, ensuring that everyone gains a better understanding of the next steps needed to help the students. A team focus on student work also promotes more opportunities to address early intervention. Team discussions may include identifying students needing similar interventions, continued practice, or enrichment. These discussions promote the collaboration necessary to make all students successful. The focus on students also allows the team to identify instructional practices that should be evident in all classrooms. All the resource teachers in the school should support those instructional practices.

Take advantage of the benefits of a team focus.

Providing early intervention for students who need it requires a team effort. Without the collaboration of resource teachers, students may not receive any intervention or may receive intervention later than they really should.

—Advice from a mathematics specialist

Collaborating with Other Resource Teachers

Reading specialists, special education resource teachers, and resource teachers who work with English language learners are three of the most common types of resource teachers in schools. Other types of resource teachers include those working with gifted students and instructional technology teachers. Additional positions for resource teachers are also defined by individual school systems.

Collaborating with a reading specialist

In many school districts, the reading specialist identifies students who require additional remedial instruction in reading and teaches them in a location away from their regular classroom. This model contrasts with the mathematics specialist model assumed in this handbook. The focus of the mathematics specialist is on increasing the effectiveness of the mathematics program for all students by collaborating with teachers to support students' learning in classrooms. Although their roles may vary within the school, the reading specialist and the mathematics specialist can work with each other to increase students' opportunities to be engaged in and to learn mathematics. For example, the reading specialist may enhance the mathematics specialist's coaching repertoire by sharing comprehension strategies to discuss with teachers when addressing possible ways to help students break down the meaning of a multi-step problem. When the instructional strategies used by the reading specialist are mirrored in the mathematics specialist's work, the impact on teaching and learning is powerful. A variety of collaborative opportunities are possible:

- Identifying children's books that focus on the mathematics content under study
- Sharing graphic organizers such as story maps and "show-me" wallets for use during class
- Co-planning and then teaching lessons that require students to use reasoning to facilitate mathematics learning and generate phonetic rules and reading strategies
- Co-planning and then teaming to deliver staff workshops addressing current instructional practices that relate to both reading and mathematics, such as brain research
- Leading a "teachers as readers" group focusing on instructional practices that apply to both reading and mathematics

Identify intersecting instructional approaches for a powerful impact.

During my first year as a mathematics specialist, I was surprised to see that some of the reading specialist's approaches for working with students mirrored approaches that I was using with some teachers and their students during mathematics instruction. For example, in work with the reading specialist, students were completing a sorting activity to display generalized phonemic patterns in words. This was similar to the sorting activities that students completed during mathematics class, like sorting triangles on the basis of their sides and angles. By using techniques that students were familiar with, teachers had more class time to spend on the mathematics. Talking about these similarities was the beginning of an ongoing discussion between the reading specialist and me about how people learn. As our discussions continued, I could see that together we could influence teachers' perspectives of classroom instruction within our disciplines, allowing all students to advance their understanding of both mathematics and reading.

—Reflections from a mathematics specialist

Collaborating with a special education resource teacher

Special education resource teachers carry the responsibility of educating students who are diagnosed with physical, mental, and emotional disabilities. They work with learners who have a range of disabilities, from mild to severe, using specialized techniques to help the students reach their goals in the least restrictive environment. The special education resource teacher's work must comply with federally mandated paperwork referred to as the Individualized Educational Program (IEP). This plan outlines the necessary supports, accommodations, and goals for a particular student. These goals can encompass both academic and behavioral concerns. Special education resource teachers also direct meetings with parents and staff regarding a student's plan and make necessary adjustments to it and to services for the student throughout the year. The mathematics specialist and the special education resource teacher may collaborate to accomplish the following:

- Define and apply modifications that will benefit an individual student's learning needs during mathematics instruction, using methods such as tiering, scaffolding of tasks, or assisting the classroom teacher in understanding the actions of a student with autism spectrum disorder
- Create a student intervention plan, outlining teaching tasks that will support and advance the student's level of mathematical knowledge and skills
- Review samples of students' work to analyze mathematical misconceptions and decide the next steps in instruction
- Create formative mathematics assessments that contain modifications according to a student's IEP
- Demonstrate ways to use a variety of manipulative materials that will support the growth of a student's conceptual understanding by working from the concrete to the abstract

Collaborating with ELL teachers

The ELL resource teacher typically works with the faculty to build teachers' expertise in instructing students who are learning to speak, read, and write English. This resource teacher also usually works directly with students to support their learning of spoken and written English and communicates frequently with families, providing them with information about language and literacy development. The ELL resource teacher can inform the mathematics specialist about where students are on the language acquisition spectrum. Other opportunities for collaboration between the mathematics specialist and the ELL teacher include tasks such as the following:

- Creating advanced organizers and visual cues
- Developing students' vocabulary through the use of mathematics word walls
- Modeling lessons by using signals, and repeating directions to ensure students' comprehension
- Applying modifications such as tiering and scaffolding, and creating and implementing tasks that will benefit individual student learning during mathematics instruction
- Creating a student intervention plan to provide instructional tasks that will support the level of processing skills identified for a student
- Reviewing samples of student work to analyze mathematical misconceptions and decide next steps in instruction
- Creating formative assessments for mathematics that contain modifications according to students' ELL levels
- Demonstrating ways to use a variety of mathematics manipulatives that will increase conceptual understanding by working from the concrete to the abstract
- Co-teaching evening parent classes with ELL teachers to help adults learn more about the school's mathematics program and how they can help their children with homework

Take the initiative in making contact with resource teachers.

One of the smartest decisions that I made during my first year as a mathematics specialist was to take the initiative to seek out the resource teachers before the year began. By spending time helping the ELL teacher at my school set up her bilingual math word wall, I was able to show her how much I respected her position and the bilingual student population. Once the school year began, she was very open to using an inquiry-based lesson format to promote problem solving, reasoning, and communication. She told the classroom teachers, and me, that mathematics vocabulary was often viewed as a large hurdle for students whose primary language at home was not English. However, promoting student discussions during mathematics class was eliminating these obstacles, and students were more likely to participate during class. Throughout the year, she became an advocate for the types of teaching practices that I was suggesting. This support made it much easier for me to earn the trust of the classroom teachers.

—*Reflections from a mathematics specialist*

Collaborating with other resource teachers

Schools also have a variety of other resource teachers, each presenting an elementary mathematics specialist with unique opportunities for collaboration. These activities include the following:

- Planning quality enrichment opportunities with the gifted resource teacher to challenge mathematically gifted learners by compressing instruction and providing mathematically rich tasks
- Partnering with instructional technology teachers to embed the use of mobile devices, interactive boards, and social media within mathematics instruction
- Working with the media specialist to identify and secure mathematics literature for students, as well as a collection of professional mathematics education resource books for teachers
- Working with other resource teachers on a schoolwide mathematics committee
- Collaborating with other specialists and teachers on schoolwide family nights or parent workshops
- Modeling a mathematics lesson that a team of resource teachers observes and then participating in the discussion of the lesson with the resource team, analyzing student understanding and reviewing samples of student work
- Working with the media specialist or the technology teacher to use communication media to convey information about the school's mathematics program as well as to distribute suggestions for how parents might help their children "do math" at home

Developing Trust through Communication and Common Priorities

The following vignette provides an example of how a new mathematics specialist and a veteran special education teacher began to develop an understanding of each other's instructional methods and expectations, while keeping the students' achievement as their common priority.

Ms. Morris is a special education teacher who has taught in a rural elementary school for the past eighteen years. She describes her job as "serv[ing] to provide students with disabilities the greatest opportunities to learn in the least restrictive learning environment." Her school recently welcomed its first mathematics specialist, Ms. Smith. Ms. Smith noticed that when students with IEPs were struggling to provide answers during a mainstreamed class, Ms. Morris would quietly tell the students the answers. During one of their common planning periods, Ms. Smith and Ms. Morris discussed the students' IEPs. Ms. Morris explained that she provided the students with answers at times because she was "concerned about the students being embarrassed during class," and she "wanted to give them the needed support." Ms. Smith asked Ms. Morris not to provide any answers to her students during one mathematics lesson in the following week, so that they could see how the students might approach a problem on their own. Ms. Morris accepted the invitation, and the two began to plan the lesson that Ms. Smith would teach.

The lesson that Ms. Smith delivered to the entire class focused on creating equivalent fractions. The lesson consisted of students modeling fractions by using plastic eggs and egg cartons. Ms. Smith reviewed the class's definitions of numerators and denominators and challenged the students to represent $6/12$ of a dozen eggs. Ms. Morris's students created several different representations of the fraction by placing the six eggs in different row and column patterns in the carton.

One of Ms. Morris's students filled the carton with all twelve eggs, but after discussing her strategy with another student she removed six of the eggs, so that six of the twelve positions in the carton had an egg. The students were then instructed to see whether they could create equal groups of eggs and empty spaces in the carton. Ms. Morris's students created various clusters of eggs and empty spaces. One of the students in the class remarked to his partner, who was a special education student, "It kind of looks like $3/6$, if you are just looking at this." He gestured to the three columns of two eggs each and the three columns of two empty slots (see fig. 6.1). The special education student didn't understand. So his partner patiently explained again, rewording his reasoning and pointing to the eggs arranged in the carton.

Fig. 6.1. Six eggs grouped as three sets of 2 in a collection of six sets of 2

Eventually, the special education student caught on and quickly created two clusters, each with three eggs, and two more clusters, each with three empty spaces, to show that $6/12$ is equivalent to $2/4$ (see fig. 6.2). Then he made a second display with a cluster of six eggs and a cluster of six empty spaces showing that $6/12$ is equivalent to $1/2$ (see fig. 6.3).

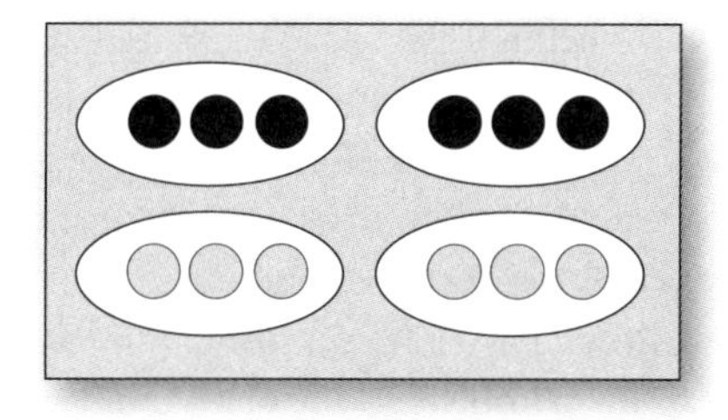

Fig. 6.2. Six eggs grouped as two sets of 3 in a collection of four sets of 3

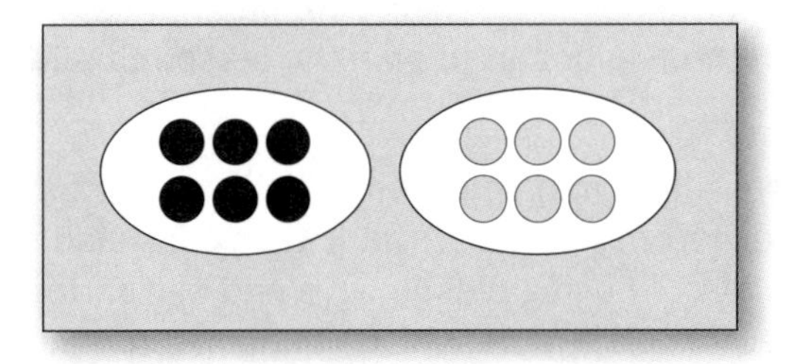

Fig. 6.3. Six eggs grouped as one set of 6 in a collection of two sets of 6

Although Ms. Morris desperately wanted to show her students several correct examples, she sat and observed patiently as they continued to connect the multiple representations to their numerically written fractions. The special education students had difficulty with the additional activity of creating equivalent fractions for 8/12 with the eggs, but Ms. Morris mentioned that the special education students "were interacting more and working harder then they usually do." When all the students came together to create a list of classroom generalizations on chart paper, Ms. Morris stated, "The special education students spoke out for the first time in a long while."

In a short post-lesson conversation the following day, Ms. Smith commented on the strategies that Ms. Morris's students were able to contrive and complimented the special education teacher on her ability to "let go and observe her students." Ms. Morris agreed that the experience had been "eye opening," but said that she was still planning to pull her students out of class to review the procedural process for finding equivalent fractions. Nevertheless, Ms. Morris and Ms. Smith agreed to continue to meet to discuss lessons and ways of addressing students' needs.

Reflecting on different perspectives

The first step that Ms. Morris and Ms. Smith took in developing a successful collaboration was determining a common time to plan with one another. During this time they were open and honest about their concerns. Ms. Smith's agenda was to allow the students to struggle more with the mathematics to give them time to develop a deeper conceptual understanding of equivalent fractions. Ms. Morris felt comfortable expressing her concerns that her students might feel embarrassed about not being able to give the correct answers during class. Ms. Morris and Ms. Smith were able to develop specific norms that they would follow during the lesson. By clearly defining and acknowledging their roles, these teachers could focus on their number one priority, the students.

At the conclusion of the lesson, Ms. Smith believed that she had taken a large step forward in encouraging Ms. Morris to observe her special education students as they solved, or attempted to solve, a problem with only limited assistance or direction. Ms. Smith interpreted the students' conversations and representations as robust and valuable, and she believed that Ms. Morris had the same thoughts. However, in their post-lesson discussion, it became clear that Ms. Morris thought her students struggled with the task, and she interpreted that as an undesirable occurrence. Further, she believed that her students needed and should receive additional instruction targeting computation procedures for creating equivalent fractions. On the one hand, this vignette highlights the importance of focusing on developing a learning environment that allows students to have the greatest opportunity to learn. On the other hand, it also shows the misconceptions that may arise if open communication and shared planning are not in place.

Admittedly, the complex schedules of mathematics specialists and resource teachers frequently limit time for common planning. Moreover, their perspectives regarding both student knowledge and misconceptions may differ. These differences can have consequences for the student if both the mathematics specialist and the classroom teacher are unaware of a resource teacher's instructional practices. At the same time, because resource teachers frequently have limited mathematical expertise, small daily encounters and clear communication between the mathematics specialist and resource teachers may lead to significant changes for both teachers and students.

Expand a resource teacher's mathematical repertoire.

An ELL teacher approached me for advice. She had been working with a fourth-grade student who had limited English fluency and was having difficulty learning multiplication procedures. She felt the classroom instruction was confusing for the student. I shared with her a typical multiplication task that I had observed being discussed in the student's class and asked the ELL teacher how she would work with the student on that task. She immediately started using the traditional algorithm. But the classroom teacher and students had been investigating a partial products strategy. No wonder the child was confused! She was being exposed to two approaches. In the student's mind these approaches were entirely different. When I demonstrated the procedure and described the discussion that was taking place in the classroom, the ELL teacher remarked that she had never seen that method for multiplying, but that she could see how it might make more sense to the student. So we worked together for a couple of weeks to expand her repertoire of differing computational algorithms, as well as the mathematical ideas underlying those procedures, so that she could support her students' conceptual understanding. She was so excited to have some "new" skills that she registered for a summer workshop to learn more about mathematics teaching.

—Reflections from a mathematics specialist

Developing Successful Collaboration

Resource teachers work with a spectrum of students in a variety of settings. It is not only that the instructional perspectives and responsibilities of resource teachers may differ; their scheduling configurations may be completely unlike one another. Some resource teachers work in small groups and meet only with students identified from across the entire school enrollment once or twice per week. Other resource teachers may work daily with selected students but only within particular grade levels. Communicating often and clearly about these settings will help resources teachers maintain common understandings and an appreciation of one another's work. It can be very useful for a mathematics specialist and a resource teacher to take the time to sit down together and determine any limitations in time, resources, or experiences that may inhibit a consistent working relationship. Doing this at the beginning of the collegial interaction can pay off as resource teachers reinforce efforts with students over time.

Resource teachers' schedules are time-bound, since these teachers must meet a range of classroom schedules. It is important to establish a common planning time when all the resource teachers in a school and the mathematics specialist can meet. Finding a time requires considering conflicting schedules. Once a mutually suitable planning time has been scheduled, the team should meet with the principal to talk about priorities for the school and to suggest that future regular meetings can help the team address those priorities. The successes achieved from regular meetings will show the importance of planning together, and this knowledge may lead to revising the schedule in the future to allow for more meeting opportunities. If team members have discussed one another's job descriptions previously, then the team may agree that a common responsibility in their job descriptions is working collaboratively and regularly with the team of all resource teachers in the school. Having a common responsibility in all job descriptions can demonstrate to the principal that the team is serious about working together. In the following vignette, one mathematics specialist shares a successful collaboration plan that he and his principal designed together.

When speaking to our principal about how resource teachers could work collaboratively with a mathematics specialist, we found that the school improvement plan was a good place to start. The principal stated that bringing all participants together and making a list of personal priorities could help determine a common goal that everyone would be invested in accomplishing. One day after school, the school's instructional technology staff member, special education teachers, gifted and talented teacher, reading specialist, ELL teacher, and I met to share ideas about how we could assist one another and create a common goal.

When it was my turn to speak, I said that I had decided to implement mathematical discussions at the beginning of each class next year, discussions that would address and build mental mathematics strategies. It was amazing to see how the other resource teachers could find a small way to assist in making these more effective. The instructional technology staff member offered to include mental mathematics questions and strategies each month on the county website for each grade level. The ELL teacher offered to join classrooms during their discussions and provide vocabulary assistance for her students. The special education teachers and the gifted and talented teacher agreed to include additional conversations as part of their pullout programs.

Some of the resource teachers had programs that I agreed to contribute to throughout next year. At the conclusion of the meeting, each person completed a personal contract for the contributions to

which they had committed. The contracts were posted in the teachers' lounge throughout the next year as a constant reminder of our collaboration and focused objectives.

Celebrating success

Celebrating success helps to further collaborative working relationships between the mathematics specialist and the other resource teachers, while building a shared confidence. Setting aside time on a regular basis to share instructional practices that are working stimulates proactive rather than reactive instructional decisions. Discussing successes related to students' growth or teachers' professional growth in knowledge or skills enhances the significance of the collegial accomplishments.

Celebrate with students.

Ms. Long works with gifted and talented students in a statewide initiative that challenges students to solve problems in their communities. I collaborated with Ms. Long and her students on a project with the goals of demonstrating the importance of mathematics and raising awareness of mathematics within the community. The students worked with a local grocery store to set up a mathematics night. Parents, students, and teachers came to the store and solved problems involving shopping and nutrition. They found the necessary information throughout the store. This group also organized some mathematics contests for the school, such as problems of the day, which were read during the morning announcements. They created flyers describing mathematically related activities that children and their parents could engage in together. I was so appreciative of their hard work. I had twelve cheerleaders spreading the word about mathematics throughout the school. At the end of the school year, Ms. Long and her students invited me to a party with cookies and punch to celebrate their successful school year. What a rewarding moment!

—Reflections from a mathematics specialist

Celebrate with staff.

My school's principal believes strongly in shared leadership roles among resource teachers. So, early in the school year, the reading specialist and I observed classes when student discourse was occurring. We made notes about student and teacher behaviors. We also reviewed student achievement data that suggested that teachers needed to look at student work as formative assessment. We designed a yearlong professional development series for classroom and resource teachers in which we shared ideas for enhancing classroom discourse and for using protocols to analyze student work. Many teachers commented that they were noticing increased student conversation focused on content rather than miscellaneous chatter. The teachers also held several extended planning sessions, learning to use protocols to analyze student work in both writing and mathematics. Through team reflections, the teachers composed new directions for better-informed instruction. The reading specialist and I were amazed that we could have such an impact on the entire staff. Our collaborative work over time actually enhanced instructional capacity within the entire school.

—*Reflections from a mathematics specialist*

When the mathematics specialist and a resource teacher collaborate, they should take time at the end of the school year to reflect on the goals achieved by students and teachers. Feedback allows the mathematics specialist to gain information about the resource teacher's perspectives. This information can guide or inform steps for the following school year. Both individual and group reflections at the end of the year involve thinking through the effective work that has been accomplished. Discussing successes related to students' academic growth or teachers' professional growth in knowledge or skills enhances the significance of the collegial accomplishments. When resource teachers work together collaboratively, they can build capacity in the school and school district.

Supporting Teachers' Work with Special Education Students

LouAnn H. Lovin and Margaret M. Kyger

Mathematics specialists have the unique opportunity to work with both special education and general education classroom teachers as they develop and implement effective instruction for students with disabilities. A variety of instructional approaches in use in schools today address students' challenges with mathematics. The most effective approach for students with disabilities coordinates regular in-class instruction, intensive small-group instruction, and individualized instruction (Owen and Fuchs 2002). This means that the mathematics specialist must help special education and classroom teachers establish common instructional goals, develop shared understandings of effective instructional interventions, and implement consistent assessments to monitor progress as they strive to support special education students in learning mathematics.

This is no easy feat, for a number of reasons. Classroom and special education teachers may have differing perspectives about what constitutes student knowledge, conceptual understanding, or misconceptions. Furthermore, their perspectives may differ from those of the mathematics specialist. In addition, because of their varying backgrounds and experiences, teachers are likely to need different types of information and different levels of support as they explore ways to help struggling students be successful in learning mathematics. Traditionally, special education teachers have employed interventions focused on procedural routines, with little emphasis on developing or appraising students' conceptual understandings (Woodward and Montague 2002). Classroom teachers may be unsure about how to develop appropriate lesson modifications for students with disabilities. Special education and classroom teachers may not be aware of student-centered mathematics instruction, which requires the teacher to pay careful attention to students' ideas. Consequently, the mathematics specialist, the special education teacher, and the classroom teacher must merge their areas of expertise to find the most effective ways to support special education students as they learn mathematics.

Help special education and classroom teachers move from a procedural focus.

I have worked with only a handful of special education teachers, but all of them have told me that their students cannot do mathematics that involves conceptual knowledge, problem solving, or reasoning. The most intense conversations that I have are with classroom teachers and special education teachers about the potential of students with disabilities. We can guide a teacher who is a learner to move beyond procedurally based lessons. The buy-in comes when she sees her students grasping concepts through these concept-based strategies.

—Reflections from mathematics specialists

What Can the Fields of Mathematics Education and Special Education Offer?

The fields of mathematics education and special education each provide unique insights into ways that teachers can support students as they learn mathematics. For example, numerous frameworks emerging from mathematics education research describe learning trajectories that elementary students tend to move along as they develop their understanding of particular mathematical concepts and skills. Research in special education has supported the development of instructional strategies that are effective in helping students with disabilities learn mathematics. Although much of this research has been conducted in classrooms with students with learning disabilities, the identified strategies can support the learning of all students. Combining ideas from both fields will inform teachers' work with special education students.

Research-based developmental frameworks for learning mathematics

In mathematics specialist preparation programs, prospective elementary specialists often learn about a variety of developmental frameworks that have emerged from teaching experiments as well as interviews with and observations of children doing mathematics (Association of Mathematics Teacher Educators 2010). If not, mathematics specialists should become familiar with these research-based developmental frameworks for learning mathematics. As an example of one such framework, consider the program called *cognitively guided instruction* (CGI) (Carpenter et al. 1999).

CGI is based on research that investigated how young children reason about whole number computations that are embedded in word problems. This research identified four strategies that children use to make sense of and solve word problems: direct modeling, counting strategies, derived facts, and known facts. Initially, children directly model the numbers and actions in the word problem by using manipulatives, tallies, or their fingers. Later, children use counting strategies, such as counting on. Over time, children move to solving word problems by using derived facts—that is, they use a number fact that they know to figure out a solution involving a number fact that they do not immediately know. Eventually, as children know more and more of their basic facts, they solve word problems by using known facts.

CGI research has identified other important aspects for teachers to consider. First, addition and subtraction word problems have different structures: joining, separating, part-part-whole, and comparison. Second, the structure of a word problem affects the level of difficulty of the problem for students. For example, a word problem that includes an action, such as joining two quantities or separating two quantities, tends to be relatively easy for children to solve because they can readily act out the problem. The placement of the unknown in the problem also affects its level of difficulty. For instance, problems with a "start unknown" are more difficult than those with a "result unknown," especially for children at the direct modeling stage, because they do not know how to model an unknown quantity. (For examples of word problems categorized by their structure, see the Common Core State Standards for Mathematics [National Governors Association Center for Best Practices and Council of Chief State School Officers 2010, p. 88]).

A mathematics specialist can assist teachers in developing a better understanding of how *all* children learn mathematics by drawing on research-based developmental frameworks that describe how children make sense of mathematical concepts and skills. Using these research-based developmental frameworks can help teachers plan and implement effective lessons. For example, these frameworks can help teachers gather meaningful information as they listen to and observe their students doing mathematics. This, in turn, can help teachers plan subsequent tasks and follow-up lessons.

Research-based instructional strategies

The developmental frameworks for learning mathematical concepts and skills can serve as the foundation for designing mathematics lessons. Moreover, these frameworks can be coupled with evidence-based instructional practices that have been shown to be effective for teaching mathematics for students with disabilities (Gersten et al. 2009b). Systematic and explicit instruction, student "think-alouds," and visual and graphic depictions of problems are examples of these highly effective instructional practices (NCTM 2007). These strategies support students as they *reason* about mathematical concepts and solve problems, moving beyond procedural proficiency to develop a deep understanding of mathematics. Although instruction involving these kinds of strategies supports *all* students, this form of instruction is necessary for students with disabilities. This means that the mathematics specialist should encourage both the special education and the general education teachers in her school to incorporate these strategies in mathematics lessons.

Systematic and explicit instruction

Research has shown that systematic and explicit instruction has a significant, positive impact on the achievement levels of students with learning disabilities (Gersten et al. 2009b). But all forms of explicit instruction are not alike. The mathematics specialist can help teachers minimize use of explicit instruction that relies on teachers' direct modeling of arithmetic procedures. She can help teachers focus instead on promoting problem-based, student-centered learning that uses explicit instruction to highlight the problem types and appropriate problem-solving strategies (Jitendra and Star 2011; Scheuermann, Deshler, and Schumaker 2009). In this approach, explicit instruction focuses students' attention on the key features of the problems that they are working to solve and the significant ideas in student-generated solutions.

Students with disabilities in mathematics often exhibit memory deficits, specifically with verbal working memory. In particular, students with these deficits have difficulty storing and retrieving information. This affects their ability to retrieve facts accurately and solve problems (Swanson and Jerman 2006). If students do not have something to which they can"hook" the information in their minds, then it gets stored in a haphazard manner in their memories.

To understand why this matters, consider the following analogy. Suppose you were looking for a particular blouse in your closet. The ease with which you found that blouse would differ enormously depending on whether over time you had been throwing clothes in a heap on the closet floor or organizing them by function, color, or season. Similarly, with respect to memory, although the precise organizational structure varies from person to person, an individual typically generates an organizational structure that enables him to locate and retrieve a piece of knowledge from memory when he needs it. Students with disabilities need help in using strategies to create this organizational structure. Because these students tend to use a limited number of strategies and do not effectively apply familiar strategies to new situations, explicit instruction is an excellent teaching intervention for working with special education students on strategy development.

Encourage explicit modeling in mathematics.

It behooves us to support teachers' problem-solving delivery with their students. We can explicitly model the "unpacking" of rich tasks and rubrics, blending in "accountable talk" with students to guide them to a correct and reasonable solution that they can explain and justify. We must ensure that all students have strategies in *their* toolkits—ones that are accurate and seem reasonable to them.

—Advice from a mathematics specialist

Think-alouds

Talking about mathematical concepts and ways to use problem-solving strategies are important parts of developing reasoning skills. As students generate solutions, they should be expected to describe how they solved the problems, as well as what they were thinking that led them to use those strategies and why their approach makes sense. Using think-alouds is an instructional practice that helps all students understand and generate ideas. Students with disabilities may initially need their teachers to ask questions that serve as scaffolds for think-alouds. Answering leading questions guides students to learn how to describe and explain their thinking. This process has a positive impact on students' metacognition—a necessity for effective problem solving (Garrett, Mazzocco, and Baker 2006). In addition, student think-alouds provide teachers with valuable formative assessment information about students' understandings of concepts and skills and their use of problem-solving strategies. They also allow teachers to model ways to use and highlight language that emphasizes mathematical thinking.

Effective use of problem-solving skills is strongly correlated with mathematics achievement. Students with disabilities often have difficulty in developing these types of skills. In particular, they exhibit difficulty in choosing strategies and then using them appropriately. When they learn a strategy, they may use it without evaluating its appropriateness for a given task. Furthermore, they have difficulty in monitoring their own learning and have limited success in using repair strategies to get back on track after making an error. Think-alouds provide a sequenced, explicit way to help students predict, monitor, and evaluate their problem-solving strategies. Students' verbalizations through think-alouds can also be particularly useful for students who act impulsively or who have difficulty distinguishing relevant information from irrelevant information in a problem (NCTM 2007). Additionally, think-alouds can provide another organizational structure to help students integrate new information with previous information.

Emphasize having special education students talk about mathematics.

Student-centered mathematics instruction requires the teacher to listen and pay attention to students' ideas. Using wait time, asking students to explain their thinking, asking students if they agree or disagree with a peer and why, restating another student's idea—these are all strategies that give teachers opportunities to evaluate students' thinking and ideas. These strategies allow teachers to really get into their students' heads.

Sometimes, the teachers that I work with are hesitant to call on a student with a learning disability, or they call on these students only for easy one- or two-word answers. In reality, these are the students who should be doing most of the talking, to help the teacher understand their current understanding and to help the students develop their thoughts through communication.

—Advice from mathematics specialists

Visual and graphic depictions of problems

Using visual representations has a positive impact on student achievement. When visual representations are used in combination with other effective instructional strategies, the impact on student achievement is even greater (Gersten et al. 2009b). Visual representations of mathematical problems are an important feature of mathematics programs in countries where students have performed well on international assessments (for example, Singapore and the Netherlands). Mathematics specialists can help teachers learn how to incorporate representations when working with students on different mathematical concepts.

As an example, consider one of the most commonly used visual representations for solving problems—a bar diagram (see fig. 7.1). Another effective visual representation is a manipulative known as an "arithmetic rack"—a rack with one or two rows of ten beads evenly divided between two colors. This device helps students visualize the benchmarks 5 and 10 (see fig. 7.2), as do ten frames. Research shows that using arithmetic racks in instruction has a positive impact on children's understanding of numbers as well as on their understanding of addition and subtraction (Tournaki, Bae, and Kerekes 2008).

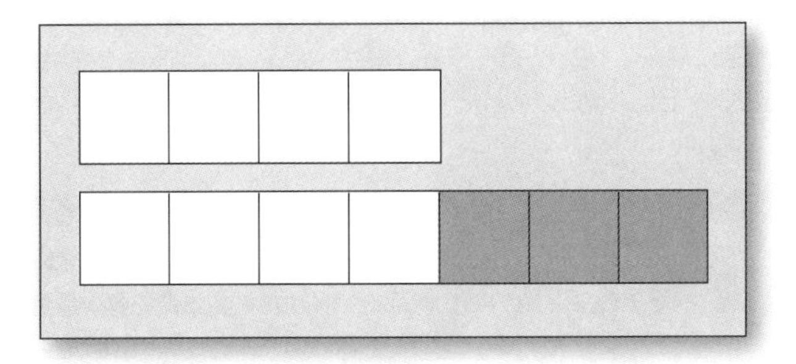

Fig. 7.1. A bar diagram showing that 7 is 3 more than 4

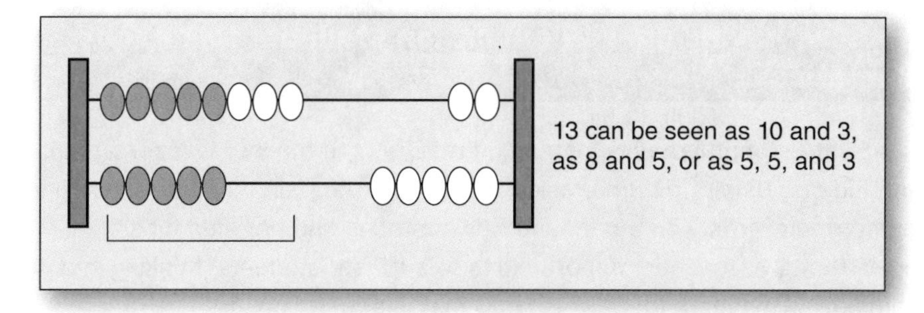

Fig. 7.2. An arithmetic rack providing a visual model of the benchmarks 5 and 10

Students with disabilities often have difficulty with attention, particularly with attending to the relevant information in a task or problem situation. Often they focus on details that are extraneous or unrelated to the problem at hand. Visual and graphic depictions of a task or problem can provide structure for students who have difficulty with recall, attention, or "seeing" the overarching structure or relationships between the information and quantities involved in a task or problem situation.

Where the Two Shall Meet: Response to Intervention

Along with helping special education and classroom teachers understand how students develop various mathematical concepts and skills, the mathematics specialist also works with them to plan instruction based on formative assessment results. Formative assessment is critical in working with students with disabilities and an integral part of the system of instruction and intervention known as *response to intervention* (RtI). However, even without this intervention focus, teachers need to be sure that they accurately assess the mathematical understandings of students with disabilities and design their instruction to address the learning needs of these students.

RtI is a multi-tiered system that focuses a school's remedial program on early prevention so that students receive immediate intervention when they need it (Swanson et al. 2012). From one tier to the next, the degree of intervention increases as the number of students decreases. However, in all tiers, the mathematics instruction within this model should involve progress monitoring and data-driven decision making as well as evidence-based teaching practices.

Tier 1 RtI instruction

To prevent or minimize students' difficulties in learning mathematics, RtI begins with high-quality instruction within the general education classroom—instruction that is informed by the periodic formative assessment of all students in the classroom (Gersten et al. 2009a). Mathematics specialists can assist general classroom teachers in designing formative assessments and interpreting results.

Demonstrate that students' explanations offer authentic formative assessment.

It's important to communicate to teachers that expecting students to explain their work or to describe their thinking is an authentic form of formative assessment. Model this for teachers by asking questions of students and probing their answers so that teachers can see firsthand how instruction for their students can be adjusted "on the spot" on the basis of this type of formative assessment.

—Advice from a mathematics specialist

Tier 2 RtI instruction

Instruction in tier 2 focuses on the same learning objectives as in tier 1 but supplements tier 1 instruction by serving as an intervention conducted in a small-group setting. The intervention targets identified mathematics content with particular students to address the difficulties that these students demonstrated during tier 1 instruction. Typically, tier 2 instruction takes place several times a week and uses evidence-based practices and continual progress monitoring (Gersten et al. 2009a). Tier 2 instruction should offer multiple opportunities for students to respond to tasks and questions and to receive corrective feedback (Crawford and Ketterlin-Geller 2008).

Tier 3 RtI instruction

Students who do not respond to the interventions in tier 2 move to tier 3, which involves individualized instruction with more intense interventions. Research shows that approximately 4 percent of students may not respond sufficiently to the support given in tier 2 (Fuchs, Fuchs, and Compton 2012). Although student data should be the basis for instructional decisions at all tiers, relying on data is particularly meaningful at tier 3 because this instruction is designed to target individual students' specific needs (Gersten et al. 2009a). Tier 3 provides the student with even more intense interventions as identified in a prescribed intervention plan that possibly includes supplemental work on previous concepts and skills as identified by assessments.

A teaching vignette: How to support tier 1 instruction

The following vignette illustrates how a mathematics specialist can support teachers in their work with students with disabilities during tier 1 instruction.

Ms. Fresco, a first-grade teacher, is planning lessons that target the addition and subtraction of numbers up to 20. In the past, Ms. Fresco has begun these lessons by presenting a numerical problem, such as 5 + 8. She has shown her students how to use manipulatives to display the two sets, and then after restating that there are 5 in the first set, she has demonstrated counting on from 5 to find the answer. She has given her students about eight to ten problems to work on their own, expecting them to solve the problems in the way that she has demonstrated.

At one of the meetings at the beginning of the school year, Ms. Fresco heard the mathematics specialist, Mr. Matherly, mention the benefits of using word problems and class discussions when teaching mathematics. Ms. Fresco wants to try these ideas in her instruction. So she decides to meet with Mr. Matherly to share her ideas and get some feedback. Before the meeting, she identifies some word problems as well as some key words that she wants to introduce to her students. She thinks that knowing these key words will be helpful to her students when they are solving word problems.

Mr. Matherly suggests that they also meet with Ms. Spangler, the lower-grades special education teacher who is assigned to Ms. Fresco's class, to hear her suggestions for working with the whole class. He also wants to ensure that both teachers are comfortable with the learning objectives that will be developed for these lessons.

Promote collaborative learning experiences with special education and classroom teachers.

Working in special education is the most intensive collaborative learning experience that I have had thus far. As mathematics specialists, we are in a position to increase the teachers' content knowledge as well as to collaborate to learn strategies supportive of each child's learning experience. It is a very delicate balance, but one of the most rewarding. We are also well positioned to promote students' strengths to the regular education teacher. One way we can do this is by sharing conceptually based strategies that can be successfully used by students with special needs. This can be a door-opening opportunity for us to model these same strategies in the inclusive classroom for all students.

—Advice from a mathematics specialist

As Mr. Matherly listens to Ms. Fresco's ideas, he recognizes several areas in which he can provide support. First, he suggests that they all review prior assessment results for Ms. Fresco's class to identify students who may need some additional support. Next, to highlight issues that arise when the focus is on key words, he shares some word problems that are appropriate for first graders and do not have key words as well as some word problems from the third-grade state assessment that do not have key words. In this way, Mr. Matherly justifies avoiding word problems with key words without demeaning Ms. Fresco's assumption that key words constitute a useful problem-solving strategy. But he makes a mental note to himself to discuss this approach with Ms. Fresco at a later time, when Ms. Spangler is not present for co-planning.

At this point, Mr. Matherly shares the CGI framework that describes children's strategies for solving word problems. Because this framework is new to both Ms. Fresco and Ms. Spangler, Mr. Matherly offers to teach the lesson that they are planning while the other two teachers observe. While they are planning the lesson together, Mr. Matherly shares his reasons for different instructional choices. For example, he explains that a significant part of his lesson will be for the children to share their ideas and strategies after they have had time to work on a problem. For this reason, Ms. Fresco and Ms. Spangler agree with Mr. Matherly that it would be a good idea to expect the students to work on only a few word problems, leaving time for discussion. Together, they identify two word problems with a structure that is appropriate for direct modeling because their review of the students' assessment results suggests that many of the children are at a level of understanding that makes direct modeling natural and accessible. They also select two more word problems with structures that are a bit more challenging for the children who complete the first two problems quickly and accurately.

Ms. Spangler explains to Ms. Fresco and Mr. Matherly that for students with disabilities, the most effective instructional strategies are explicit and systematic instruction, think-alouds, and visual and graphic depictions of problems. Mr. Matherly suggests that they brainstorm about ways to incorporate these into the lesson as they continue to plan.

Promote the benefits of deep planning of lessons.

Many times teachers believe that planning is mapping out lessons over the course of a quarter. Deep planning should be one of our goals when working with teachers. Deep planning looks at big ideas, essential questions, differentiation, and assessment—all based on data. This type of planning takes a lot of time but is rewarding and reflective. Try to do as much of this type of planning as you can with teachers. Often it is easier to begin with individual teachers.

—Advice from a mathematics specialist

With the collaborative planning completed, the lesson unfolds. To begin, Mr. Matherly poses a simple word problem to the children as they are seated on the class rug:

> **Three puppies were sitting on a chair. One more jumped on the chair. How many puppies are on the chair now?**

This problem has small numbers and can be solved by acting it out. Students have access to various manipulatives as well as the number line on the wall. After they have had a chance to work, Mr. Matherly asks two or three students to give an answer and to explain how they found that answer. As students explain their thought processes, Mr. Matherly models their ideas by using visual representations, such as linking cubes, tally marks, and the arithmetic rack that he knows Ms. Fresco has been using to help her students develop benchmarks of 5 and 10. In each case, he explicitly models or helps students explicitly model the numbers and the action in the problem. Mr. Matherly has noticed that one student counted on his fingers, and so he asks the student to stand and show the rest of the class how he used his fingers to count. Mr. Matherly noticed that another student used the number line, so he asks the student to demonstrate how she used the number line. As she does so, Mr. Matherly points out to the class that she is counting the spaces between the numbers, not the numbers themselves. Another student shares how he counted on by recognizing that 4 comes right after 3. Mr. Matherly lists the different ways that the students solved the problem on chart paper so that they have a visual record to refer to when working independently.

After writing another word problem on the board, Mr. Matherly reads it with the class, explaining to the children that they may solve the problem by using any strategy they want, with any of the available materials. He reminds them that they should be ready to explain to the class how they thought through the problem and solved it. As children work on the problem, he walks around the room, asking children questions about what they are doing and how they are thinking about the problem. As he circulates, he decides which children he will ask to share ideas and strategies, depending on whether they have demonstrated a significant idea that he wants to highlight for the rest of the class. He notices that some children used direct modeling, some used counting on, and a few used derived facts.

As Mr. Matherly discussed with Ms. Fresco and Ms. Spangler when they were planning, he will choose children to share ideas and explanations that demonstrate a range of strategies. Because he knows children move through different levels of strategies in sequence, he wants to make sure the children can make sense of at least one of the shared strategies. But he also wants the children to start grappling with a more advanced strategy so that they can eventually move to more sophisticated ways of reasoning. As Mr. Matherly walks around, he uses a monitoring sheet to record which students use which strategies. These data will be helpful for Ms. Fresco and Ms. Spangler as they plan their next lessons.

Once students have had time to work, Mr. Matherly brings them back to the rug area. Before he asks particular students to share their ideas, he asks students to pair-share so that all students have an opportunity to engage in think-alouds. During the whole-class sharing, Mr. Matherly probes some of the children's thinking with questions to help them share explicitly, discussing the steps that they took to solve the problem and why they used a particular strategy. At different points, he rephrases their explanations and models their ideas in a step-by-step manner as the students share their solutions. This process not only helps all the children learn how to describe and explain their work, but also provides direct instruction for those students who will benefit from the organized reiteration. On chart paper, he uses color coding to distinguish between parts of one student's solution to emphasize the relationship between what the student *did* and what he was *thinking*. To wrap up the lesson, Mr. Matherly restates the primary strategies that the students used and emphasizes the significant ideas that the discussion addressed.

The Role of the Mathematics Specialist

By co-planning and teaching a demonstration lesson, Mr. Matherly guided Ms. Fresco and Ms. Spangler to think about how to use high-quality instructional strategies that are informed by a developmental framework. In future meetings, he can work with these teachers to introduce additional models, representations, and visualization strategies, such as bar diagrams and part-part-whole mats (see fig. 7.3), to help students visualize the quantities and the relationships between them in word problems.

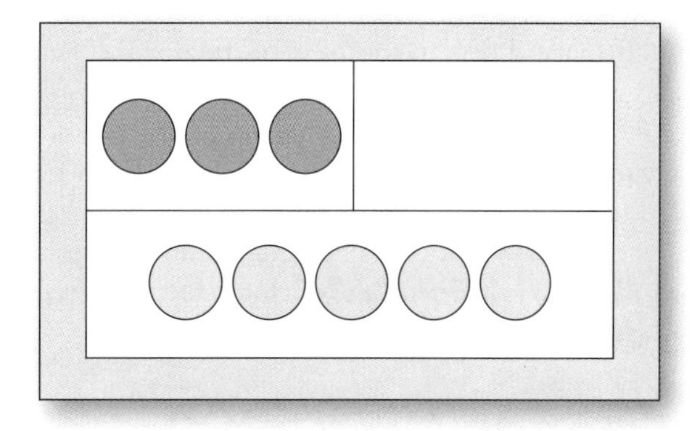

Fig. 7.3. A part-part-whole mat providing a visual model for the following problem: "Keira had 3 coins. A friend gave her some more. Now she has 5 coins. How many coins did Keira's friend give her?"

Even with high-quality whole-class instruction, some students may struggle with the content of the lesson. On the basis of his observations of the students at work and their responses to questioning during this session of tier 1 instruction, Mr. Matherly can work with Ms. Fresco to identify any struggling students and help her design more intense interventions to use in a small-group setting so that she can target and support the students' thinking.

For example, if ongoing assessments reveal that particular students are not moving beyond direct modeling to the counting-on stage, Mr. Matherly might suggest that Ms. Fresco begin with a word problem in which the amount in the initial set is known but hidden, as in the following problem:

Devon had 4 smooth stones. He didn't want to lose his stones, so he put them in a box with a lid that he could close. Then he found 2 more smooth stones. How many smooth stones does Devon have now?

Ms. Fresco could ask children in a small group to model the numbers and the action in the problem directly, including counting to determine the total without opening the box (except to check to see whether the stones are still there). At the same time, she could use questioning and think-alouds to make the reasoning more explicit. Mr. Matherly can help Ms. Fresco develop a sequence of words problems based on the developmental framework so that her instruction is moving from easier to more difficult problems as students build their repertoire of strategies. Using the developmental framework, he can also help Ms. Fresco design an observation sheet for monitoring student progress.

Offer tools to help teachers clarify their student expectations.

Developing student observation sheets has been one method that I have used to make sure all team members are clear about the student expectations. These sheets also serve as a great graphic organizer for a teacher who is inexperienced at facilitating or leading a layered classroom discussion.

—Advice from a mathematics specialist

On the basis of observations and results from progress monitoring, Ms. Fresco may still find that a few of her students are in need of even more intense support. At this point, she may seek help from Ms. Spangler, the special education teacher, in offering tier 3 instruction. It is imperative that students at the different RtI tiers all engage in instruction focused on the *same* concepts and skills. The mathematics specialist can work with both teachers to ensure an instructional focus and facilitate instructional planning that will allow students to benefit from having whole-group instruction as well as small-group instruction. An important role of the mathematics specialist at tier 3 is to ensure that the special education teacher is aware of any available developmental frameworks that describe how children learn the mathematics in question. She and the special education teacher can discuss how this information can help determine which instructional strategies to use to support students during tier 3 instruction.

Addressing Needs through Collaboration

The mathematics specialist has to be a collaborative learner, and this is especially true when the specialist is working with teachers to support the instruction of special education students. This chapter highlights one developmental framework addressing how children learn addition and subtraction concepts, as well as three instructional strategies that are effective for working with students with disabilities as they learn this content. Additional frameworks and strategies target other mathematics content, and investigations are in progress that will yield further suggestions. But the fact remains that no single comprehensive curriculum is ideal for all learners. The mathematics specialist must be willing to engage in a learning journey with the general and special education teachers in her school as they identify, implement, and reflect on various instructional approaches to support all students, including their special education students, as they learn meaningful and worthwhile mathematics.

References

Association of Mathematics Teacher Educators. *Standards for Elementary Mathematics Specialists: A Reference for Teacher Credentialing and Degree Programs.* San Diego: AMTE, 2010.

Carpenter, Thomas P., Elizabeth Fennema, Megan Loef Franke, Linda Levi, and Susan B. Empson. *Children's Mathematics: Cognitively Guided Instruction.* Portsmouth, N.H.: Heinemann, 1999.

Crawford, Lindy, and Leanne R. Ketterlin-Geller. "Improving Math Programming for Students at Risk." *Remedial and Special Education* 29 (January–February 2008): 5–8.

Fuchs, Lynn S., Douglas Fuchs, and Donald L. Compton. "The Early Prevention of Mathematics Difficulty: Its Power and Limitations." *Journal of Learning Disabilities* 45 (May–June 2012): 257–69.

Garrett, Adia J., Michele M. M. Mazzocco, and Linda Baker. "Development of the Metacognitive Skills of Prediction and Evaluation in Children with or without Math Disability." *Learning Disabilities Research* 21 (May 2006): 77–88.

Gersten, Russell, Sybilla Beckmann, Benjamin Clarke, Anne Foegen, Laurel Marsh, Jon R. Star, and Bradley Wizel. *Assisting Students Struggling with Mathematics: Response to Intervention (RtI) for Elementary and Middle Schools* (NCEE 2009-4060). Washington, D.C.: National Center for Education Evaluation and Regional Assistance, Institute of Education Sciences, U.S. Department of Education, 2009a. http://ies.ed.gov/ncee/wwc/PracticeGuide.aspx?sid=2.

Gersten, Russell, David J. Chard, Madhavi Jayanthi, Scott K. Baker, Paul Morphy, and Jonathan Flojo. "Mathematics Instruction for Students with Learning Disabilities: A Meta-analysis of Instructional Components." *Review of Educational Research* 79 (September 2009b): 1202–42.

Jitendra, Asha K., and Jon R. Star. "Meeting the Needs of Students with Learning Disabilities in Inclusive Mathematics Classrooms: The Role of Schema-Based Instruction on Mathematical Problem Solving." *Theory into Practice* 50 (January 2011): 2–19.

National Council of Teachers of Mathematics (NCTM). *Effective Strategies for Teaching Students with Difficulties in Mathematics.* NCTM Research Brief. Reston, Va.: NCTM, 2007. www.nctm.org/news/content.aspx?id=8452.

National Governors Association Center for Best Practices and Council of Chief State School Officers (NGA Center and CCSSO). *Common Core State Standards for Mathematics. Common Core State Standards (College- and Career-Readiness Standards and K–12 Standards in English Language Arts and Math).* Washington, D.C.: NGA Center and CCSSO, 2010. http://www.corestandards.org.

Owen, Rhoda L., and Lynn S. Fuchs. "Mathematical Problem-Solving Strategy Instruction for Third-Grade Students with Learning Disabilities." *Remedial and Special Education* 23 (September–October 2002): 268–78.

Scheuermann, Amy M., Donald D. Deshler, and Jean B. Schumaker. "The Effects of the Explicit Inquiry Routine on the Performance of Students with Learning Disabilities on One-Variable Equations." *Learning Disability Quarterly* 32 (Spring 2009): 103–20.

Swanson, H. Lee, and Olga Jerman. "Math Disabilities: A Selective Meta-analysis of the Literature." *Review of Educational Research* 6 (Summer 2006): 249–74.

Swanson, Elizabeth, Michael Solis, Stephen Ciullo, and John W. McKenna. "Special Education Teachers' Perceptions and Instructional Practices in Response to Intervention Implementation." *Learning Disability Quarterly* 35 (May 2012): 115–26.

Tournaki, Nelly, Young Seh Bae, and Judit Kerekes. "Rekenrek: A Manipulative Used to Teach Addition and Subtraction to Students with Learning Disabilities." *Learning Disabilities—A Contemporary Journal* 6, no. 2 (2008): 41–59.

Woodward, John, and Marjorie Montague. "Meeting the Challenge of Mathematics Reform for Students with LD." *Journal of Special Education* 36 (August 2002): 89–101.

Supporting Teachers' Work with English Language Learners and Gifted Mathematics Learners

Susan Birnie and Catherine Lamczyk

Teachers must meet the challenge of providing instruction that will advance the mathematics learning of each student in their classrooms. As a result, mathematics specialists are likely to be called on to support general education teachers in their efforts to teach significant mathematics to diverse learners, including special groups of students. When working with a teacher to support diverse learning needs, an elementary mathematics specialist begins by considering whether the teacher is already employing general strategies for differentiated instruction—strategies such as small-group instruction, cooperative learning, and frequent formative assessment. However, this catch-all approach to differentiated instruction may overlook learning needs particular to English language learners (ELLs) and gifted learners. This chapter addresses how a specialist can assist classroom teachers in providing effective mathematics instruction for these two groups of learners, much as the preceding chapter addressed working with teachers to support the instruction of special education students.

Instructional Practices That Facilitate the Learning of Diverse Students

Because the mathematics specialist's primary role is to support teachers, she needs to look for ways to address two interrelated demands at once. First, she must support teachers' efforts to plan differentiated instruction so that *all* students come to understand mathematics through active engagement in problem solving, and second, to do the first, she must work with teachers to accommodate the special needs of mathematically gifted students and students who are also learning to speak English.

Building from what students know

A critical first step in planning appropriate differentiated instruction is to set a clear mathematics learning target for the unit or the lesson. This ensures that the same high expectations are established for every learner. The mathematics specialist and the classroom teacher should discuss how to scaffold instruction to incorporate prerequisite knowledge and skills, since some students may need this support, and how to incorporate challenge tasks to extend the learning of advanced students.

Support teachers in reaching every student.

One of my first challenges as a mathematics specialist was working with a fourth-grade teacher who had several ELLs in her classroom. These students were approximately a grade level behind in mathematics. The teacher wanted the children pulled from her classroom for remedial mathematics instruction. Instead, I told the teacher that we would work on this challenge together. When I shared this concern at a mathematics specialists' meeting in my school district, the other specialists reported that they also had teachers who were requesting that either the specialist or a resource teacher serve as the mathematics teacher for ELL students. The group brainstormed about ways to encourage teachers to work with all students in the classroom. We identified four levels of support that we could provide for teachers:

1. **Curriculum level.** Collaborate with the teacher to incorporate objectives in and across units to provide support for differentiated instruction in lessons as well as to address prerequisite understandings prior to lessons.
2. **Teacher level.** Provide a set of "look-fors" for a teacher to use while observing a specialist teaching a differentiated lesson, and then debrief the lesson afterward.
3. **Student level.** Plan lessons and activities that expect students to represent their thinking, use a variety of tools (including concrete materials as well as pictorial and graphic representations), and explain their thinking by talking and writing.
4. **Professional learning level.** Use grade-level meetings and individual coaching opportunities to discuss instructional strategies to meet the needs of English learners. These include supporting oral language with written language and nonverbal communication (such as body movements and expressions), using visual materials (such as pictures, diagrams, objects, manipulatives, and graphs), using auditory materials (such as video and songs), and providing direct experience (such as walks around the school or field trips).

Today, the teacher who wanted me to offer her students remedial mathematics instruction in pull-out sessions is one of my fans. She is very appreciative of the support that I gave her in finding ways not only to differentiate instruction for her students who still were learning to speak English, but also to improve the learning of all her students.

—Reflections from a mathematics specialist

The second important step is to determine what students already know about the learning goal or mathematical expectation. By helping the classroom teacher develop formative assessments to establish her students' level of skill and understanding, the mathematics specialist helps her gain a better understanding of her students as well as the mathematics in upcoming lessons. Formative assessments should include—

- open-ended problems that require students to demonstrate their thinking about the mathematics;
- prompts for concept maps or graphic organizers that allow students to describe the connections within a mathematics topic;
- interviews that permit the teacher to listen as students explain their thinking.

Analyzing and discussing the results of a formative assessment naturally leads to collaboration as the teacher and the specialist plan lessons to address particular skills and understandings. Depending on the assessment results, these lesson plans will include different instructional approaches for supporting students' learning of the mathematics content, reflecting students' current levels of understanding. (See chapter 9, "Using Assessment to Inform Instruction on the Basis of Data," to consider additional ways to support teachers' use of formative assessments.)

Vignette: Differentiating across fractions

The following vignette portrays one classroom teacher's work with a mathematics specialist to offer differentiated instruction related to fractions.

One day early in the school year, Ms. Cortez came to Ms. Jenson, the mathematics specialist at Washington Elementary School. Ms. Cortez had given her third-grade students a pre-assessment for an upcoming unit on fractions, but now she was unsure how to proceed, given the varied results. Ms. Cortez reported that last year the fraction unit had been difficult to teach because the students had come from second grade with many different levels of understanding about fractions. Some students had arrived with a good understanding of how to use fractions to name parts of a whole while others were still struggling with what "$1/2$" or "$1/3$" actually means. This year, Ms. Cortez had both ELLs and mathematically gifted students in her class, so student differences were even more pronounced.

Ms. Cortez and Ms. Jenson planned to meet the following day, giving Ms. Jenson time to review the mathematics concepts and skills included in the pre-assessment. Ms. Jenson decided that it would be helpful for them to examine the progression of concepts and skills for fractions identified for kindergarten–grade 5 in their state's curriculum standards for mathematics and also to identify mathematics learning targets or goals for the upcoming third-grade unit. Ms. Jenson encouraged Ms. Cortez to look beyond the unit she was planning to consider how students might use the mathematics in the unit to extend their understanding of fractions. Knowing that students were at many different levels of understanding, the specialist helped Ms. Cortez use the progression for fractions as a continuum to map out where the students appeared to be in their understanding according to the students' pre-assessments. This was an exciting opportunity for Ms. Jenson to collaborate with Ms. Cortez on the meaning of the mathematics content expectations and the importance of meeting the needs of all students in the classroom.

Ms. Jenson's review of the students' work on the pre-assessment revealed that the students clustered into three groups on the basis of their understanding. Students in group A could write the unit fraction name for one part of a given number of equal parts of a whole and could represent a fraction with a drawing. These students were ready to begin the grade 3 unit. Students in group B did not realize that the whole had to be partitioned into equal-sized parts when naming unit fractions, so they would need to work on that prerequisite knowledge before beginning the unit. Students in group C, by contrast, had already mastered the mathematics concepts identified for the unit on fractions. They were able to use the area, number line, and set model to represent fractions, and their work indicated that they were using the idea of a unit fraction to help them name the parts of the whole for fractions such as $3/5$ or $8/5$. This advanced group could find combinations of fractions that were equal to 1—for example $1/3 + 1/3 + 2/6 = 1$—and they were able to add and subtract proper fractions with like denominators.

All the students would remain in Ms. Cortez's classroom for their mathematics instruction, so it was important for Ms. Jenson to provide support for planning the lessons and make helpful suggestions about ways to differentiate instruction on the basis of students' learning needs. Ms. Cortez and Ms. Jenson discussed how the differentiation could be organized with flexible grouping based on the three readiness levels for the fraction unit. Ms. Cortez wanted to provide all her students with rich tasks that would challenge them, but she also wanted her students to be able to work on tasks without needing her to guide them step by step through the mathematics.

Ms. Jenson shared some resources addressing differentiated fraction goals, including textbook exercises and activities in other supplementary materials. Together, Ms. Cortez and Ms. Jenson looked for rich tasks that offered multiple entry points and called for students to use various representations to solve problems or to explain their work. Ms. Jenson helped Ms. Cortez select tasks that matched the mathematics goals of the unit. The state standards called for students to use the area, number line, and set models to work with fractions, so Ms. Jenson and Ms. Cortez identified manipulatives and pictorial representations to emphasize those different models during the unit. They discussed ways to use the same tasks while scaffolding the learning of students who needed more assistance. Ms. Cortez identified some online resources that she had used before to support students' learning about fractions, and Ms. Jenson added that she knew some fraction games that the students

could play. At the end of the meeting, Ms. Jenson told Ms. Cortez that she would do some additional research on ways to support ELLs and mathematically gifted learners. They agreed to meet again to discuss specific instructional considerations based on what Ms. Jenson found.

Instructional Strategies That Support Differentiation

As illustrated in the vignette, Ms. Cortez and Ms. Jenson planned for the students who needed additional support to advance their understanding, as well as for the learners who already had an advanced understanding of the content but needed instruction to challenge them to extend their understanding. Various instructional strategies can be employed to achieve the learning goals for all students. These include strategies that focus on learning mathematics by experiencing, thinking about, and solving nonroutine problems and communicating one's thinking. Instruction that begins with a clear learning goal and includes rich tasks requiring student communication can further support differentiation through use of cooperative grouping strategies and tiered lessons. A performance-based assessment can also support differentiation as it builds on and reveals students' prior knowledge and skills.

Mathematically rich tasks

Mathematically rich tasks are open-ended problems that are cognitively challenging and can be solved by using various strategies. These tasks are designed around an interesting context or intriguing mathematics situation. They are called "rich" because they encourage discussion and justification and require students to communicate their thinking in ways that others can understand. When students apply problem-solving skills to rich tasks, they often model their thinking with concrete materials, pictorial or graphic representations, or symbolic notation. Making connections among the different models will strengthen students' understanding of the concepts, as well as their understanding of the processes behind the mathematical procedures that they are using.

Emphasize the value of planning for and using mathematically rich tasks.

I began a fourth-grade planning meeting with three teachers by asking them to solve this problem:

There were 2 pieces of chocolate fudge and 4 1/2 pieces of the same size of vanilla fudge on the counter. If Andrea and 6 of her friends wanted to share each kind of fudge equally, how much fudge would each person receive?

I suggested that the teachers work alone for a few minutes before sharing their solution strategies and discussing the mathematics. The teachers were surprised at the different ways that they had worked the problem, as well as how many fraction concepts were involved in solving it.

We then discussed how to scaffold instruction and launch this problem for students with differing strengths. The group thought there could be two versions of this problem. Some students could solve a problem that ended: "Andrea and 3 of her friends wanted to share the fudge so each person would get the same amount of each kind of fudge. How much fudge will Andrea and her 3 friends get?" while other students would solve the problem as presented to the teachers. The teachers then discussed whether they should modify the directions and require students to use a pictorial representation or a symbolic representation to show their thinking.

—Reflections from a mathematics specialist

Cooperative grouping

Cooperative grouping is an instructional strategy in which the teacher assigns each student to a small group of learners, thus establishing multiple learning communities within the classroom. When students work in groups, they have more opportunities to talk about their ideas and to learn from one another as they work together to solve a problem. Another advantage of the cooperative grouping strategy is that having students work interdependently in their small groups allows the teacher to work more closely for extended periods of time with students in selected groups. For independent cooperative group work to be productive, the students must first be taught how to be effective team members. The mathematics specialist can work with teachers to define what cooperative learning behaviors they want to use in their classrooms. The specialist may also co-teach when introducing students to group expectations, both behavioral and mathematical.

Hill and Flynn (2006, pp. 58–59) identified ways for instructors to help students learn effective cooperative group behaviors:

- Model. Role-play or show a video clip in which effective team behavior and meaningful collaboration is taking place.
- Explain. Discuss examples of effective team behavior(s), as well as what would happen if the team did not function effectively or if a team member were called away from the activity.
- Practice. Ask students to think of real-world situations in which everyone must work as a team and must depend on one another to get the job done. Possibly ask students to role-play situations in which various workers interact and are interdependent.

Cooperative learning situations can range from simple, on-the-spot interactions, such as listen-think-pair-share activities, to more complex and formalized structures, such as mixed ability groups or similar ability groups. Sometimes, students in cooperative groups have different roles related to the conduct of the group, such as serving as the recorder who produces the group's final product or serving as the reporter who shares the group members' work with the whole class. Cooperative group work is valuable because through it students may become more confident in their mathematical understanding while collaborating with others. These opportunities allow students to "think like mathematicians" while exploring different ways to solve problems.

Tiered assignments

When teachers use tiered assignments to differentiate instruction, the mathematical focus of the lesson does not vary from tier to tier. All students will be learning the essential understandings and skills identified in the curriculum, but students will experience the lesson at different levels of complexity, abstractness, and open-endedness (Tomlinson 2001). The teacher may use information gained from formative assessments to vary the tasks assigned to students in an effort to ensure that each student engages in challenging yet accessible mathematics while investigating concepts, using skills, and developing understanding that builds on what the student already knows. The mathematics specialist can help a teacher investigate the mathematics behind the content or skill being targeted and then develop effective tiered assignments advancing each student's learning.

Performance-based assessment

Performance-based assessments are a type of formative assessment. They can be assigned before, during, or after a unit of instruction. Performance-based assessments require students to explain their thinking, allowing the teacher to evaluate their proficiency when solving novel or nonroutine problems or applications. At the same time, performance-based assessments permit the teacher to identify or uncover student misconceptions that need attention. When teachers use rich tasks in their classroom lessons, performance-based assessments are a natural extension of the instructional process. The mathematics specialist can partner with a teacher to develop performance-based assessments as well as the accompanying assessment rubrics for interpreting the students' work.

Collaborate with teachers to develop performance-based assessments.

During my first year as a mathematics specialist, I was assigned to work with an experienced teacher who was highly respected because of the high standardized-test scores that her students earned. I was nervous—no, I was scared—about collaborating with her. She had more classroom teaching experience than I did, and she was very assertive about what she thought were best practices for teaching mathematics. What could I offer her that she did not already know? I decided that I would broach the topic of using performance assessments and rubrics. This strategy was new to her, and she was skeptical of it. So I decided that first I would talk with her about the idea of using tasks and rubrics during instruction, so that students might become aware of what they understood and what they still needed to learn. I was so nervous when I presented these ideas to her that I came prepared with a research article to support my ideas! To my amazement, she agreed to try this approach. This set the stage for our ongoing work together over the rest of the year. We were a team helping students to monitor and regulate their own learning as they solved problems. We were also using what we learned about her students' understanding to design lessons.

—Reflections from a mathematics specialist

Supporting Classroom Teachers of ELLs and Mathematically Gifted Students

As an experienced teacher, a mathematics specialist may feel confident about his ability to help teachers design lessons to engage students in doing mathematics. Because of his specialist preparation program and teaching experience, he may also feel confident that his knowledge of mathematics and his understanding of various instructional strategies allow him to collaborate with classroom teachers to differentiate instruction. But, depending on their prior teaching experience, many specialists are less confident about their ideas for modifying mathematics instruction to meet the special needs of ELLs or mathematically gifted students. At the conclusion of the vignette about Ms. Jenson and Ms. Cortez's planning, Ms. Jenson recognized that she needed to strengthen her own understanding of ELLs and gifted learners before she could provide Ms. Cortez with more targeted support.

The ELL and gifted resource teachers in the school or school district are valuable sources of information. The mathematics specialist can also locate resources that are available through the school, the school district, or the state's department of education to support instruction for these special groups of learners. Then the specialist and teachers can work together to try out some of those approaches. (See chapter 6, "Working with Resource Teachers," for more information about how a mathematics specialist and resource teachers can work together.)

Instructional strategies to support ELLs

Students must have English language proficiency to use their mathematical knowledge and skills for solving problems in real-world situations, reading and comprehending word problems, communicating their mathematical thinking, and working with other students on mathematical tasks. However, ELLs face great challenges related to using and understanding the English language. The mathematics teacher whose class includes ELLs must make mathematics lessons understandable for her English language learners. This includes making certain that students have the vocabulary necessary to understand instruction and to express their ideas about the mathematics concepts both orally and in writing (Felux et al. 2009). For example, in a fourth-grade measurement lesson, the students were told that during spring break their classroom would be covered with new carpet and the students needed to tell the principal how much carpet to order. The teacher informed the students they could use yardsticks to help them determine the area. Then she noticed that two of her English learners were looking out the window with confused looks on their faces. When she talked with them, she realized that they associated the word "yard" only with the ground outside.

Teachers in the upper-elementary grades may also notice that their ELLs seem to speak English with greater ease when interacting with other students in the lunchroom or during recess than they do in class. It takes students much longer to develop what is termed the "language of schooling" than to acquire the language that is used in daily social communication (Schleppegrell 2004). Research suggests that although an ELL may take only six months to two years to learn how to communicate in social settings, he or she may need five to seven years to become fluent in English as it is used in school (Cummins 2008). A specialist could discuss this difference with teachers to help them understand the uneasiness with English that many ELLs experience every day during instruction.

Building background knowledge

When teachers work with students, they are constantly tapping into and building students' background knowledge of mathematics content, enlarging their mathematical vocabulary, and supporting the development of their language and skills for communicating their mathematical reasoning and understanding. Although these instructional goals are essential for work with all learners, they are especially important in work with ELLs. Each student has a unique understanding of mathematics vocabulary, ranging in complexity and sophistication as he continues to grow as a mathematical thinker. Many mathematics vocabulary words are confusing because of different meanings associated with them. Consider, for example, *beside/besides*, *whole/hole*, *table*, *difference*, *left*, and *face*. When teachers are introducing new mathematical concepts, they can support their English learners by discussing key vocabulary words and posting an illustration on a word wall for ongoing student reference. Using visual supports such as illustrations, demonstrations, graphs, objects, body movements, and nonverbal expressions, as well as auditory materials such as videos, makes mathematical content more understandable and supports communication.

If students are confused by either essential or nonessential information in a mathematics problem, they may be distracted and not focus on the mathematics. For example, in the carpeting example, the teacher could display a yardstick, post a labeled picture of a yardstick, and, after asking a volunteer to show how to use a yardstick to measure, post a sketch of a square yard. These instructional supports are useful for many students, but they can be critical for ELLs.

When co-planning, keep ELLs in mind.

As a former ELL, I feel a real commitment to support ELLs. Vocabulary and language development are so important for English learners. When I plan a lesson with a teacher, I stress the use of think-pair-share opportunities. These give the students the chance to talk about what they know informally and then to report back as a team. Next, the teacher and I discuss and clarify possible unfamiliar words, giving examples of the different meanings of words that have multiple meanings. For example, when a problem asks how much is *left*, ELLs need help to understand that *left* is not your *left* hand. We also plan lots of opportunities for students to explain their thinking in writing. We frequently use tasks with sentence starters. For instance, I know that 30 – 5 = __________ because .

—Reflections from a mathematics specialist

As the specialist partners with a teacher to plan instruction, particularly in classes that include ELLs, she can use the following steps, identified by Marzano (2004, pp. 70–87), for effective vocabulary development:

- Step 1: The teacher provides a description, explanation, or example of the new term.
- Step 2: Students restate the explanation of the new term in their own words.
- Step 3: Students create a nonlinguistic representation, such as a symbol, picture, or graphic organizer for the term.
- Step 4: Students periodically engage in activities that help them add to their knowledge of the new terms. For example, they may use comparisons and classifications, generate metaphors and analogies, revise initial descriptions and explanations, and apply understanding of roots and affixes to deepen vocabulary use.
- Step 5: Students are asked to discuss the terms with one another, with the key academic vocabulary becoming a daily part of classroom discourse.
- Step 6: Students are periodically involved in games and competitions that allow them to use the terminology.

Classroom discourse and wait time

Mathematics instruction for ELLs must create opportunities for the students to develop and practice their mathematics language skills by participating in oral communication. These opportunities can range from think-pair-share activities to small-group work to whole-class discussion.

One of many useful strategies for working with ELLs is providing sufficient wait time after asking a question (Echevarria, Vogt, and Short 2000). Specialists can discuss with teachers why it is important to refrain from calling on students who volunteer to respond right away, as well as why it could be useful to tell all students that they should first wait and think before answering or raising their hands, with the teacher indicating to the class when he is ready for a response. Ample wait time for responses gives all students an opportunity to think. But for English learners, it is also time to process the question in English, to think of the answer in their first language, and then to formulate their response in English. Planning for instruction should include ways to structure classroom learning so that, as the situation requires, the teacher and the students use wait time appropriately. For example, during whole-class instruction the teacher can pause periodically during a presentation to give students some personal think time to reflect on what has been shared.

Supporting classroom teachers of mathematically gifted students

Just as the different levels of English language proficiency call for various levels of support for ELLs, different levels of understanding and interest in mathematics necessitate various levels of support for mathematically gifted students (Gavin 2003). Keeping the mathematically gifted student engaged in interesting mathematics can pose an even bigger challenge to teachers in a mixed-ability classroom. The mathematics specialist can work with classroom teachers to identify mathematics tasks and ways to stimulate and enhance the learning of these students.

The mathematics specialist should consider the generally accepted learning characteristics of gifted students as she supports classroom teachers' efforts to plan lessons to challenge mathematically gifted students. Often gifted students demonstrate exceptional reasoning ability. Many gifted students have unusually good memories, enjoy posing problems, and are skillful in solving problems in unexpected ways and noticing and describing regularities, patterns, and relationships. Mathematically gifted students often enjoy working abstractly and demonstrating rapid learning. When planning for these students, teachers need to take into consideration their long and highly focused attention spans when presented with tasks that interest them, their capacity for self-directed activity, and their preference for mathematical activities involving original problems. A mathematics specialist can collaborate with the classroom teacher to supplement and differentiate the mathematics curriculum for high-ability students in ways that build on and extend what they already know, while maintaining their engagement in important and interesting mathematics.

Differentiation strategies such as cooperative learning, use of rich tasks, expectations for student communication, tiered assignments, and performance-based assessments may not be sufficient to provide a rigorous and challenging learning experience for mathematically gifted students. Additional options for differentiating instruction for these students include curriculum compacting, mathematically complex tasks, and problem-based learning.

Curriculum compacting

Curriculum compacting is a differentiation strategy that is beneficial to gifted mathematics students because it opens up the grade-level curriculum to provide time for students to study mathematics content or applications of mathematics that they might not otherwise be able to study. The purpose of curriculum compacting is to create a rigorous alternative mathematics learning experience in which students who have already mastered the concept for the grade level are provided with an opportunity to learn more complex content or to apply the grade-level content within investigations of real-world situations.

Curriculum compacting involves three steps: (1) defining mastery for a particular grade-level concept, (2) pre-assessing students, and (3) identifying alternative mathematics concepts or applications for students who demonstrate mastery on the pre-assessment. A mathematics specialist can support the classroom teacher in each of these steps. The alternative mathematics assignments must offer mathematically gifted students rigorous and interesting problems or tasks that will foster their understanding of significant mathematics concepts and relationships. In addition, the alternative assignments should strengthen students' creative problem-solving skills, enhance their ability to conjecture, and foster more sophisticated logical reasoning skills.

Mathematically complex investigations

Mathematically gifted students will develop their sense of self-worth and identify learning goals that they believe are worthwhile when given the opportunity to partner with the teacher to reflect on their mathematics learning and interests. When gifted students struggle and then succeed as they investigate a task or problem that they helped to identify, they gain more satisfaction than when simply completing a task assigned by the teacher. Gifted students still need support from their teachers, but it may be a different kind of support. For example, they may need assistance in identifying and gaining access to resources to help them with their investigation. The students may need access to someone other than the teacher who has expertise in the topic—an expert such as a mathematically gifted high school student, a high school mathematics teacher, or even a community member who works in a field that applies mathematics. These students may require help in locating or using online sources of information. Most important, mathematically gifted students need daily interaction with their teacher so that they continue to feel that they are members of the class and the teacher can monitor their progress and determine whether they need particular guidance or resources.

Assist in developing related, but more complex tasks for gifted students.

I was working with a third-grade teacher to plan a fraction lesson addressing the use of unit fractions to name the fractional part of a whole. Having worked in this classroom many times, I knew that some students had already grasped this idea and would quickly lose interest in the lesson. Knowing that the teacher was cautious about deviating from the goal of the lesson, I suggested that perhaps the advanced students could explore a question that would still involve unit fractions but be more complex:

> **Can you find consecutive unit fractions that when added together sum to a total of 1? If your answer is yes, give some examples, and if your answer is no, how would you convince someone that it cannot be done?**

The teacher became intrigued by the problem, but she was concerned that it might be too tricky for the students. I encouraged her to let the students wrestle with it. I explained that if these students were struggling, instead of giving them hints, she should ask them to explain what they had discovered so far and then ask what they could try next. I suggested, in other words, that she get the group members talking to one another. If their answer was that it is impossible to get to 1, then the teacher could ask the group to explain how close they could get and push them to develop at least one way to prove their idea. After she used this problem, she could not wait to tell me about how many different ways the students could prove that it is possible to get closer and closer to 1, but never arrive at 1 exactly!

—Reflections from a mathematics specialist

Problem-based learning

Problem-based learning (PBL) is an instructional approach that allows gifted students to be self-directed learners while the teacher serves as guide and consultant in the learning process. Working in a small group, students are presented with an authentic problem situation and must identify what they want to investigate, on the basis of the questions raised by the problem. PBL investigations are cross-disciplinary and engage the students in using mathematics to investigate a real-life situation. In PBL, students are required to think both critically and creatively and to monitor their own understanding. Throughout a PBL investigation, students conduct research to find information that will give them a better understanding of the problem. Students are expected to make conjectures, develop potential solutions, and evaluate the merit of each solution. In addition, they have to communicate and evaluate their thinking about the problem, develop a way to share the solution with an audience, and justify their recommended solution.

Authentic or real-world problems requiring the students to use and extend their understanding of the mathematics in the grade-level curriculum come from many sources. Resources for problem-based learning investigations can be found by searching the Internet for engineering or STEM projects for elementary students or NASA educational resources. Searching the Internet under "problem-based learning activities" can be another useful way to identify problems suitable for PBL.

PBL can be a challenging strategy for teachers to implement, and the specialist should be prepared to provide a great deal of support for teachers. This may be a strategy that a specialist first begins to learn about on his own so that he can introduce it to teachers in subsequent years.

Establish and Build from Strengths

No strategies are guaranteed to advance the mathematics learning and achievement of ELLs and of mathematically gifted students. For this reason, the elementary mathematics specialist should honestly tell teachers that together they are going to figure out approaches as they collaborate to meet the needs of students. Then, just as teachers should work from students' strengths, the mathematics specialist should work from teachers' pedagogical strengths. It is through this collaboration that teachers will find support for working with their English language learners and mathematically gifted students and, at the same time, have the opportunity to improve their instructional practice and find support.

References

Cummins, Jim. "BICS and CALP: Empirical and Theoretical Status of the Distinction." In *Encyclopedia of Language and Education*, 2nd ed., vol. 2, *Literacy*, edited by Brian S. Street and Nancy H. Hornberger, pp. 71–83. New York: Springer, 2008.

Echevarria, Jana, Mary Ellen Vogt, and Deborah Short. *Making Content Comprehensible for English Language Learners: The SIOP Model.* Needham Heights, Mass.: Allyn & Bacon, 2000.

Felux, Carolyn, Rusty Bresser, Kathy Melanese, and Christine Sphar. *Supporting English Language Learners in Math Class: A Multimedia Professional Learning Resource, Grades K–5.* Sausalito, Calif.: Math Solutions, 2009.

Gavin, Katherine M. "Meeting the Needs of Talented Elementary Math Students." *Understanding Our Gifted* 16 (January 2003): 19–22.

Hill, Jane D., and Kathleen M. Flynn. *Classroom Instruction That Works with English Language Learners.* Alexandria, Va.: Association for Supervision and Curriculum Development, 2006.

Marzano, Robert J. *Building Background Knowledge for Academic Achievement.* Alexandria, Va.: Association for Supervision and Curriculum Development, 2004.

Schleppergrell, Mary J. *The Language of Schooling: A Functional Linguistics Perspective.* Mahwah, N.J.: Lawrence Erlbaum, 2004.

Tomlinson, Carol Anne. *How to Differentiate Instruction in Mixed-Ability Classrooms.* 2nd ed. Alexandria, Va.: Association for Supervision and Curriculum Development, 2001.

Supporting the School Mathematics Program

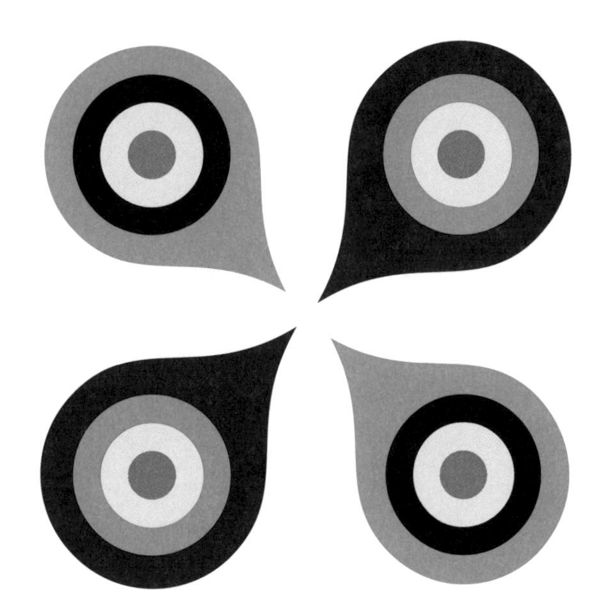

Using Assessment to Inform Instruction on the Basis of Data

Denise M. Walston and Sandra S. Overcash

Assessment should not only furnish useful information about what students have or have not learned, but also provide guidance for future teaching (National Council of Teachers of Mathematics [NCTM] 2000). When it comes to assessment, an elementary mathematics specialist assumes many roles. A specialist organizes and interprets assessment data to provide meaningful feedback to teachers, students, and administrators. She does this with the intention of providing information that will be useful in making decisions about future instruction—instruction that might lead to improved student achievement. A specialist may work with grade-level teachers to design assessments. She does this to enable the teachers not only to evaluate student learning, but also to gain insights into their teaching. Frequently, a specialist collaborates with teachers to review student work and interpret student thinking. She does this to develop teachers' understanding of student learning and to support teachers' efforts to meet students' needs. In each of these settings, the mathematics specialist is using assessment as a vehicle for providing useful information to school administrators and teachers as she partners with them to improve mathematics teaching and learning.

The mathematics specialist uses assessment data to gather information that will benefit teachers' practice and students' learning in a positive way. When the mathematics specialist organizes assessment data, he does so with one of two purposes in mind. First, he may be preparing to work with teachers in sessions where they will use the assessment results to inform instruction. In this case, the purpose of assessment is *for* learning. When teachers and the mathematics specialist review and interpret organized assessment data, teachers get information that helps them decide where and how they should next focus their work with students. This work involves specifying learning goals and strategically planning how this learning will occur during classroom instruction. However, it may be that the specialist is organizing assessment data for a different purpose: so that he and the teachers can interpret them to evaluate student performance and summarize what students have already learned. In this case, the purpose of the assessment is to provide a measure *of* learning, with the data allowing a comparison of each student's achievement, as measured by the assessment, with a standard or expectation. Assessment data also offer evidence for comparing the achievement or test-item responses of one student with those of another student.

This chapter highlights the ways in which specialists can use assessment data to focus their work with teachers and principals. It also describes how specialists can use assessment data to support and enhance collaborative discussions among teachers and administrators as they attempt to identify and address the challenges that students may be facing when learning mathematics.

Don't let the idea of assessment *for* learning go missing in action.

The fifth-grade teachers had been struggling to help children understand the distributive property and decomposing numbers. In one class, the teacher worked with students on the concept for three days and then gave a quiz. Her class pass rate was 32 percent. I stopped in her room to offer a suggestion for the next lesson on the distributive property, and she immediately said, "I'm done. I taught it for three days, and if I offer another strategy, it will only confuse the children." I'm sure my chin dropped about three inches. I couldn't believe that she thought she was finished with this topic when 68 percent of her class did not understand it. I knew that this was not the time to press the teacher. But I also knew that at the next grade-level team meeting I wanted to discuss some student responses to assessment items on this topic so that teachers could think about their students' understanding and needs in planning for upcoming lessons.

—*Reflections from a mathematics specialist*

Opportunities for Formative Learning with Teachers

Classroom assessments can be more than a collection of scores for the grade book. But for this to happen, teachers need to take the time to analyze what students understand and where they are confused. Positive changes occur in student learning when teachers regularly use the results of assessment to make adjustments to their instructional plans. But teachers typically need some help to do this. They frequently do not know how to organize or interpret assessment results in ways that will help them infer what their students do or do not understand. They also need support as they figure out how to use the information from an assessment to plan their instruction.

When the specialist and teachers work together, classroom assessments become a valuable source of data that can help them design future lessons. These lessons will need to include rich mathematical tasks that introduce students to new material while simultaneously filling in gaps associated with their areas of weakness. By starting the planning process with what students understand, teachers and their specialist can blend previous and upcoming mathematics content and curricular requirements with instructional strategies that build on students' strengths to improve their understanding. Some of the most useful evidence for planning based on students' prior knowledge is gathered through a process called *formative assessment*.

The formative assessment process

The process of formative assessment is characterized by three stages (Wiliam 2011, p. 45):

1. Finding out where the students are in their learning
2. Knowing where the students will be going
3. Figuring out how to get the students to their destination

Although students are the focus of each stage, these steps also describe a pathway for the mathematics specialist to follow in her work with teachers. Formative assessment becomes an effective tool to guide instructional decisions as the specialist and teachers work through these three stages together.

Using formative assessment to identify student learning goals

State standards and local school district curricular guides identify an intended mathematics curriculum. These guides are key sources for defining intended targets for student learning. The specialist supports teachers by working with them to develop a deep understanding of the meaning of the mathematical concepts in an upcoming unit, as well as the connections among those concepts. This discussion may also consider what prior knowledge students might need to tap into or build on when learning this content.

The mathematics specialist can then work with individual teachers or, even better, grade-level teams to create a formative assessment. That is, the teachers and the mathematics specialist will define mathematics problems or questions for students to respond to, to give the teachers and the specialist a better grasp of their current understandings and misunderstandings related to this content. The grade-level team and the specialist then compare students' responses to these tasks or questions, the presumed prior knowledge base, and the intended curriculum objectives or standards. Interpretation of this information allows the team to identify student learning goals. In addition, with the help of the specialist, the teachers may identify those concepts and skills that the students must progress through to reach a particular learning target. Once they have established this learning progression, teachers have the information that they need to make choices about which specific concepts and skills they will need to emphasize or introduce during classroom instruction.

The mathematics specialist is actively engaged during these collaborative planning sessions as he leads discussions among teachers, provides feedback, and supports teachers through the process of designing instruction and planning one or more lessons. The critical characteristic of these plans is that they include questions and tasks that allow teachers to assess students' in-progress learning. Planning collaboratively with teachers allows the mathematics specialist to steer the discussion to ways of inserting ongoing assessment of student learning within classroom instruction. In this manner, the specialist can support teachers' efforts to lead effective classroom discussions, to phrase questions that help bring out students' thinking, and to use activities and tasks that elicit evidence of their learning. Once the lesson has been taught, the specialist and the teachers should come back together to analyze student work, as well as any other evidence that has been gathered during the lesson and uncovers or reveals student thinking.

Learning from student work

Discussions of students' work and thinking can become rich learning opportunities for teachers. When teachers consider the reasoning behind students' wrong answers or incomplete responses, they are establishing a basis for addressing their misunderstandings about a particular mathematics concept. This discussion deepens the teachers' own understanding of the mathematics and how students learn it. As the partnership among teachers and specialist grows and trust deepens, discussions about student performance can expand to consider variations among classrooms and candid examination of instructional practices that worked or did not work in individual classrooms. These discussions allow teachers to serve as learning resources for one another and to strengthen their knowledge about the connections among content, instruction, and assessment.

Planning a unit

Working collaboratively with teachers on a grade-level team allows a mathematics specialist to support the team in unit planning. During the planning discussions, the specialist can help teachers identify a group of related standards to be addressed within a unit, describe what constitutes evidence of student learning, and identify ways to gather that evidence. The specialist should work with the teachers to design tasks and activities aligned with the unit's learning goals. When teachers agree to use these tasks with their students and to bring samples of student work back to future grade-level meetings, the team is assured of having data that members can discuss together. During these discussions, teachers can evaluate student performance. They do this as they decide what criteria to use to determine student understanding and what quality of work represents good understanding. These discussions can lead teachers to think about existing rubrics and also how to develop their own rubrics. These discussions can ultimately lead teachers to create and use common assessments.

Unwrapping the Standards

Discussions about student performance are most productive when the specialist and the teacher—

1. understand the mathematics content in the state or local curriculum standards;
2. know how the mathematical learning expectations develop across the grade levels; and
3. know which classroom experiences help students develop their understanding of the mathematics content.

One way that a specialist can support this process is to lead teachers in "unwrapping" the state or local standards. They should do this *before* having discussions about assessment results or planning lessons based on those results. These unwrapping discussions help teachers identify the concepts and skills that together compose a group of interrelated standards. Focusing on these interrelated standards can be useful when identifying what students are expected to know to be ready for a particular unit of study. Identifying interrelated standards can also reveal useful content connections for investigation during instruction.

For example, during an unwrapping discussion about the concept of multiplication with whole numbers, the specialist could highlight the usefulness of the commutative property as well as the concept of area. This discussion could lead teachers to identify the concepts and skills in a learning progression. This learning progression would lay out expectations for students' development of an understanding of multiplication over time. The learning progression would end with the standard of fluency in whole-number multiplication.

Demonstrate the usefulness of "unwrapping" the standards.

While reviewing the results of the latest third-grade common assessment, the teachers determined that students had struggled with subtraction because they did not understand place value. They thought that the second-grade teachers could do more to develop this concept. I needed to find a way to work with second-grade teachers without being critical of what they were doing. Because we had new state standards that year, I figured that they would be a perfect place to start. I went through the new K–3 standards and pulled out all that related to place value, addition, and subtraction. Then I planned an "unwrapping the standards" activity. The teachers and I went through each of these standards in grade-level order and used chart paper to track the progression of the concepts and skills across the grade levels. We also spent time talking about the changes in the verbs describing what students were expected to do as we moved up the grade levels. That conversation led to a discussion about what students needed to know and be able to do by the end of second grade to be ready for third grade. During the discussion, the teachers realized that first graders really needed to understand what they called grouping 10 ones for 1 ten and ungrouping 1 ten for 10 ones, while second graders also needed to understand grouping and ungrouping 10 tens for 1 hundred for numbers up through 999.

—*Reflections from a mathematics specialist*

Designing instruction and assessments

The information and ideas developed during the unwrapping process may lead to a discussion addressing not only learning goals for a unit, but also students' current understanding of the mathematics in the unit. On the basis of their experience, teachers can share insights about potential student misconceptions and overgeneralizations. The specialist can ask them to consider what constitutes evidence of student learning throughout the unit, perhaps asking, "How will you know when students understand and can do these things? What will you accept as evidence of student learning?" (National Council of Supervisors of Mathematics [NCSM] 2008). This discussion may then branch to teaching ideas. Teachers may share effective practices while collaboratively designing tasks and instructional activities to assist students in meeting the learning goals of the unit. The specialist's role is to ensure that mathematics content anchors the emerging unit of instruction and is clearly evident in any chosen task or activity.

The Common Assessment Process

When all teachers at a particular grade level agree to administer the same assessment instrument and to score the students' work collaboratively, the assessment is called a *common assessment*. During the scoring process, teachers will discuss the mathematics content that the instrument assessed. They will also talk about student responses that represent either solid or incomplete understanding of the assessed concepts and skills. In this discussion, the mathematics specialist can draw attention to how particular expectations, such as those identified in the Standards for Mathematical Practice (National Governors Association Center for Best Practices and Council of Chief State School Officers 2010), can affect student understanding.

Although using a common assessment developed by someone else can offer grade-level teachers rich learning opportunities, creating their own common assessment can increase the potential impact on instruction. When grade-level teams plan units of instruction together, the mathematics specialist can encourage the teachers to take the extra step of planning a common assessment for the unit. If the team does this before they start teaching the unit, the teachers are more likely to discuss their students' progress throughout the unit because they have their expectations clearly in mind. Teachers may develop a routine of discussing errors that they find in student thinking and in the generalizations that students make during classroom lessons. This allows teachers to consider how to address students' misconceptions prior to administering the common unit assessment.

Lend support to teachers' development of unit tests.

In my school, I had to be careful to back away from making assessments for teachers. Just last week, I had a teacher come to me worried that she did not have time to make an assessment for her students. I talked with her about the resources that she had available for the assessment and pointed out material from the textbook and the online testing tools that our school had purchased. I also encouraged her to talk about developing the assessment with the other grade-level teachers and with the special education teacher who co-teaches with her. Once she saw that the assessment was not something she had to do on her own but could collaborate on with others while drawing on available resources, she became less stressed. She chose to work with the special education teacher to put an assessment together, using some materials provided with our textbook. She brought the test to our grade-level team meeting, and we reviewed the test items and made a few changes. The grade-level teachers decided to use the questions on their own unit test and to bring the student papers to our next meeting.

—Reflections from a mathematics specialist

The mathematics specialist will find that the difficult step in the common assessment process is not related to interpreting the standards or developing the assessment items. The most challenging task is to work with teachers to analyze the assessment data and translate those findings into real changes in curriculum implementation, instructional practice, and student learning opportunities (NCSM 2008). The specialist needs to plan carefully how to introduce classroom data, including samples of student work, into the discussion with teachers so that the link between student learning and classroom tasks and activities can be examined. In this discussion, the specialist can also introduce information about current practices for teaching particular mathematics concepts.

Using Assessment Data to Support Collaboration

The mathematics specialist is in a unique position. He can use assessment data and examples of student work as a starting point for encouraging teachers and the principal to join with him in a concentrated effort to improve the school's mathematics program. The effort will include curriculum analysis, data analysis, and analysis of instruction. As a collaborative team, a specialist and his teachers can focus on the following:

- Implementing and analyzing frequent formative assessments
- Planning powerful instruction based on students' understandings as revealed in formative assessments
- Delivering a rigorous curriculum
- Evaluating high expectations for student performance
- Returning to implementing and analyzing frequent formative assessments to restart the cycle

At the same time, this process allows a specialist to evaluate whether he is holding high, yet appropriate, expectations for teacher performance (Killion 2008). In this way, assessment is a tool that specialists may use to focus the work they do with teachers.

Using Assessment Results to Focus Work with Teachers

The following vignette illustrates the efforts of a mathematics specialist to use results from assessment to focus her work with teachers:

Ms. Brown was a mathematics specialist working in an elementary school located in a large suburban school district. She had received the initial results of the most recent common formative assessment developed and administered by three fourth-grade teachers to all their students. The common assessment addressed fraction equivalence and ordering fractions. Ms. Brown was to meet soon with the fourth-grade teachers to discuss the results of the assessment and to support the teachers in their planning. Fractions had been a school focus, and Ms. Brown's principal, Ms. Ames, had also asked to meet with Ms. Brown to discuss the assessment results. Ms. Brown knew that in addition to looking at the results of this latest common assessment, Ms. Ames would be interested in knowing how Ms. Brown would support the teachers in using the results to improve student learning.

Organizing and analyzing the data

Ms. Brown examined the students' work to determine what percentage of the students had correctly answered each of ten short-answer questions on the common assessment. Using this information, she created a bar graph (shown in fig. 9.1), to display the results by question.

The graph showed that fewer students had given correct responses to questions 4, 6, 7, and 9; on these items, more than 20 percent of the students had provided incorrect responses. Ms. Brown then scanned a clean copy of the test, with no student responses, and identified the mathematics content addressed by each of these four questions. Next, Ms. Brown pulled a random sample of incorrect student responses for the four questions to help her determine the misconceptions and patterns of error that she would discuss in the collaborative meeting with the teachers.

Ms. Brown's analysis of the students' work revealed that many students were using whole-number thinking, resulting in errors in their work with fractions. For example, some of these students claimed that $3/8$ of a candy bar is more than $3/4$ of the same candy bar because 8 is greater than 4. As Ms. Brown looked at the work samples, she noted that the students appeared to be comfortable using an area model to find the solutions to questions but had much more difficulty with items involving a number line. Ms. Brown also determined that rather than using reasoning skills and benchmark fractions to help them order fractions, some students were rewriting every fraction in the test item to make common denominators. However, these students did not recognize when their incorrect application of the procedure gave them a new fraction that was not equivalent to the original fraction. On the basis of the error patterns and misconceptions that she was seeing, Ms. Brown concluded that the students needed more experiences with a variety of concrete and pictorial models to develop their understanding of the relationships between whole numbers and fractions.

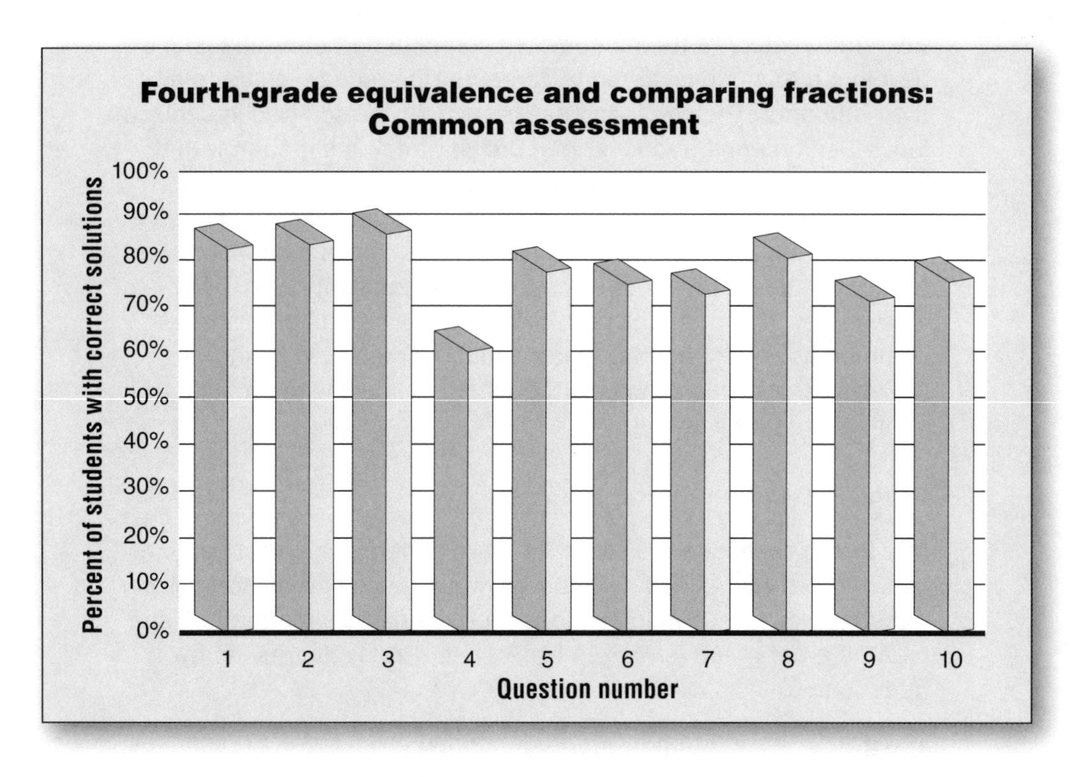

Fig. 9.1. A bar graph showing grade 4 common assessment results by question

Ms. Brown planned carefully for her meeting with the teachers. She wanted the teachers to identify and use students' misconceptions to plan their next lessons. However, determining student misconceptions and error patterns requires analyzing students' responses question by question. Ms. Brown thought that by focusing on questions 4, 6, 7, and 9, she could use the teachers' conversations about error patterns to discuss the important relationships between whole numbers and fractions that students needed to understand. Ms. Brown planned to raise the idea that students need to use both the area model and the number line model to reason about fraction equivalence and to develop a procedure for finding equivalent fractions.

Ms. Brown realized that some of the weaknesses that the fourth graders were demonstrating were the result of limited understanding of fraction concepts that were identified in the third-grade curriculum standards. As a result, she wanted the teachers to focus on the important mathematical understandings that support learning about equivalence, instead of thinking only about the mathematics objectives specified in their fourth-grade curriculum standards. Knowing that their local school curriculum was based on the state standards, Ms. Brown chose to focus on the state standards. She would ask the teachers to examine the learning progression for equivalence and ordering fractions in the state standards so that she could emphasize the important mathematical ideas in the progression. Using the state standards could also allow Ms. Brown to highlight effective instructional strategies.

Grade-level collaborative meeting

When Ms. Brown met with the teachers, she posted her bar graph and led a brief discussion in which the teachers shared what they noticed in the graph. Next, the group reviewed the learning progression for equivalence and ordering fractions, as presented in the state standards, and the group discussed the important understandings identified in the progression. Ms. Brown posted the four assessment questions on which the students' performance had been weakest (see fig. 9.2). She reminded the teachers that these questions were answered incorrectly by over 20 percent of the children. Then she asked the teachers what they thought students needed to know to find a correct solution for each of these four questions.

Question 4: Three boys each had the same kind of candy bar. Each boy ate part of his candy bar. One ate $5/10$, one ate $3/8$, and another ate $3/4$. Who ate the most? Use a number line to justify your answer.

Question 6: Place the fractions $5/7$, $5/6$, $5/9$, $1/8$, $3/8$ in order on a number line.

Question 7: Determine which of two equal-sized pans has more brownies left in the pan: $4/5$ of a pan of brownies or $5/6$ of a pan of brownies. Justify your reasoning.

Question 9: Justify that $3/6$ and $4/8$ name the same point on a number line.

Fig. 9.2. Common assessment questions for discussion with the grade 4 teachers

One teacher shared the observation that students needed to know that when fractions have a common denominator, the smaller the numerator, the smaller the fraction. Another teacher pointed out a similar mathematical idea: when fractions have a common numerator, the smaller the denominator, the larger the fraction. Another teacher connected these ideas with the learning progression that the group had examined in the state curriculum standards, developing the related ideas that the denominator determines the size of the unit fraction, and the numerator determines how many times the unit fraction is iterated, or repeated. The group went on to discuss the strategy of using benchmarks, such as 0, $1/2$, and 1, to order fractions. The teachers wondered how many of their students used 1 as a benchmark when comparing $4/5$ and $5/6$. One of the teachers said that after looking at the learning progression in the state standards, she was curious about the models her students had used to find their solutions. The group decided to examine samples of student work to see what representations the students had used.

As the teachers examined the students' work, they began to notice some general patterns of error. For example, for question 4, about which of three boys had eaten the largest portion of a candy bar, several students in each class gave a response similar to that of Steven, who wrote, "I know the order is $3/4$, $3/8$, $5/10$ because 5 is bigger than 3, so $5/10$ is the biggest. Then because both of the other two fractions have a 3 on top, I looked at the bottom numbers. I knew that 8 is bigger than 4." One of the teachers located two student papers to show the group that although the students had written the correct answer for question 7, about which of two pans of brownies had more left ($4/5 < 5/6$), they had found their solution by using Steven's incorrect way of thinking. Ms. Brown pointed out that by examining students' work, the teachers had uncovered the fact that although some students reached a correct solution, they still had some misconceptions about the mathematics. The teachers decided that these students had used whole-number thinking to solve fraction problems. They asked if Ms. Brown would collaborate with them to develop tasks that would engage the students in reasoning about unit fractions and then extend their thinking to develop their understanding of relationships among fractions.

The teachers' examination of the fourteen incorrect responses to question 9, which asked students to justify that equivalent fractions name the same point on the number line, revealed that ten students had not attempted the problem, and the teachers were unsure how to interpret the work of the other four students. The teachers wondered whether the students understood how to use the number line. An analysis of correct responses to the question revealed that many students had used an area model to think about $3/6$ and $4/8$ and show that $1/2$ of the area was shaded. The teachers began discussing how they incorporated representations in their lessons and concluded that the area model received more attention than the number line. They went on to consider how the tasks that the specialist and teachers developed collaboratively could use the instructional suggestions included in state standards for using the number line.

Meeting with the principal

The following day, Ms. Brown began her meeting with Ms. Ames by displaying the bar graph and the four assessment items that she had used to frame her work with teachers. She shared selected student responses with the principal. These responses illustrated some of the student misconceptions that had come to the surface in the common formative assessment and had been discussed by the teachers. Ms. Brown also reported that she and the teachers would collaboratively develop lessons to fill in the gaps, address student misconceptions, and move the students forward in their learning. She explained that she would visit the teachers' classrooms to observe or co-teach some of the lessons.

Ms. Brown also reported to Ms. Ames that she had used the state standards to focus the teachers' attention on the learning progression for equivalence and ordering fractions. Because some of the student misconceptions reflected inadequate mastery of grade 3 learning expectations, Ms. Brown suggested that she meet with all the teachers of third- and fourth-grade mathematics in a cross-grade-level meeting. She told Ms. Ames that she would like to have the teachers work through the learning progressions for fractions presented in the state standards. The principal agreed that a cross-grade-level meeting could be a good idea if it were carefully planned; she thought that teachers would be able to differentiate more effectively if they understood how the mathematical ideas developed. Ms. Ames said she would explore the possibility of scheduling the cross-grade-level meeting during the school day. She asked Ms. Brown to meet with her again the following week and to bring a detailed plan showing how she would engage the teachers in positive discussions during the meeting.

Opportunities for Formative Learning with Principals

As the vignette illustrates, data drawn from formative assessments may allow a mathematics specialist to plan for a session in which she and the principal will review what students do or do not understand. Student data from summative assessments can be a basis for similar conversations between a specialist and a principal. Interpreting the data creates a focus for discussion between the specialist and administrators as they plan how the specialist will collaborate with the teachers to improve the mathematics instructional program. The principal can identify ways to support the specialist in his efforts to support teachers and advance their work to improve student learning. Not only is it important for the specialist, the teachers, and the principal to work together, but it is also important for the specialist and the principal to discuss ways to monitor whether the plans that they put in place are effective.

Organizing and Interpreting Assessment Data

The mathematics specialist may have access to a variety of data related to student learning, including the results of summative classroom assessments, district and state assessments, benchmark common assessments, common formative assessments, and formative classroom assessments. As the mathematics specialist works to organize and display the data so that analyzing it is a manageable task, she can make some initial interpretations to suggest where students may be having difficulty. As illustrated in the vignette, this initial work with the data helps the specialist plan for meetings with the principal and the teachers. Assessment results can help the specialist identify students' learning problems so that she can focus her work with teachers.

Drilling down into the data

To make sense of data generated from multiple sources, the specialist needs to "drill down." Drilling down into data means looking first at broad categories and then reexamining the same data again and again, each time recategorizing them by smaller groupings, and finally examining the data for individual students.

The advantage of starting with large categories of data, called *aggregated data*, is that the "big picture" permits looking for trends. What do the data reveal about how each of the different grade levels in the school are performing in relation to those same grade levels in the district or the state? This information can be helpful in identifying problems across the school's entire mathematics program or within one or two grades. These concerns may require changes in the pacing of the curriculum, access to instructional materials, or emphasis in the instructional program.

Next, the specialist recategorizes, or disaggregates, the data, reexamining the data to compare performance between student subgroups in the school as defined by race, gender, economic disadvantages, English language status, or disabilities. Identifying any gaps among the various subgroups may point to equity and opportunity-to-learn issues.

For a specialist to plan his work with teachers, he will need to get specific information about student learning. This means that he must examine grade-by-grade data on student performance within mathematics strands or topics, as well as on specific items. Analysis of achievement by strand allows the specialist to make some determinations about what mathematics content to focus on in his work. The item-by-item interpretation of student performance provides him with insight into how students are thinking and responding to specific kinds of questions within a content strand. Finally, drilling down to individual student work provides the specialist with even more specific information about students' understanding or confusion.

Jump right into the data.

If I were speaking to a new mathematics specialist, I would say, "Jump right into looking at the data and having conversations with teachers." Data are tools for focusing the work. They take subjective beliefs and make them objective. It is so easy as a teacher to form inaccurate opinions about what children know on the basis of what they hear during a class discussion. Teachers will often tell me, "I thought they had it. I don't know what went wrong on the test." The data are real. They don't lie about what students know. It is what it is!

—*Advice from a mathematics specialist*

Sharing assessment data with teachers and interpreting the data with them allows a school's specialist to involve teachers in joint data-based decisions about the impact of the curriculum. These decisions lead them to scrutinize classroom instruction as they try to decide what might be most effective for student learning. The specialist may also discover indications of student-learning problems that need additional investigation. Team members will need to be relatively confident that they have discovered the reasons why students are having difficulties. Then they can move to the next step, outlining methods for addressing those difficulties.

Facilitating a Data-Driven Collaborative Inquiry Meeting

When the specialist meets with the teachers or the principal, she can display data in a large and vibrant format. Her display will focus attention on interpreting the data to determine what they reveal about student learning. Establishing norms for collaborative discussions can help remind group members to maintain an inquiry focus as they study the displayed data to identify learning problems. The goal of this discussion is to consider how the school's instructional and administrative staff can address identified problems. It is not an opportunity to make excuses for low student performance.

In the vignette about Ms. Brown, the specialist prepared a large bar graph of the question-by-question grade-level results from the common assessment and used her graph to identify four assessment items to investigate further. The teachers then drilled down and considered individual student-level data for those four questions. By collaboratively analyzing the data, the teachers and the specialist not only uncovered possible explanations for the results but also developed a plan to address apparent misconceptions.

Four phases of data-driven discussion

Nancy Love (2009) describes a process for facilitating data discussions through four phases of inquiry. The data-driven dialogue process begins with identifying a student learning problem and ends in specific instructional decisions. In phase 1 of a data-driven inquiry meeting with teachers, including the principal perhaps, the specialist asks the participants to predict what they think the data will show about student performance. The participants state their conjectures, but no discussion takes place at this point. The specialist then posts graphs—preferably large and colorful—that he has prepared, thus moving the group to phase 2: visual examination of the data. In phase 3, the specialist asks participants to focus on what they notice about the graphs. The participants make factual statements, supported by evidence from the data displays, but still no discussion takes place. Finally, in phase 4, the mathematics specialist asks participants to share their explanations of what the data reveal and possible implications for instruction. During this phase, the participants may ask questions that will require the specialist to do additional research.

Don't let "because" become a way to offer excuses.

I was thinking after our data meeting about how important it is to steer teachers away from "because," and how glad I was that I had a poster in my room with a big red line through the word "because." At our meeting today, a teacher was venting about all that she had done to prepare her students for an assessment. As she continued talking, she said, "Billy didn't pass because he sits through math class with his sweatshirt pulled over his head. I can't help Anna because she is absent at least once a week. Sam didn't pass because he doesn't know his multiplication facts." I pointed to the poster and reminded her that "because" couldn't be used in the discussion. She was frustrated, but it really helped move the conversation in the direction of what we can do to help students, on the basis of the data.

—*Reflections from a mathematics specialist*

Supporting Instructional Decisions with Data

The purpose of collecting and analyzing data is to improve instruction. As Love (2009) points out, "Student learning does not improve unless what is taught, how it is taught, and how learning is assessed changes" (p. 133). Once the data are reviewed, teachers and the mathematics specialist have specific evidence about what students understand and what they are missing. Then the specialist can focus her work. She can support teachers' efforts to identify materials and instructional strategies and plan subsequent lessons, with continuing attention to evaluating and addressing students' understanding.

The mathematics specialist is a data coach. Part of the responsibility of this role is to help teachers and the principal use data to make decisions about how to address student learning problems. In addition, the specialist works with teachers to deepen their understanding of the content as well as how to teach it to improve student learning. Assessment results can help a specialist decide what professional development activities he should use with the teachers in his school.

Supporting Teachers to Develop Effective Classroom Assessments

The mathematics specialist can work with teachers to develop more effective summative classroom assessments, measuring students' progress toward achieving particular local and state curriculum standards. When teachers examine assessment items with a standard in mind, they can talk about two things—the mathematical demands of the item and the level of understanding and application that students will need to achieve if they are to demonstrate mastery of it.

The specialist might begin by asking teachers to analyze released items from state or other standardized tests or to review assessment items from curriculum materials. Together, the specialist and teachers can discuss the assessment items to determine whether each one meets the intent of the standard and if not, why. Part of this work is learning how to modify questions or test items so that they allow students to demonstrate their understanding while providing the teacher with information that permits them to pinpoint where students' understanding is not fully developed. In this work, the specialist should encourage teachers to include in their classroom assessment items that—

1. provide opportunities for students to demonstrate their understanding in multiple ways;
2. uncover a variety of errors, including computational errors; and
3. reveal a range of difficulties with mathematics vocabulary and notation.

When a grade-level team designs a summative unit assessment before teaching the unit, the specialist can help the teachers accomplish two related goals. First, they must clarify the skills and concepts to be assessed. Second, they need to consider the level of understanding that students will be expected to demonstrate on the assessment.

Once the assessment has been developed, the specialist and the teachers can review the mathematical understandings that individual test items presume. When coupled with teachers' knowledge of their students' current understanding, this information establishes learning targets for the unit. The next step is to design effective instructional approaches. Because the teachers have established their learning targets on the basis of the assessment items, they can plan a unit that is aligned with the assessment and, therefore, with the standards (Ainsworth and Viegut 2006).

Teachers begin the process of unit planning by reflecting on their prior teaching experiences and by sharing approaches that they considered successful. The mathematics specialist brings additional effective instructional approaches to the group for consideration. Then the group collaboratively develops a unit plan to implement the instructional approaches, including informal or formative assessments that may be administered within the unit to inform instruction as it progresses. This allows for mid-unit corrections before the common unit assessment.

Assessment can be a vehicle for enhancing instruction and student achievement. But many teachers do not have a strong background in assessment. Consequently, if assessment is to be used to inform instruction (NCTM 2000), the mathematics specialist plays a vital role. She is the provider of professional development addressing not only mathematics content and mathematics teaching, but also the effective use of assessment results.

References

Ainsworth, Larry, and Donald Viegut. *Common Formative Assessments.* Thousand Oaks, Calif.: Corwin Press, 2006.

Killion, Jo Ellen. "Are You Coaching Heavy or Light?" *Teachers Teaching Teachers* 3 (May 2008): 1–4.

Love, Nancy. *Using Data to Improve Learning for All: A Collaborative Inquiry Approach.* Thousand Oaks, Calif.: Corwin Press, 2009.

National Council of Supervisors of Mathematics (NCSM). *The Prime Leadership Framework.* Denver: NCSM, 2008.

National Council of Teachers of Mathematics (NCTM). *Principles and Standards for School Mathematics.* Reston, Va.: NCTM, 2000.

National Governors Association Center for Best Practices and Council of Chief State School Officers (NGA Center and CCSSO). *Common Core State Standards for Mathematics. Common Core State Standards (College- and Career-Readiness Standards and K–12 Standards in English Language Arts and Math).* Washington, D.C.: NGA Center and CCSSO, 2010. http://www.corestandards.org.

Wiliam, Dylan. *Embedded Formative Assessment.* Bloomington, Ind.: Solution Tree Press, 2011.

Managing a School's Instructional Resources for Mathematics

Kim Raines and Beth Williams

A mathematics specialist's work depends heavily on the instructional resources that are available for her school's mathematics program. Knowing what resources are on hand in the building and encouraging teachers to use them are two important aspects of the job. In fact, the specialist is often called on to be the manager of the school's mathematics resources. In addition to knowing what resources are in the building and where they are located, the specialist must determine exactly how teachers are using the materials and which materials they are not using at all. The specialist can use this information as a starting point for—

1. developing a plan to encourage teachers to use different resources;
2. planning professional development activities supporting teachers' effective use of materials;
3. identifying needed resources for purchasing.

This chapter outlines strategies for managing instructional resources and putting them to effective use in a school.

A New Mathematics Specialist Gains Access to Teachers through Resources

One of the primary ways in which a mathematics specialist gains access to the teachers in the school is through his knowledge and management of resources. Consider the following vignette, which illustrates possibilities available to the specialist for using resources to advance his work.

Mr. Grove had recently completed his coursework and earned his state's endorsement as an elementary mathematics specialist. He was excited because his school district offered him a position in a school that had not been assigned a mathematics specialist before. After meeting with the principal to determine his initial tasks, Mr. Grove considered ways to learn more about the school's mathematics program and the teachers' perspectives on mathematics teaching and learning. He began taking advantage of opportunities to meet with individual teachers and to attend grade-level team meetings. He worked out a schedule that would allow him to observe instruction in every teacher's classroom during the first two months of school.

As Mr. Grove began his work, he quickly discovered that the majority of the instructional staff had not participated in much mathematics professional development in recent years. Most of the teachers worked entirely from a traditional textbook and used the textbook worksheets as their primary resource for assigning tasks and student work. The only manipulative materials that he saw in use were snap cubes in a kindergarten class, where students were building repeating patterns with the cubes, gluing colored paper squares onto paper to record their patterns, and verbally naming their patterns with an A, B, C scheme (for example, ABAB). Throughout the school, Mr. Grove observed that the dialogue in the classroom was mainly between the teacher and the students. He saw very little intentional student-to-student talk.

Mr. Grove decided that his first steps would involve working with teachers about when and how to use instructional materials. Through this work, he believed that he would be able to build the teachers' trust. He hoped that teachers would value his support and see him as a knowledgeable colleague as he shared new manipulatives and activities that they could use in teaching their students. He hoped that these discussions could be the beginning of further interaction with the teachers—interactions that could blossom into opportunities for co-planning and co-teaching.

To determine what materials were currently available in the building, Mr. Grove asked all the mathematics teachers to complete a simple survey listing each mathematics resource housed in their classroom, providing its name, how many were in the classroom (for instance, 3 tubs of base-ten blocks), and the mathematics topics that they taught through its use. Mr. Grove wanted to know not only what was available, but also whether the teachers recognized when they could use these resources to address various topics in the curriculum. Most of the teachers willingly completed the list and returned it to him. Some teachers were reluctant to do the work of listing all their resources, so Mr. Grove offered to do the inventory with them, and these teachers accepted this offer of assistance. Mr. Grove then met with each teacher to talk over the list and gain a better sense of how the teacher used each resource. Mr. Grove found these conversations extremely beneficial. He now had an idea about resources that were being used effectively and resources that were not evident in the building.

Mr. Grove then created an "ideal" list of instructional resources for each grade. These were materials that he believed each grade-level classroom should have available for students to use as tools whenever it was appropriate. For instance, he identified pattern blocks as a resource that should be available in all the classrooms, connecting cubes as a critical material in the kindergarten and first-grade rooms, and base-ten blocks as a necessary resource for grades 2–5. Mr. Grove also created a list of resources that could be shared across classrooms, noting that these would require a storage location from which teachers could secure them when they were ready to use them with their students. These included geoboards, mathematically related children's literature, and measuring tools such as meter sticks and protractors. In creating both the grade-specific lists and the list of shareable materials, Mr. Grove reviewed the curriculum and made clear connections between the resources and the mathematical concepts that could be addressed through their use. After he shared these lists with the principal, the principal purchased shelves for Mr. Grove's workspace so that the shared resources could be stored in a secure yet readily accessible location.

Through these conversations and observations, Mr. Grove learned a great deal about the current state of mathematics teaching and learning in the school. He and the principal then determined his schedule for support for that first semester. Teachers in several grade levels seemed willing to try some new approaches. Mr. Grove decided to plan lessons with these grade-level teams and to co-teach in some classrooms in each of the grade levels, introducing the teachers to a variety of manipulative materials and choosing rich activities that encouraged student engagement.

Follow-up meetings allowed Mr. Grove to hear what the teachers thought about using each resource. More important, these sessions became settings where teachers reviewed resources and activities in terms of their effectiveness and levels of understanding evidenced or missing in their students' use and explanations. The principal thought that the best approach for the more reluctant teachers was for Mr. Grove to meet with the teams occasionally throughout the semester, introduce a few manipulatives, and offer to teach a lesson using that resource.

Every month, Mr. Grove reviewed the content that students were to learn at each grade level and sent an e-mail message to teachers calling their attention to some of the available resources that they might use when teaching that mathematics content. He offered to share with any teacher the basics of using a resource and to give any other support that he could. His room was open before and after school for any teacher to visit and to ask questions about the upcoming or current mathematical content in the curriculum and the resources.

Mr. Grove hoped that the impact of his leadership would be felt fairly quickly. However, he understood that the time spent building relationships with the principal and the teachers might not have an immediate reward but would pay off in the long run. As the year

progressed, teachers shared with one another how Mr. Grove was helping them with their own understanding of the resources available to them. Eventually, he was well established in his role as mathematics specialist, and the teachers viewed him as an accessible, nonjudgmental person who understood teaching and learning mathematics from a whole-school perspective.

Managing a School's Instructional Resources

As Mr. Grove found, managing a school's instructional resources has clear benefits. Instructional resources include any tool designed to support teachers in their efforts to build and deepen their students' understanding of mathematics concepts. Some resources are particularly important to consider:

- Adopted textbooks (hard copy and online materials)
- Manipulative materials
- Library books
- Mathematics education books
- Videos
- Online resources
- Computer applications
- Calculators
- Interactive whiteboard resources
- Websites

Manipulatives, or manipulative materials, are useful tools for students as they move from concrete representations to pictures to symbolic ways of representing their mathematical thinking. Specialists can use manipulatives to engage teachers in addressing and explaining their own ideas about mathematical concepts. The number of resources available to teachers can be overwhelming. If the mathematics specialist can help teachers focus on the most effective books, websites, and technology, teachers will see the value of his role. As the mathematics specialist reviews the school's current inventory of instructional resources, he should ask a variety of questions:

- "What resources are available to the teachers in our school?"
- "Which resources are our teachers using effectively?"
- "Which resources should we add to our inventory to teach the students in our school more effectively?"

Responsibility for managing a mathematics resources inventory

The responsibility for managing the mathematics resources inventory often belongs to the mathematics specialist in the building. She is frequently the person who is expected to be knowledgeable about instructional practices that support effective use of the mathematics resources. Many elementary mathematics specialists create an ideal list of manipulatives for each grade level, based on the content that students must learn. What resources do the teachers already have? What materials do the teachers and students need? A teacher or team leader at a grade level might know what he has in his classroom or at his grade level, but he is not likely to have an overview of the entire school's mathematics resources. Generally, a school has no one else besides the mathematics specialist who has the motivation or interest to manage the school's mathematics resources. Because she will be able to work with teachers through the resources that she inventories, purchases, or develops, the mathematics specialist will find that time spent creating a baseline of current instructional resources in her building is time well spent.

Some of the resources that a mathematics specialist believes are required for good teaching will already be in place in the building; other resources will need to be purchased. The specialist should prepare a priority list for future purchases. What is needed most? Can teachers implement it effectively in instruction in the near future? It is best to plan with care so that teachers will receive each new manipulative or new activity with interest and enthusiasm and will not feel overwhelmed by too many new initiatives.

Assessing current use of resources

As the mathematics specialist inventories his school's mathematics resources, he also considers whether teachers are making effective use of the materials that are already in place. The professional bookshelf in the school's library might include mathematics education books that address the use of materials. Have teachers been using those books, and is their use evident in classrooms? Children's literature that addresses mathematics can be powerful; such books might be housed in classrooms or in the school library. Does the school have a list of titles available for classroom use, and are those books coded in such a way that their connections with mathematics content that teachers address in instruction are obvious? Teachers might already be using the National Library of Virtual Manipulatives (Utah State University; http://nlvm.usu.edu/en/nav/vlibrary.html) or Illuminations (National Council of Teachers of Mathematics; http://illuminations.nctm.org).

Have teachers attended a professional development session on using the resources that are available in the most recently adopted textbook? Sometimes initiatives by a school district, principal, or grade-level team are not fully implemented, and previously purchased materials that could be used effectively have been placed on shelves and forgotten.

One constructive approach that the specialist can take is to envision what materials he would ideally like to see in use, and for what purposes. Then he can measure the current environment against those hypothetical best practices. Once he has completed this assessment of whether and how teachers are using materials, the mathematics specialist can build a focused plan for professional development sessions addressing use of both existing and soon-to-be-purchased materials.

Make determining resource use an early priority.

Just because teachers have a resource available to them does not mean that they are using it. And even if they are, they might not be using a particular manipulative in a variety of valuable ways. Knowing how teachers are using various resources gives a new mathematics specialist a good starting point for providing professional development.

—Advice from a mathematics specialist

Assessment of Mathematics Instructional Resources

In the vignette about Mr. Grove, one of the specialist's first actions in his new placement was to assess what mathematics resources were already available and in use by teachers and students at the school. This is a useful first step, and there are several ways to develop an inventory of existing resources. The specialist can set up a schedule to spend time in every classroom, surveying and recording all the mathematics materials throughout the school. This approach will give the specialist a sense of the materials that are on hand and a chance to think about where to start her work with teachers. An alternative is to create a survey, as Mr. Grove did, asking each teacher to list the mathematics resources that she currently has in her classroom and what mathematics objectives or units she teaches when using them. If the school or district has some sort of mathematics content code, then the teachers need only categorize their materials by the code.

The survey can serve two purposes. The first is obvious: to collect information for an initial baseline of resources. The second is more subtle: to assess whether the teacher knows potential uses for each resource. A teacher might say that he has three buckets of pattern blocks, which he uses in teaching addition of fractions with unlike denominators. Another teacher might say that she has a set of colored sticks of varying lengths—which she may not know are called *Cuisenaire rods*—and she thinks they are supposed to be useful for mathematics, but she is not sure where they would fit into her curriculum. A teacher may have some resources in her classroom simply by virtue of the fact that they were present when she was assigned to the room. But they might be collecting dust while the teacher has no idea what use students could make of them.

Meetings with teachers to review list of resources

After the teachers have completed a mathematics resource survey, the mathematics specialist should meet with each teacher in his classroom and review his responses. The specialist should ask the teacher a number of questions:

- "When do you use this resource? How do you use it?"
- "Which resources do you use most often?"
- "Do you know of manipulatives that you would like more training on or whose use with students you would like to have modeled for you?"

Co-planning and then teaching a lesson involving the use of manipulatives might be a good place to start collaborating with a teacher.

Assessing actual use of instructional resources through classroom visits

As a first step in supporting effective use of resources, the mathematics specialist can observe in classrooms to see whether and how the teachers and students are using the materials. Are they using the resources effectively? Manipulative materials can help students develop a deeper understanding of mathematics, but this happens as students reflect on and explain their use of the materials, offering their mathematical interpretations of displays. However, manipulatives can also be used in teacher-directed ways—perhaps with the teacher telling her students exactly how to move and place the materials. However, for students, this shifts the focus to learning rote procedures for moving the manipulative materials, thus making the concrete materials in effect another symbol system. The mathematics specialist should assess the use of each manipulative in relation to the content that students are expected to learn and the extent to which the instructional practice surrounding use of the materials supports students' emerging mathematical understandings.

The specialist can develop an observation tool to assess the level of use of instructional resources. Are the teachers using the resources in ways that the specialist might expect to see? The specialist should pay attention to the types of activities that each teacher chooses. He should be looking for activities that engage students in making sense of problems and that encourage them to talk about mathematics as they describe their work, explain their thinking, and justify their reasoning.

When observing in classrooms, the mathematics specialist can begin to determine which models and representations students are applying and interpreting effectively. Are some students more successful than others in using models to solve problems? Are students using their representations to justify and explain their methods and answers? Do students' responses seem to be based on interpreting the manipulative materials that were used during instruction and building on them? The mathematics specialist and the teachers can work together to assess current student work on the basis of these questions and determine whether omissions in the use of tools or manipulatives are hindering students' thinking or understanding.

Assessing use of resources through grade-level meetings

During a grade-level team meeting, the mathematics specialist could ask teachers to share their understanding of the relationship of a particular manipulative material to content that will be learned by students in the near future. How do the teachers explain the use of that manipulative to teach the content? How would they rate their own skill in using the manipulative or teaching with it? Perhaps the teachers would be willing to co-plan a lesson involving the manipulative and then permit the mathematics specialist to co-teach the lesson with one of them. When a specialist invites teachers to consider the use of a manipulative material in a grade-level team meeting, she creates a risk-free setting in which the teachers learn how to use the resource effectively with students and at the same time learn more about the mathematics content. Further, the meeting gives the specialist an opportunity to hear teachers' thoughts about the use of the manipulative, allowing her to develop a sense of how teachers are using it in their classrooms.

Consider filling a cart with materials related to an upcoming concept.

I know several mathematics specialists who load up a cart with various resources, depending on the current topic of instruction. They take the cart to grade-level planning meetings. That way, the specialist and the teachers can explore, discuss, and demonstrate the use of various manipulatives during the planning meeting. The teachers can sign out resources that they need to teach concepts right away, while the idea is fresh in their mind.

—Advice from a mathematics specialist

Assessing prior initiatives and professional development

Asking the principal or individual teachers to share the history of initiatives within the building can give the mathematics specialist a better understanding of the current state of mathematics teaching and learning in the building. Why, for example, does the school have so many sets of some materials and so few of others? Was particular mathematics content intentionally made the focus for the entire school in a prior school year? In conversations with the principal and the teachers, the mathematics specialist can also find out what professional development has already occurred in the school. Has the whole faculty ever engaged in a study of a mathematics education book? If so, what was its purpose? The effects of prior professional development and teachers' perceptions of it are important pieces of information for the specialist to consider.

Storing the Mathematics Resources

Storing manipulative materials in a central location is a problem in some schools. The school may have only one class set of a specific material to which several teachers need to have access. Working with the principal and the teachers, the specialist can help identify an effective approach for ensuring access to these resources. In a given grade, some materials should be in every classroom and available every day, but other materials are used only occasionally and can be stored in a central place in the school.

Creating a "Math Central" room

If the specialist can set up a storage area for shared manipulatives, then the teachers can go there to check out materials and tools. Every teacher needs to know where to find materials when he is ready to use them. One elementary school had an extra classroom with many tables and extra chairs. The mathematics specialist set up a room called "Math Central," where most of the mathematics tools were stored. Teachers checked out materials during their break times without disrupting a class, and the specialist invited classroom groups to work on special lessons and presentations in this setting. The room became the favorite spot for after-school professional development for the teachers.

If shared mathematics materials are stored in a central location, the specialist should be sensitive to teachers' concerns that their selected manipulative be available when they need it. Knowing what quantities of particular manipulatives are necessary to have on hand—how many geoboards the school needs, for example—is tricky at first, but if the specialist pays attention to use, he will soon know which components of the inventory need to be increased. He will also know which materials are not being used, giving him some direction for further professional development with teachers. The specialist should also be very careful about storing any resource purchased personally by a teacher. The teacher might be willing to share the resource, but because she bought it herself, she might want to keep it in her own classroom for her students' use unless another teacher asks her permission to use it in a particular set of lessons. In this case, the specialist should respect her decision to control access to her own resource.

Other options for materials sharing

If the school does not have enough space to house the shared mathematics materials in a central location, the mathematics specialist might work out a plan for sharing resources throughout the building and tracking where they are at any given time. For example, when a fourth-grade teacher needs a large set of snap cubes for a short time, the mathematics specialist should know which first-grade teacher might have extra cubes that could be loaned for a day or a week. In this way, the mathematics specialist becomes the person whom teachers can depend on to provide them with materials to support their work with students.

Building the inventory

The mathematics specialist quickly recognizes that important differences exist between the resources on her "ideal" list and those that are currently available in the school. Knowing the mathematical content in each grade's curriculum helps the specialist recommend the purchase of necessary tools and resources that will enhance instruction. By referring to the school's assessment data and then working with the principal, the specialist can create a timeline for future purchases. What are the school's most critical needs? Which purchases might have the greatest impact on student learning throughout the school? Conversations with grade-level teams and the principal will help the specialist to prioritize specific tools for use in implementing the district focus in mathematics. The work of developing a list of possible new purchases can expedite the task of budgeting funds to be spent tomorrow, next week, or three months from now, especially if the list gives an administrator a rationale for making particular purchases.

All manipulatives do not have to be purchased. Families can recycle many commonplace items in the mathematics classroom instead of throwing them away. Colored milk caps and juice lids are great for sorting and patterning activities. Egg cartons serve as excellent counting trays and fraction arrays. Dried lima beans can be spray painted on one side to make two-color counters. Seashells and old keys retrieved from kitchen drawers can be used to make a sorting center in a classroom station. Families love to donate items to the classroom collection, especially if they learn about the mathematics that they have the potential to support.

Professional Development Addressing Use of Instructional Resources

Once the mathematics specialist has created an inventory of current and available resources, he will need to create a plan to engage groups of teachers in considering effective use of the resources. As he plans, he must consider the available settings for professional development, the needs of the students, the receptiveness of the teachers, and the support that he can provide as the teachers begin teaching with a new resource. Teachers often have predetermined, scheduled times available for professional development either before or after school, as well as grade-level team meetings or staff meetings. The following vignette shows how one specialist organized a professional development session for a vertical team of teachers.

Ms. Jordan, the mathematics specialist at Oak Park Elementary, scheduled a meeting of a vertical team of third- to fifth-grade teachers to address curricular objectives on the use of the number line model for fractions. She guided the teachers in considering the use of fraction strips to support students' understanding and move them from concrete models displaying a fraction as a fair share of part of a region, such as a share of pizza or a brownie, to the number line model. During this discussion, Ms. Jordan invited the teachers to reflect on the progression of curriculum expectations addressing fractions from third to fifth grade and the importance of the number line model in the upper grades.

Next, Ms. Jordan introduced a follow-up activity that she had planned, engaging the teachers in a rich mathematical task on the use of fraction strips and the number line. After the teachers had completed the task and selected teachers had shared their responses and reasoning, Ms. Jordan summarized the practices that she had seen the teachers using as they worked through the task.

During subsequent grade-level team meetings with Ms. Jordan, the teachers planned specific lessons to engage their students in using the number line model. For example, the third-grade teachers devised a lesson that challenged students to locate fractional values less than 1 on the number line, using fraction strips as a way of interpreting and locating positions on the number line.

Following their meeting, the teachers taught the co-planned lesson in their classrooms and brought samples of student work to the next team meeting with Ms. Jordan. The teachers then shared their successes and challenges in using the activity and addressed follow-up lesson modifications as well as interpretations of student understandings.

By working with the specialist in a vertical team of faculty members, teachers can begin to see how different grade-level teachers might approach a particular task and how their content connects with the content of higher and lower grades. This interaction promotes conversations across the grades regarding use of particular materials and is a very effective way for the mathematics specialist to increase the faculty's cohesiveness in its approach to mathematics instruction.

Differentiation of work with teachers

Mathematics specialists must differentiate their professional development work with teachers. Teachers, like their students, learn and receive new information in a variety of ways. Some teachers prefer to work individually with the specialist on the use of a manipulative before they are comfortable asking questions in a grade-level team meeting. An effective way to help a teacher understand the usefulness of a particular resource is to have one teacher observe another teacher successfully using it with students. Working with the principal, the mathematics specialist can set up peer observations and follow-up debriefings that will benefit both the observed and the observing teachers.

Teachers as students

Teachers learn best by actually doing activities and working with manipulatives. A grade-level team of teachers is likely to be receptive to a make-and-take session, since the teachers know that they will have materials to bring back to their classrooms for immediate use. But the key is to schedule enough time to permit discussion of ways to use the materials to support student understanding. When a teacher works as a student would, he recognizes the advantages in using the manipulative and may become more willing to give his students sufficient time to develop a deeper understanding. Through the mathematics specialist's modeling of questioning techniques and collaboration among the team members, the teachers can learn how to ask appropriate questions and wait before giving answers. Another useful idea is to have the teachers who created a particular manipulative come back together as a group several weeks later to talk about their successes and challenges in using it.

Don't lose sight of the power of doing.

Just like students, teachers learn best by actually doing activities. After using a resource material to complete an activity, teachers have a better grasp of how it can be used, and they can then turn around and use it confidently with their students. In a recent team meeting, I heard one teacher exclaim, "Now I get it! I had no idea how to use these myself, let alone have students use them." If teachers do not have a clear idea about using a resource, it is very likely to remain unused on the shelf.

—*Advice from a mathematics specialist*

Using Instructional Resources to Engage Teachers in Discussions about Mathematics

Effective planning requires that teachers understand their students' thinking and identify their needs. This prerequisite information comes into play as the specialist and teachers discuss the evidence of mathematical understanding that they find in students' work. As opportunities for grade-level planning occur, a mathematics specialist should ask teachers to bring in samples of student work that indicate students' current level of understanding—particularly students' interpretations of the knowledge and skills expected by specific curriculum standards. As the teachers engage in the discussion of student work, they may begin to connect problem solving to reasoning and justification. They may come to understand the benefits of using multiple models to represent and explain ideas. Then the specialist can help teachers make choices about which resources to use to support their students' developing mathematical thinking.

For example, consider what may occur as students begin to develop an understanding of decimal concepts. Many teachers use base-ten blocks in the lower grades to build whole number place-value concepts spanning ones, tens, hundreds, and thousands. But in fourth grade they may redefine the blocks so that 1 is represented by the thousand cube, tenths are represented by flats, hundredths by rods, and thousandths by unit blocks. Some students are able to make this part-to-whole, whole-to-part shift in the values of the blocks as they draw or model decimal values and explain their responses. Other students find the change confusing and need a different representation. In such a case, the mathematics specialist can help a teacher select other models to support interpretation of decimals.

For example, a meter stick can provide a valuable linear model of decimals, with students breaking apart or folding paper strips that are 1 meter long into tenths (decimeters) or hundredths (centimeters). They might mark tenths of the hundredths to see the tiny value represented by thousandths (millimeters) along this line. Similarly, this concrete model often helps a child make the leap to a successful comparison of 0.31 with 0.306. Is the student now able to explain why a number with more digits to the right of a decimal point is not necessarily larger than a number with fewer digits to the right of the decimal? Through the use of a linear model, students may more readily interpret the mathematics of decimals as they connect what they see in the paper strips to the abstract symbols of the digits. Teachers also need time to work through these representations with the mathematics specialist to be comfortable in their work with students.

Plan monthly meetings involving manipulatives.

As a mathematics specialist, I have monthly meetings with each grade level. At these meetings, we solve problems and create models by using manipulatives. We look at student work and discuss what the students know and what they do not know. We also talk about the different models that students use to represent their work. If possible, we watch and discuss short video clips of students engaging in meaningful work with the manipulative or model under discussion.

—Advice from a mathematics specialist

In grade-level planning sessions, the mathematics specialist is often teaching teachers about the use of manipulatives and simultaneously deepening the teachers' mathematical content knowledge. Many elementary teachers have not had the opportunity to use multiple manipulatives to represent the same numerical idea. The specialist should work alongside the teachers to develop different activities, modeling the use of thinking strategies and manipulatives that will help more students explain the mathematics. The struggles and misconceptions of students are often at the center of these conversations. These discussions allow teachers to identify common sources of confusion and help teachers develop questions and tasks to address them.

Seeking Funds to Purchase Instructional Resources for Mathematics

The specialist is likely to discover that her school needs to purchase various materials to move the mathematics program forward. Suppose, for example, that Mr. Grove, the specialist showcased earlier in this chapter, discovered that the third- to fifth-grade classrooms had no access to base-ten blocks. He would probably quickly realize that the cost of this purchase for all the upper-elementary classrooms was beyond the budget that he had been given. Mr. Grove would need to seek other sources of funding.

Funding within the school

Schools have many different funding sources available to them. When a mathematics specialist is looking for funds to support mathematics instruction, he should go first to his administrator and share the need for resources and his rationale for their purchase. The building-level administrator is responsible for instructional funds and will direct the specialist's next step. The principal may suggest purchasing tools with grade-level funds or from a larger fund for instruction at the school. She may ask the specialist to present the need to the executive board of the PTA to see whether funds raised through the PTA might support the purchase. When community partners are made aware of a specific need and understand why particular equipment or resources would be beneficial for students' learning, they are often willing to donate money for the purchase.

District, regional, and state possibilities for funding

When funds are needed to purchase materials to support a district-level initiative, the principal and the central office staff usually try to collaborate to secure them. A specialist can help her principal by documenting the ways in which the requested materials will support the mission and goals of the school district. Sometimes the mathematics specialist may learn about state-level initiatives that include professional development and new materials for the school. The specialist should try to stay informed about any initiative that might be available to the school. She should ask state, regional, and district leadership about relevant grant possibilities.

Pursuing local grant possibilities

The mathematics specialist may be asked to write a grant proposal in an effort to secure funds for projects or materials related to the school's mathematics program. Many grants are available to teachers and school districts. The mathematics specialist should consider local businesses and business groups. Local engineering, accounting, or architecture firms are likely to see the benefits of enhancing mathematics education. Corporations that have a local office or facility near a school are often open to funding innovative ideas to improve the teaching of mathematics in the school. These corporations recognize that educational programs are an important investment in their community and their employees' families. Businesses and corporations want to support students who understand and appreciate applications of mathematics. If the specialist defines his purpose and rationale well, local companies may be very receptive to the idea of providing funding.

Grant possibilities beyond the local level

A mathematics specialist should also consider possibilities for financial support beyond the local level. NCTM's Mathematics Education Trust (MET; http://www.nctm.org/resources/content.aspx?id=198) supports teachers by funding projects that promote the improvement of mathematics teaching and learning. The MET Web page provides links for funding sources that support classroom teachers in improving classroom practices and in increasing teachers' mathematical knowledge. A mathematics specialist can view funded proposal abstracts and get ideas for successful projects by exploring this page.

Many corporations seek opportunities to invest in the future of their communities through educational grants to neighborhood schools. The Grant Resources link on the 4Teachers website (http://www.4teachers.org/profdev/index.php?profdevid=gnr) provides a listing of grants available through some of these corporations, along with explanations of their opportunities for funding support.

Working through the grant proposal process

When preparing to write a grant proposal, the first thing that the specialist should do is define the purpose of the project to be funded and develop a rationale for it. Why are specific materials necessary? How will they aid teachers and students? The funding organization will ask that the request be grounded in research. Often, the specialist can include a literature review in her grant proposal. As the mathematics specialist undertakes the writing of a grant application, she should be sure to do the following:

- Keep all administrators actively aware of, and interested in, the grant writing process
- After recognizing a need, identify the best fit for funding, develop a rationale, and know the cost
- In reviewing funding sources, read the fine print, and know the requirements
- Secure permission from the local authorities before applying for the grant
- Write the grant application in language appropriate for the audience

- After receiving a grant, use the funds as planned
- Write all required follow-up reports for the funding agency, the principal, or the school district, detailing the results of the project and how the money was used

If the proposal is not funded, the mathematics specialist might ask for a copy of reviews to get feedback before applying for another opportunity. If an organization or funding group provides feedback, the specialist should write a thank-you note and try again the next time, incorporating lessons learned from the feedback.

Enhancing Instruction through Instructional Resources

It is well worth the mathematics specialist's effort to inventory current instructional materials, enhance teachers' use of those resources, and pursue the purchase of new instructional resources in the school. Through the inventory process, she gains the trust and respect of the teachers in the building. She begins to get a sense of the current state of mathematics teaching and learning at each grade level and in the work of each teacher. As she introduces methods using existing and new manipulatives, she builds her teachers' repertoire of activities and rich tasks with the potential to expand students' thinking. The ultimate goal is to increase students' conceptual knowledge through active and engaging mathematics lessons. Having mathematics resources and materials in classrooms and the school is essential. Making certain that teachers are prepared to use the materials effectively at the appropriate time is an important goal for every mathematics specialist.

Serving as the Face of an Elementary School's Mathematics Program

Contina Martin and Fanya Morton

As Stronge, Richard, and Catano (2008) concisely express it, "Schools are in the business of student learning" (p. 51). But what exactly does this mean in the case of mathematics? Succeeding in this "business" requires much more than simply establishing the expectation that teachers will somehow either know or figure out how to teach mathematics in ways that promote student learning. What is required is a mathematics program with many interacting features, including the following:

- A perspective defining the mathematics content and practices that students are expected to learn, frequently as defined by state and district curriculum standards
- A variety and range of rich curricular materials and instructional resources, readily available for use
- A shared vision of mathematics instruction, co-created and understood by all teachers and administrators
- Responsive on-site leadership, supporting teachers' efforts to interact and learn
- Assessments aligned with learning standards and used to gauge student achievement
- Effective teaching and successful learning taking place in the school

Although a shared vision for a school's mathematics program is created through a collaboration of the elementary mathematics specialist with the principal and the teachers, the specialist is the one who will be sought out when questions arise about mathematics teaching and learning in the school. She is the one recognized by teachers, parents, and members of the school community as the "go-to person" for any questions relating to the school's mathematical agenda. She serves as the face of the school's mathematics program. As such, she must continually foster partnerships that encourage dialogue and interactions among those who are working to support students' learning of mathematics.

Recognize that the job of mathematics specialist takes more than being a good teacher.

When I started this job, I thought I just needed to be able to teach good mathematics lessons. I never imagined how big this job is. Actually, I need to understand all there is to know about the mathematics program in my school—and that includes both what is happening now and what we are working toward.

—Reflections from a mathematics specialist

The Mathematics Curriculum: A Scaffold for a School's Mathematics Program

One of the programmatic roles of the elementary mathematics specialist is to support efforts to align the curriculum delivered in the school with the intended curriculum distributed by the district and adopted by the state, as expressed in state curriculum standards. When faced with limited time for working with teachers, these alignment efforts can be challenging, especially if the school has many teachers who could benefit from enhanced mathematical and pedagogical knowledge. This work can become even more demanding if new textbooks and instructional materials have been adopted or curriculum standards and assessments have been revised. When faced with new expectations, many teachers have questions for which they need answers. Although these challenges can be daunting, at the same time they can provide a specialist with unique opportunities for access to teachers, who may be more willing to work with a specialist if they perceive him as a potential advocate or source of support.

Move quickly to help teachers make a student-centered start with new materials.

When my district purchased new curricular materials, I found myself being perceived as the "mouthpiece" for a curriculum with which I was occasionally uncomfortable. So, to model a more student-centered approach to teaching with these materials, I offered to go into classrooms to demonstrate co-planned lessons. This enabled teachers to experience specific student learning behaviors that they could work to replicate later.

—Advice from a mathematics specialist

When a school or district is implementing new or revised curricular standards or instructional materials for mathematics, teachers may want their specialist to provide information or explain the use of, or access to, the materials, instead of addressing mathematics content or instructional strategies. This can make a specialist uneasy, since she may find herself being asked to defend a position that she herself does not yet understand or being expected to provide an answer that she does not yet have. The specialist should admit what she does not know but promise to contact those in the district who will know and to get back to her teachers with clarification. When a specialist follows up and provides answers or explanations subsequently, teachers will recognize her as an asset and as someone who is learning and working with them. At the same time, the specialist can co-plan with teachers and volunteer to model that co-planned instruction, demonstrating various classroom uses for materials or standards-based approaches to the intended mathematical content or practices. This strategy not only provides a starting point for change, but also allows the conversation to shift to the overarching goal of teaching mathematics for understanding.

When a specialist meets with teachers, either in a grade-level team or one on one, to review a state's or district's mathematics standards and consider the meaning, order, or pacing of mathematical content, she sends an important message. Planning mathematics lessons is more than identifying the content that a teacher is going to teach or reviewing the approach that a textbook presents. Lesson planning encompasses the knowledge and needs of the teachers. When teachers plan, they are drawing on their mathematical strengths, their beliefs about teaching, and their prior teaching experience, as well as their knowledge of the needs of their students. Mathematics teaching involves a delicate balance between asking and telling and requires knowing when to do which. Planning mathematics instruction also involves deciding whether to expect students to complete investigations, to explain ideas, to solve problems, to justify methods, or to practice independently, while simultaneously determining what steps to take to encourage students to persist in the work of making sense of the mathematics. A curriculum helps frame those decisions. Shared lesson planning may not only yield a planned lesson, but also promote discussions addressing these perspectives. When this occurs, the result will be not only sample lessons aligned with a curriculum, but also a strengthening of the mathematics program delivered in a school.

Illustrating a Different Image of Mathematics Instruction

The mathematics program in a school is not fixed. Ideally, a school's mathematics program changes for the better as a mathematics specialist and his faculty and school administrators work together. These individuals engage in conversations in which they establish shared goals, describe what kind of student engagement they want instruction to elicit, and clarify what they mean by evidence of learning during a lesson. But sometimes these changes do not originate internally, within a school. Sometimes they are prompted by external demands, as when a school district or a state adopts new curricular standards. Whether the origin of the changes is internal or external, the mathematics specialist is the person to whom many in a school will turn for leadership. The vignette that follows illustrates how a specialist addressed an external demand for instructional change.

Ms. McMurphy is an elementary mathematics specialist whose school district has released new curriculum guidelines that call for instruction that supports students' active engagement with mathematics. The intent is to build student understanding. Ms. McMurphy knows that the teachers in her school are not opposed to the goal of having students understand and be successful with mathematics. But she also knows that her teachers emphasize the learning of skills, demonstrating how to complete tasks and helping students who are "stuck." Ms. McMurphy realizes that her teachers will benefit from seeing their students figure out a solution without being told exactly what to do. She wants these demonstration sessions to show different methods and explanations of reasoning from the students. At the same time, the sessions need to be relatively short and focused, so the teachers can feel that managing discussion of the differing methods is something that they can do.

Ms. McMurphy decides that "number talks" (Parrish 2010) offer an approach that can serve her purpose. A number talk consists of a teacher presenting a problem that can be solved in a variety of ways by noting numerical relationships before adding, subtracting, multiplying, or dividing. The expectation is that the students will solve the problem independently, in ways that have meaning for them. Young children may work with concrete materials to help them consider how to compose or decompose numbers, but the intention is not for them to use these materials to "get the answer." For example, a second-grade student who is challenged to solve 47 + 28 = ? during a number talk session might respond, "30 plus 47 would be 77. But that is 2 too many... So the answer is 75." If asked, "Where did you get the 30?" the student might reply, "I changed the 28 to 30, but then I had to give back the 2 extra." Given the same problem, another student might respond, "67. Forty-seven plus 20 is 67, and then plus 3 would be... is 70, plus 5 more is 75." If asked, "Where did you get the 3?" the student might reply, "I broke the 8 into 3 and 5."

In number talks, students are given time to determine their solutions, with the expectation that they will share not only their answers, but also their thinking. They have opportunities for self-correction since they can view initial answers as conjectures until the class confirms their approach and reasoning. The teacher selects the problem, allows adequate time, and decides which methods will be shared or summarized. The teacher also shows that thinking is valued by focusing his questions on understanding a solution strategy and clarifying through restatement as he records students' approaches. Number talks are most effective when used regularly for 5 to 15 minutes as an adjunct to the established curriculum, enabling students not only to become more computationally proficient, but also to gain confidence in their ability to think, reason, explain, and justify.

By modeling number talks, Ms. McMurphy gains entry into teachers' classrooms. Once there she is able to demonstrate how to manage classroom conversations that engage students in mental mathematics. She also models how to ask questions that help students explain and communicate their ideas. After Ms. McMurphy has modeled a few number talk problems and discussions, she helps teachers create problems and supports them as they lead class discussions focused on the mathematics. Through Ms. McMurphy's in-class modeling and co-facilitation of the student discussion with teachers in their classrooms, individual teachers gain more insight into how to support their students in learning to share their mathematical thinking and to question one another in respectful and nonconfrontational ways. Some teachers are clearly reassured by seeing how readily the students accept Ms. McMurphy's explanation that the purpose of questioning one another is to understand all the different solution methods and ways of thinking about the problem.

Ms. McMurphy's next hurdle is to address the district's new content expectations and build on number talks to advance the teachers' vision of mathematics instruction. Grade-level team meetings can afford an opportunity to address teachers' questions and consider the meaning of standards-based instruction, as well as how mathematical practices might play out in classrooms. Although no one presumes that this will be an easy task, Ms. McMurphy's decision to begin slowly with number talks has established a level of trust. Looking back later on what she has done, Ms. McMurphy realizes that as a result of this approach, the teachers have decided that she is there to work with them, not simply to tell them what they need to do.

Connecting with Parents

An important way in which the mathematics specialist supports a school's mathematics program is by interacting with parents and facilitating their involvement. Although it is important for parents to understand aspects of the mathematics program being implemented in their child's school, it is critical for them to understand the positive influence that they can have on their child's mathematical development and achievement. Therefore, mathematics specialists must be committed to learning how to communicate effectively and build relationships with parents.

Project a positive attitude about mathematics.

At my school, the message that I share most often is that everyone can "get" mathematics and that it is important for parents and teachers to instill in children and in one another a positive attitude toward mathematics.

—Advice from a mathematics specialist

Mathematics classrooms have changed dramatically in the last twenty years. In many schools, the intent is not for students to sit in isolation working on pages of "naked" computational problems. Today's elementary mathematics classroom is abuzz with activity and discussion; students employ many sorts of mathematical tools and manipulatives as they work to make sense of the mathematics and share their solution strategies. To a visiting parent, the mathematics classroom may look chaotic and unlike a place of learning. Similarly, when new curricular materials are adopted that look very different from the textbooks that they remember using as students, many parents become concerned. This anxiety may result from their uncertainty about how they will help their children with homework or answer questions that they ask. Or it may result from a lack of understanding about how these new materials will help their children learn mathematics successfully. In each of these situations, many schools rely on their mathematics specialist to help parents understand the focus and purpose of the mathematics program.

Use back-to-school nights as opportunities for establishing contact with parents.

A new textbook adoption gave me the opportunity to address parents during back-to-school night. Both my principal and the teachers were happy to let me explain the features of the new materials and let parents know that I would be available to answer their questions about the new books. This not only allowed me to be introduced to the school community, but did so in a way that established me as a knowledgeable resource and as the person for parents to seek out if they wanted to discuss any aspects of the mathematics program. My challenge, then, was to keep those lines of communication open.

—Reflections from a mathematics specialist

Many specialists find that their interactions with parents fall into two categories: helping them understand what their child's mathematics instruction entails and helping them learn how to support their children's mathematics work at home. Many parents have a strong desire to help their children in the academic process but do not know how to help their children learn. Or children may be resistant to accepting instruction from a parent. Mathematics specialists can assist parents in understanding how to create realistic mathematics experiences at home to reinforce specific grade-level expectations. A mathematics specialist can use a variety of approaches to do this.

One effective way to help parents understand what mathematics instruction is like for their child is to set up an opportunity for parents to observe in the classroom; one such opportunity, called "BEAM Day," is described in the following section. Two other effective ways of establishing rapport with parents are family mathematics nights and parent luncheons, also described in sections that follow. Both of these establish a friendly and positive setting for meeting and collaborating with parents. During these events, parents have opportunities to participate in hands-on learning activities that provide them with skills that they can use to enhance their child's mathematical understanding.

BEAM Days

Some mathematics specialists organize a "Be Excited about Mathematics Day"—BEAM Day, for short—as an opportunity for parents to visit an actual mathematics classroom and experience a standards-based mathematics lesson. BEAM Day provides an opportunity for the elementary mathematics specialist to promote the school's mathematics program while communicating what mathematics instruction looks like in the classroom.

Although the elementary mathematics specialist coordinates BEAM Day, the regular classroom teacher should teach the mathematics lesson. Working together, the principal, the specialist, and the teachers establish the date for BEAM Day and issue invitations to parents. Parents are asked to respond to the invitation so that teachers can not only prepare the lesson, but also prepare their students for visitors. The parents should go to a central location where the elementary mathematics specialist can meet them. Ideally, the principal will also be present to welcome them to the school. The specialist should provide a short summary of what they are about to see, perhaps discussing expected elements of a mathematics lesson. The specialist might distribute a "look for" handout as a tool for parents to use as they observe the teacher and students during the lesson. This tool can prepare parents to look for a variety of behaviors:

Teachers—

- presenting a problem or task to the whole class, or different questions or tasks to different students, but without demonstrating or telling any students how to solve problems assigned to them;
- asking questions about a problem and about relationships in a problem, before "turning students loose" to solve that problem or task;
- asking students questions as they work independently, in pairs, or in small groups.

Students—

- sharing their work with others in the class;
- engaging in a conversation about that work with both the students who are explaining it and the teacher.

Specialists should caution parents that they probably will not see every behavior listed on the sheet, which can also provide information about the district's mathematics curriculum, citing websites and links to other resources, such as the Common Core State Standards for Mathematics (National Governors Association Center for Best Practices and Council of Chief State School Officers 2010) and *Principles and Standards for School Mathematics* (National Council of Teachers of Mathematics 2000).

Specialists can encourage parents to take notes for a debriefing of the lesson after the classroom visit, when they will return to the central location to discuss their observations and ask questions. During this session, the specialist can also invite parents to contact her or the teacher if they have questions in the future.

Family mathematics nights

Family mathematics nights are usually held in the early evening. Some schools host these events several times during the school year to showcase the kinds of hands-on activities and technology-enriched tasks that students are experiencing regularly in mathematics class. Mathematics specialists can work with teachers to create activities for the night, setting up games and stations in the school's hallways, classrooms, or the multipurpose room. Families move from center to center, guided by their children. Indeed, the children serve as docents, explaining to their caregivers or siblings what the intent of the task is, how to use the materials, and, most important, what the expectations are for sharing and defending their approach. These activities provide parents with an opportunity to understand that mathematics is more than memorizing rules and to communicate with teachers about the activity. They also allow parents to work with their children on mathematical tasks in a supportive, nonthreatening setting, with opportunities to display enthusiasm, persistence, and skill.

The mathematics specialist might set the agenda for a family mathematics night. Some schools target activities during the event, focusing on particular mathematical topics. For instance, if a school's data indicate that students are having difficulty with measurement, geometry, and estimation, activities for the family mathematics night could focus on those strands. Through family mathematics nights, parents can learn of the types of activities, materials, and everyday concrete materials that they can use to reinforce and recreate mathematics at home. References are available to help a school or a specialist organize these events (see, for example, Taylor-Cox [2005]).

Use family math nights to showcase engaging math, aligned with standards.

At my school we focused family mathematics night activities on ways to keep mathematics learning centered on student understanding through the use of games and activities. But by labeling the tasks and by providing a handout with a website reference, I was able to introduce the parents to the new mathematics standards required by our state curriculum while at the same time promoting the importance of our goal of teaching for understanding.

—*Reflections from a mathematics specialist*

At the varied centers and game locations, the mathematics specialist and teachers can demonstrate the types of questions that parents can ask their children, explaining to parents that posing such questions will encourage their children to talk about mathematics and demonstrate their understanding. The intent is to help parents understand that asking good questions can enable a child to make sense of mathematics, but telling a child how to solve a problem may cause the child to shut down or back away. Many parents simply do not know what types of questions to ask their children. For this reason, some specialists and teachers prepare a sheet for parents to take home, providing sample questions and ideas about ways to continue having fun while practicing mathematics with their children at home.

Parent mathematics luncheons

Some specialists organize mathematics luncheons as opportunities for a group of parents to come to a school during the day, eat, and meet with the elementary mathematics specialist. Although goals for this luncheon vary, the specialist should have one or two aims in mind. The primary intent might be—

- to encourage parents to be more involved in their children's mathematics work at home;
- to strengthen parents' understanding of particular mathematical content;
- to offer some techniques for having children practice mathematical skills; or
- to help parents understand how mathematics is being taught at the school.

Once the specialist has determined the focus, he should prepare for the luncheon by gathering some evidence to justify the approach that he will present or to establish the need that he is addressing, without targeting any student. Beyond building good will and respect by extending the invitation to lunch, the specialists should focus the session on enabling the parents to experience engagement in the kinds of mathematical tasks that their children are working on in school. When planning these tasks, the specialist must remember that it is important not only for parents to be engaged, but also for them to be comfortable. At the same time, the specialist should anticipate questions that parents might have and prepare answers in advance. Finally, the specialist should plan for follow-up communication so that the parents trust that their future questions and needs will be addressed. Consider the experience of Ms. Ryerson, an elementary mathematics specialist in an urban school district.

Ms. Ryerson received several messages from teachers in her school, all sharing a common concern. Their students were not completing their homework assignments, and the teachers expressed concern that parents were providing inadequate support to reinforce the mathematical skills that students would be expected to demonstrate on the next benchmark assessment administered by the district. Ms. Ryerson asked her principal for permission to host a parent mathematics luncheon in an effort to get parents involved in their children's mathematical learning and increase student achievement on the mathematics benchmark assessments. The principal readily gave permission, and the PTA agreed to sponsor the event. Ms. Ryerson and some members of the PTA purchased food, door prizes, participation certificates, and gift cards as incentives for the parents' participation. The principal announced the mathematics luncheon at a PTA meeting. Invitations were sent home to parents of students in grades 3–6, encouraging them to participate. Ms. Ryerson and the principal promised the PTA that the parents of students in kindergarten–grades 2 would be invited to participate in a parent luncheon in the future, after the assessments were completed.

To Ms. Ryerson's surprise, a large number of parents showed up for the parent luncheon. Although Ms. Ryerson had prepared several activities to engage parents in learning specific mathematics content, she began the luncheon by talking to parents about the rigor of the new mathematics curriculum and the complexity of the standards that their children were expected to master. Ms. Ryerson showed the parents how to visit the state department of education website and find the standards for various grade levels, as well as sample questions for the end-of-the-year state assessment. After eating lunch, the parents completed activities at several stations that Ms. Ryerson had set up to show what students were doing to meet the standards that instruction was addressing at the time.

One of the activities required parents to measure their heights and post them anonymously in either centimeters or inches. Once all the data were collected, some of the small-group activities included ordering and comparing numbers; estimating and rounding; finding the mean, median, mode, and range; working with whole numbers, decimals, and percents; and creating multi-step word problems. Ms. Ryerson's parents enjoyed working in small groups to complete these activities.

In addition to having the parents engage in the activities at the centers, Ms. Ryerson talked to them about creating meaningful mathematical learning experiences for their children at home. She handed out sales advertisements for local grocery stores and department stores. She modeled for parents how to use information in newspapers or real shopping experiences as a basis for creating problems or asking questions to foster critical thinking and promote applying mathematics and engaging in mathematical problem solving. Ms. Ryerson gave the parents a sample question:

> **David wants to buy a bicycle that costs \$140.00. If he pays the store $1/5$ of the total cost of the bike, they will hold it for him and let him make regular payments. How much will he owe the store if he pays $1/5$ of the cost of the bicycle today?**

When challenged to come up with another question that they could ask a child about this setting, the parents suggested the following:

> **How much will David have to pay each week if he plans to pay the same amount each week and finish his payments in 8 weeks?**

Parents discussed how they could challenge their children to create pictorial and numerical representations and additional word problems to demonstrate their understanding.

Many of the parents asked questions and discussed ways in which they could extend these learning experiences at their homes. Ms. Ryerson's parent luncheon was an inviting, successful way to partner with parents and to solicit their support for the mathematics program.

Community Involvement

The PTA can be instrumental in supporting mathematics specialists' efforts to connect with parents, but specialists should also reach out directly to the community to get support for the school's mathematics program. Retired adults, military personnel, and members of various local organizations may be willing to give time to assist in reinforcing skills to promote student success. Specialists can write letters, make phone calls, and visit community representatives to ask for volunteers or donations to strengthen the school's mathematics program, to assist with parent luncheons, or to support family mathematics nights. Through these community relationships, students can gain access to rewarding mathematical support and experiences.

Concluding Thoughts

Although arranging schoolwide events such as BEAM Day, setting up family mathematics nights, and organizing a luncheon session for parents take a specialist out of the classroom and establish a different form of interaction with teachers, facilitating such activities is part of serving as the face of a school's mathematics program. Yet, for teachers and administrators to view the specialist as the go-to person for a school's mathematics program, the key is to stay informed about resources and policies that will affect the school's program while simultaneously working with teachers to advance their teaching and their students' learning. Ultimately, it is mathematics teaching and learning that make a school's mathematics program. A specialist's primary allegiance must be to support instruction and student achievement.

References

National Council of Teachers of Mathematics (NCTM). *Principles and Standards for School Mathematics.* Reston, Va.: NCTM, 2000.

National Governors Association Center for Best Practices and Council of Chief State School Officers (NGA Center and CCSSO). *Common Core State Standards for Mathematics. Common Core State Standards (College- and Career-Readiness Standards and K–12 Standards in English Language Arts and Math).* Washington, D.C.: NGA Center and CCSSO, 2010. http://www.corestandards.org.

Parrish, Sherry. *Number Talks: Helping Children Build Mental Math and Computation Strategies, Grades K–5.* Sausalito, Calif.: Math Solutions, 2010.

Stronge, James H., Holly B. Richard, and Nancy Catano. *Qualities of Effective Principals.* Alexandria, Va.: Association for Supervision and Curriculum Development, 2008.

Taylor-Cox, Jennifer. *Family Math Night: Math Standards in Action.* Larchmont, N.Y.: Eye on Education, 2005.

4

Other Considerations

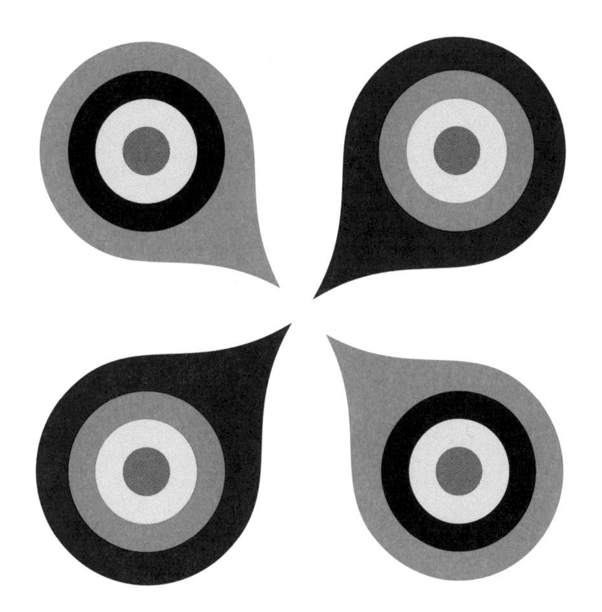

Turning Challenges into Opportunities

Sarah M. Minervino, Patricia A. Robertson, and Joy W. Whitenack

The elementary mathematics specialist faces many challenges as she seeks to shape mathematics instruction and advance student learning in her school. To do this work, the specialist must first gain access to classrooms. This means that she must gain credibility with both the veteran and the novice teacher and earn their trust. So, for example, while the specialist is engaging in collaborative dialogue with one teacher, she will be offering intensive mentoring and support to another. She must recognize that the type of interactive strategies that work well with one teacher may fall flat with another. Indeed, learning to juggle different challenges is one of the unique aspects of being a successful mathematics specialist.

Of course, working regularly and successfully with teachers is more likely if the specialist has supportive administrators. The savvy specialist will need to develop relationships with administrators, clearly communicating his goals for mathematics instruction at the school and brainstorming about ways to achieve them. As part of his responsibilities, he will need to provide opportunities for teachers to increase their mathematical and pedagogical knowledge. But what kinds of challenges is he likely to face, and how can he meet them? This chapter highlights some of the more common challenges faced by specialists and offers some strategies for transforming these challenges into opportunities.

Gaining Access

A newly assigned specialist needs to understand a school's culture, communicate her role, and gain access to teachers' classrooms. Doing so can be quite challenging. How can a specialist help the principal and the teachers understand her responsibilities as she engages in her work? And what should she do so that teachers will invite her into their classrooms?

Getting to know the principal and the teachers

Consider how Ms. Simon, the first mathematics specialist assigned to Beacon Elementary School, met the challenge of building relationships and gaining access to mathematics classes in her new school.

When Ms. Simon arrived at the school, Ms. Carson, the principal, was very welcoming. Ms. Carson offered to help Ms. Simon in any way she could. However, Ms. Carson was also still learning about the role of the mathematics specialist, and she was not yet ready to discuss job specifics with Ms. Simon. During the first teachers' meeting before the start of school, Ms. Carson expressed her enthusiasm about having a mathematics specialist in the school building and stated that she wanted each of the teachers to work with Ms. Simon this year. However, Ms. Carson did not explain Ms. Simon's job or how Ms. Simon would work with the teachers. What could Ms. Simon do to help everyone learn more about her role? Then Ms. Simon had an idea! She would write the teachers a letter describing the different ways in which she could support their work. But before she distributed the letter to the teachers, she would first meet with Ms. Carson and get her input.

One of the mathematics specialist's challenges is to clarify her role with the principal and the teachers at the beginning of the year. Ms. Simon met this challenge by crafting a letter to teachers explaining some of the ways that she could work with them (see fig. 12.1). By sharing the letter with the principal first, not only did she create another opportunity to meet with the principal and explain her role as a mathematics specialist, but she also established a line of communication and a relationship with her administrator. Ms. Simon's next step was to deliver her letter in person to the teachers.

As the new mathematics specialist at Beacon Elementary School, I am eager to collaborate with you during mathematics instruction. Let me tell you about some of the many ways that I hope we can work together this year. I am ready to—

- attend team meetings to dialogue about mathematics instruction, to do mathematics together, and to examine student work;
- participate in grade-level curriculum planning and in lesson planning, in either individual settings or within grade-level teams, as we work through mathematical expectations and establish a mathematical agenda as part of that planning;
- work with individual teachers, grade-level teams, and assessment groups as together we learn from, analyze, and make decisions based on student work;
- conduct demonstration lessons in your classroom that we can talk about afterward, so we can discuss ideas based on your observations;
- observe you working with your class, so I can learn more about the needs and strengths of your students;
- co-plan and co-teach classes with you and then debrief the lesson afterwards—this will help us identify the understandings and misunderstandings of particular students;
- work with you, implementing units or lessons;
- assist in the design and interpretation of grade-level mathematics assessments and in preparing for state testing by analyzing test results and student work;

Fig. 12.1. Ms. Simon's letter to teachers at her new school

- work with you to identify and pace your yearly goals in mathematics;
- present an in-service or mini-workshop for a large or small group of teachers and teaching assistants;
- talk with parents about mathematics or give a mathematics presentation to our PTA;
- share resource materials, tools, and professional literature to support lessons.

Please feel free to e-mail me, find me in room 22, or just tap me on the shoulder! Let me know how I can support mathematics instruction in your classroom and at Beacon Elementary!

Looking forward to a great school year,
Ms. Simon

Fig. 12.1. *Continued*

To begin building relationships with the teachers, Ms. Simon decided to visit each teacher in the days following the first teachers' meeting and before the children's first day of school. As she visited with each teacher, she introduced herself and personally gave each teacher a copy of the letter that she had written. She also took this opportunity to ask the teachers whether they had any questions for her. If a teacher had time, Ms. Simon used this conversation as an opportunity to find out more, such as the teacher's instructional practices, his level of confidence about teaching mathematics, his willingness to work with other teachers, and his perceptions of the school. These informal conversations gave Ms. Simon a chance to gain a better understanding of her new school's culture.

By taking the time to understand the teaching staff, Ms. Simon began to build the rapport that she would need to establish relationships. Investing this time at the beginning of the school year can make access to teachers' classrooms easier for a mathematics specialist.

Working in teachers' classrooms

The next step for a specialist is preparing to work with teachers in their classrooms. One of the first issues that a specialist then needs to deal with is scheduling.

Scheduling times to meet with teachers was a challenge for Ms. Simon at the beginning of the school year. Some teachers taught mathematics at the same or at overlapping times, making working all classrooms difficult for her. Teachers' schedules had been finalized during the summer before Ms. Simon arrived. This was a problem that she would need to address before the beginning of the next school year. Now, however, she needed to talk with the principal about ways to work around the scheduling obstacles in the current school year. In the meeting, Ms. Carson told Ms. Simon that she would take a look at the schedule to see whether and where a few changes could be made so that Ms. Simon could have access to a few more classes this year. The principal also said that she would take the scheduling issue into consideration when making the master schedule for the next school year.

To tackle the challenge of scheduling time to meet with teachers, Ms. Simon decided to provide the teachers with a copy of her schedule. She distributed a monthly calendar, noting times when she would be working in the classrooms each week. She also provided a cover letter (shown in fig. 12.2) with a list of ways in which she might help while in the classroom.

September Mathematics Resources

Dear teachers,

Attached you will find my calendar and schedule for the month of September. I thought it would be helpful for you to see when I am scheduled to be in which classrooms.

Once the first week of school and the beginning-of-year assessments are completed, I look forward to working with you on the start of unit 1. Please let me know how I can work to support your mathematics program this month. In addition to observing the lessons and student learning during our scheduled time, I can help in other ways. Simply e-mail me, catch me before or after school in room 22, or fill out the form below and return it to my mailbox.

Ms. Simon

During September, my mathematics class will be learning about ____________________
units or topics)

Put a check mark by whatever you would like me to do (check however many apply):

_____ Model a lesson in my class

_____ Collaborate to plan and teach (or co-teach) a lesson

_____ Share some additional resources or activities related to ____________________

_____ Meet with me to plan and discuss a lesson or unit

_____ Other *(please explain)* ____________________

A convenient time for us to meet would be: ____________________

Requested by: ____________________

Fig. 12.2. Ms. Simon's cover letter for her September schedule

This year, the principal expected Ms. Simon to work each week with Ms. Lee and Ms. Bowen, two fifth-grade teachers. Ms. Lee was eager to work with Ms. Simon to learn the newly adopted, innovative curriculum at the school, as well as different methods for teaching mathematics. Ms. Lee welcomed Ms. Simon's support and asked Ms. Simon to model or co-teach lessons regularly in her classroom. Ms. Simon realized that one of her challenges would be to support a teacher who was new to teaching mathematics. Ms. Lee had never taught math before this year, and she would be learning how to teach for understanding. The first unit they planned together focused on investigating multiple representations of rational numbers. Not only was teaching this content a new experience for Ms. Lee, but she was also unfamiliar with the new curricular materials that emphasized exploring relationships among fractions, decimals, and percents.

Access to Ms. Lee's classroom was easier because of the principal's expectation that Ms. Simon work with both fifth-grade teachers. What might the specialist do when the principal does not require all the teachers to work with her? A specialist in such a situation can do any number of things:

- Tell all teachers that she will be asking to visit every classroom to learn more about how students engage in mathematics at each level. This approach is particularly helpful for a mathematics specialist who has not had teaching experience in certain grades.
- Consider working with one or two first-year teachers before the students arrive and then during the first week of school, when veteran teachers may prefer to work independently. First-year teachers may be more open to receiving support in areas such as classroom set-up and to discussing topics such as classroom management or establishing norms for discussion and "on-task talk" during mathematics instruction.
- Share problems of the week, either schoolwide or by grade level, to engage students in problem solving. This strategy not only generates excitement about mathematics throughout the building, but also provides opportunities for the mathematics specialist to engage teachers in dialogue about students' solutions.
- Offer to co-plan and co-teach (or teach) a few lessons addressing new content in the curriculum so that teachers can learn how to provide better support for students' understanding.

These are only a few of the strategies that a new mathematics specialist might use to begin his work with teachers. His overarching aim is to focus his work on helping teachers support students' learning. But to do that, he must understand the culture of the school, and the teachers, in turn, need to learn what his responsibilities are and understand what they entail.

Working with Reluctant Teachers

When a teacher is willing or eager to work with the mathematics specialist, the coaching situation is ideal. Sometimes creating these types of working relationships can take a great deal of time, effort, and patience on the part of the mathematics specialist. In fact, even if the principal requires all teachers to work with the specialist, they may not be enthusiastic about—or may even be resistant to—working with her. How might the mathematics specialist work with teachers who do not wish to work with her? In some cases, the teacher may be uncomfortable about the idea of the mathematics specialist working in her classroom. Then the specialist has the challenge of helping the teachers feel at ease. Also, once the mathematics specialist begins her work, she must find ways to sustain this collaborative relationship. So how did Ms. Simon work with Ms. Bowen, the other fifth-grade teacher?

Working with Ms. Bowen was more challenging than working with Ms. Lee. Ms. Bowen had taught fifth grade for nine years, and her students had always done well on the state-mandated tests. From Ms. Bowen's point of view, she did not need the mathematics specialist's help. In fact, Ms. Simon might not ever have worked with Ms. Bowen if the principal had not required it.

Because Ms. Bowen was an experienced teacher, Ms. Simon decided to begin by drawing on Ms. Bowen's strengths—namely, her knowledge of the fifth-grade mathematics curriculum. Ms. Simon asked Ms. Bowen whether she had some time to talk about strategies that she had found successful in teaching fifth-grade mathematics. The question seemed to please Ms. Bowen, and she talked openly about her teaching experience. By beginning their early interaction in this way, Ms. Simon hoped to establish a working relationship that would allow her to take a more active role in the classroom.

After visiting Ms. Bowen's classroom a few times, Ms. Simon noticed that students rarely had opportunities to talk about mathematics or to explain their strategies for solving problems. Ms. Bowen tended to focus her instruction on using procedures, but her students showed little understanding of why those procedures worked.

Although Ms. Bowen was not comfortable with Ms. Simon modeling or teaching the lesson, she agreed that Ms. Simon could ask the students questions. As class time permitted, Ms. Simon also exchanged comments briefly with Ms. Bowen about different students' work. She focused her comments and suggestions on ways to actively engage students, offering remarks like, "It looks as if they have all completed the problems that you assigned. Would you mind if I asked them to explain their solution methods?" As the students explained their thinking, Ms. Simon modeled how to promote more productive discourse.

Over time, Ms. Simon wanted Ms. Bowen to realize that having more opportunities to talk about mathematics could help her students develop a deeper understanding of mathematical ideas. Ms. Simon hoped that a goal that she and Ms. Bowen could establish together would be to facilitate more effective student discussion of mathematics during Ms. Bowen's lessons.

Making teachers more comfortable

In the vignette, Ms. Simon recognized Ms. Bowen's reluctance. She then capitalized on the opportunity offered by Ms. Bowen's knowledge about and experience with the fifth-grade curriculum, initiating conversations that communicated her respect for Ms. Bowen. After gaining access in that way, she began to build a working relationship with Ms. Bowen that would enable the two of them to delve more deeply into Ms. Bowen's practice.

Help teachers become more receptive by visiting other teachers' classrooms together with them.

When teachers were not very receptive to having me in their classrooms, I made the suggestion that we go to other classrooms together to observe students. I asked teachers to visit a classroom that is one grade below and one grade level above the grade that they teach to observe how the mathematics content being taught at those levels connects with concepts that they teach. By thinking through how the concepts are related across the grade levels, the teachers and I could focus on student thinking. This vertical look provided opportunities for teachers to extend their understanding of the mathematics content as well as how those concepts are taught at different grade levels. Additionally, the experience allowed teachers to see the importance of developing lessons that promote understanding that is addressed at other grade levels or that needs to be extended differently.

—*Reflections from a mathematics specialist*

The specialist may try other approaches that can be useful when working with teachers who are hesitant or seem resistant to working with her:

- Work with a teacher who models best instructional practices, is respected by his colleagues, and is seen as a leader in mathematics instruction. By choosing this teacher, the mathematics specialist may help debunk the stereotype that coaches are Band-Aids for struggling teachers. This is also a way for the specialist to begin to build professional capacity within the school.
- Listen to what teachers may really be saying. Sometimes teachers mask their own confusion by appearing to be resistant. For this reason, the mathematics specialist needs to be sensitive to the meaning behind the teachers' words. If a teacher says, "I don't want to introduce that strategy—I think it will just confuse the students," perhaps she is communicating her own confusion. The teacher may really be thinking, "I don't really understand this strategy, so I don't want to use it." The mathematics specialist might offer to introduce the strategy and could ask the classroom teacher to watch how the students respond. Then they could discuss students' responses after class.
- Ask the teacher to observe a strategy or technique that the mathematics specialist models. The specialist might request an opportunity to try out a new strategy, at the same time enlisting the teacher's participation by saying, for example, "I have been trying to ask more open-ended questions that require students to explain their thinking. Would you do me a favor and record the questions I ask during the lesson?" This is an opportunity for the mathematics specialist to use a strategy that can also serve to entice the teacher to discuss or learn about the strategy.

Sustaining the working relationship

Sometimes a teacher may view his work with the mathematics specialist as a temporary interaction. A reluctant teacher may go through the motions of collaborating with the specialist for a month, all the while waiting for the opportunity to return to his traditional ways of teaching. Once the specialist gains access, how can she continue the partnership and help the teacher continue to grow? To remain focused on improving instruction and increasing student learning, the specialist might consider some of the following strategies for strengthening a working relationship:

- Continue to work with teachers as they teach more challenging content, perhaps identifying a topic, such as fractions, that the teacher might not feel completely confident about teaching. The specialist and the teacher can cultivate their collaboration as they engage in dialogue about the content during planning.
- Always bring the conversation back to the students' thinking and understanding. For example, if students are struggling with a particular topic or need more of a challenge, the specialist can continue to work with the teacher to address their academic needs. The specialist can provide suggestions for how to differentiate instruction for a wide range of learners.
- Use formative and summative data to help start conversations with teachers about instruction, always focusing the discussion on how the students perform, solve problems, or explain their ideas. The key for the specialist is to communicate to teachers what their students do or do not understand and make suggestions for using additional strategies to help students learn the content.

Help teachers understand that you are creating learning partnerships with them.

I know that I am working hard to help improve instruction in the classrooms, but I remind myself continually that I am learning too. As I work with teachers, I make sure they know that I am learning with them. This makes our work together a true partnership.

—*Reflections from a mathematics specialist*

The specialist can use these strategies with teachers as she continues to work with them throughout the school year. Each strategy is valuable and provides more than one possible benefit for teachers' professional development. For instance, by taking time to address challenging content, teachers have opportunities to understand the mathematics that they teach more fully. Then teachers can use this knowledge to plan lessons that help students build conceptual understanding. Consider how Ms. Simon's work developed with Ms. Lee as the specialist helped the new teacher understand the content that she was teaching in fifth grade.

The big ideas associated with teaching fractions were new to Ms. Lee. She didn't know how to use a 10×10 grid as a tool to help students develop an understanding of percent equivalents for different fractions. She was completely stumped about how the students could use the grids to show $1/3 = 33\,1/3$ percent. Ms. Lee and Ms. Simon talked about some of these ideas as they planned the lesson.

After the lesson, as they reviewed student work, Ms. Simon realized that Ms. Lee was still confused. Ms. Lee was not sure how Johnny had arrived at $33\,1/3$ percent—he had divided his grid into groups of 25 (see fig. 12.3). Through their discussion, Ms. Lee seemed to understand that he had taken the fourth group of 25 and divided it by 3 to get 8 in each group. Next, he had taken the one remaining square and divided it into three equal parts. Then he had three groups of 25, three groups of 8, and three $1/3$'s. Finally, he had added 8 and $1/3$ to 25 to yield $33\,1/3$ squares or $33\,1/3$ percent of the grid.

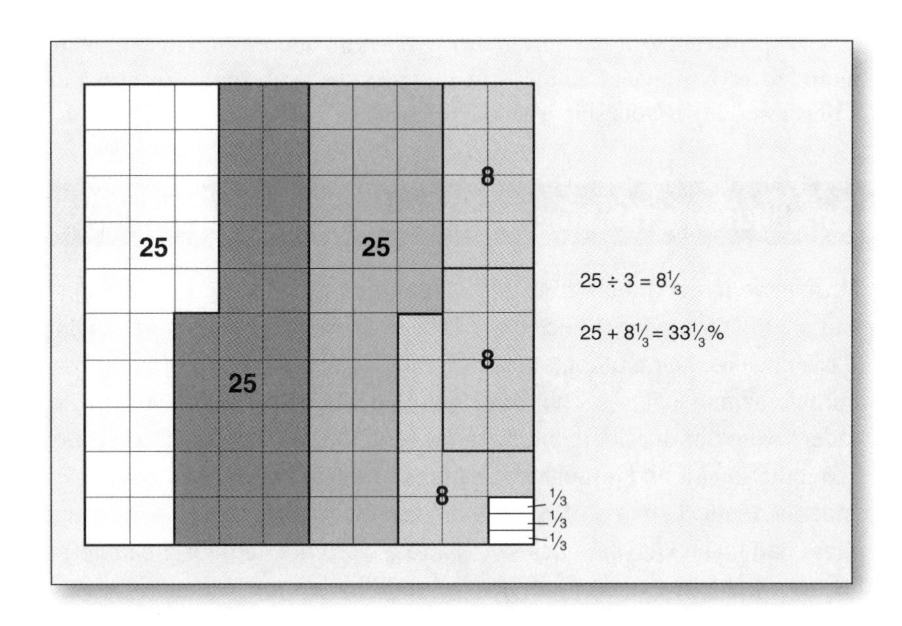

Fig. 12.3. Johnny's way of showing $33\,1/3$ percent on a 10×10 grid

As they discussed Johnny's and other students' work, Ms. Lee began to understand how students could make connections among fractions, parts of 100, and percents. Because of this interaction, Ms. Lee appeared to be more confident about teaching this content. She and Ms. Simon were now ready to move forward and plan the next lesson.

The vignette illustrates the important role that the specialist can play in helping a teacher grow in her understanding of the mathematics she teaches. By exploring students' work with a specialist and with other teachers, teachers can delve more deeply into the mathematics behind a lesson. Student work during lessons can also be used for a formative assessment of student progress. When the specialist examines summative data from unit tests or state assessments, he can gather useful information about topics to focus on with teachers, addressing both content and instructional practices. The specialist might begin these conversations with teachers by asking some of the following questions:

- "What surprises you about your students' results?"
- "Why do you think students struggled with that question?"
- "How did you teach the content?"
- "Now that you have seen how the students responded to these questions, what do you think we should consider before teaching it again?"

Asking these questions during a team meeting can help teachers be more reflective and learn from their experiences. This not only allows teachers an opportunity to engage in collegial conversations and to learn from one another, but also gives the mathematics specialist opportunities for sustaining a working relationship with the teachers.

Reflect on children's thinking with teams of teachers.

Last year, I struggled to get a team of veteran first-grade teachers to do anything in mathematics other than present procedures and rules. They even had procedures specifying how the children should manipulate their mathematics materials. I asked them to present the children with some word problems and just see what the children could do on their own. They assured me that first graders were not developmentally ready for this, and that solution strategies for word problems had to be taught and retaught many times before the children could even begin to do a problem independently. I shared with the team the fact that at the beginning of the year, our second graders had fallen flat when asked to write a word problem for a simple equation such as $3 + 5 = 8$. As a team, we made it our goal to address word problems as real problem solving throughout the school year. Then, after the children solved some word problems without being told exactly what to do, we met to discuss the children's thinking and share their approaches. Reluctantly, the teachers admitted that the children had engaged in a lot more thinking than they had initially believed possible.

—Reflections from a mathematics specialist

When Teachers Make Mathematical Mistakes

A particular challenge that a mathematics specialist may encounter is deciding what to do when a teacher makes a mathematical error. The decision may depend on the specialist's relationship and prior experiences with the teacher. If Ms. Simon observed Ms. Lee making a mathematical error during instruction, she addressed the mistake as they continued to teach the lesson because that was what she and Mrs. Lee had agreed on when planning the lesson. But if Ms. Simon observed Ms. Bowen making a mathematical mistake, Ms. Simon waited until students had begun their work before she made suggestions or talked with Ms. Bowen about different ways to think about the content. A short scene illustrates Ms. Simon's approach:

One day when Ms. Simon worked in Ms. Bowen's classroom, she noticed that when Ms. Bowen solved a problem like 34.75 + 48.26, she referred to the digits to the right of the decimal point as "5" and "6," "7" and "2," and so on. Ms. Bowen did not name the numerals as the decimal quantities "7 tenths" and "2 tenths," and "75 hundredths" and "26 hundredths," and so forth. Although she arrived at the correct answer, when she explained the procedure to the students, she simply continued to recite and add digits as whole numbers. Her students were struggling to understand decimals, partly because they did not have opportunities to make sense of the relationships represented by the digits. Ms. Simon also noted that they did not have opportunities to explore different computational strategies, such as the following:

$$0.75 + 0.26 = 0.75 + (0.25 + 0.01) = (0.75 + 0.25) + 0.01$$
$$= 1.00 + 0.01 = 1.01.$$

Ms. Simon decided to talk with Ms. Bowen about these ideas after the lesson. She began the conversation by mentioning that the students seemed to be struggling with decimals. Next, she asked Ms. Bowen whether she thought it would help students to think about how the values of the digits were related. Asking this question gave Ms. Simon the opportunity to talk with Ms. Bowen about ways that they might help students understand these relationships.

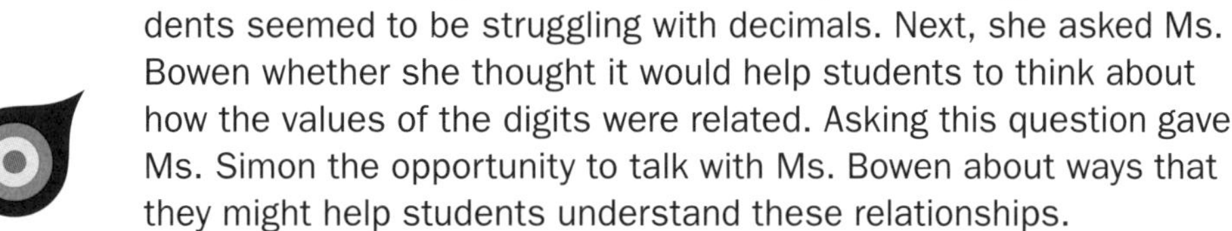

Like Ms. Simon, the mathematics specialist may talk with the teacher after the lesson to address any missteps that the teacher made. She might begin the debriefing by saying,

> **"This is what I think I heard you say: ________________. But the correct math idea is ________________. Let's consider how we can clarify this misunderstanding in the next lesson."**

Alternatively, she might *carefully* address the mistake during the lesson, redirecting the instruction tactfully by offering a brief remark such as the following:

"What I think your teacher is trying to say is ________________."

"Boys and girls, another way of thinking about this is _____________________."

By using this approach, the mathematics specialist is able to steer the instruction in the right direction and ensure that the content that is presented is correct. A significant advantage of addressing mistakes during instruction is that students then are likely to leave class with a stronger understanding before beginning their assigned homework. An equally significant disadvantage is the possibility that the teacher will be embarrassed. Therefore, the specialist needs to give careful consideration to her approach before addressing a teacher's error, weighing her working relationship with the teacher.

Propose a way for a teacher to ask for guidance during the lesson without losing face.

Some teachers are comfortable asking the mathematics specialist for guidance during instruction. If a teacher is reluctant to seek guidance, the mathematics specialist can propose a way for her to do so while maintaining the respect of her students. For example, the specialist might suggest that when the teacher is uncomfortable about responding to a student's question or unclear about some of the content, she can turn to the specialist and say, "Let's see what Ms. Simon thinks about this." In this way, the specialist removes some of the stress from the teacher—she does not need to admit to her students that she does not understand. Additionally, the specialist can talk with the teacher after the lesson to provide more content support and to help address the teacher's mathematical misunderstandings.

—Advice from a mathematics specialist

A mathematics specialist has other opportunities to address teachers' mathematical misunderstandings outside the classroom. Below are three suggestions that she could employ to provide job-embedded professional development connected with mathematics content:

- Offer to score assessments with the teachers, and then talk about the findings and the content. This conversation can be a good time to discuss the mathematics that is proving to be difficult for students to learn and may also be difficult for teachers to teach.
- Explore and discuss the mathematics in an upcoming unit when planning with a grade-level team.
- Have teachers bring individual student work to a team meeting, and analyze and discuss it together. As teachers analyze student work, they become more familiar with the ways that

students think about and solve problems. At a different team meeting, have teachers bring one low-level response and one high-level response to a cognitively demanding problem provided by the specialist. By focusing on this task, the specialist places no judgment on the quality of tasks assigned by individual teachers but instead creates an opportunity to talk in greater depth about the mathematics content and the quality of students' responses. Taking this approach may also help the mathematics specialist gain the trust of the teachers on the team.

Final Thoughts

Mathematics specialists play a vitally important role in supporting teachers and their students' learning. If the mathematics specialist can implement effective strategies and approaches to support teachers' work, she can make it possible for more students to reach their full potential. As Guskey (2002) points out, change occurs in teachers' beliefs only when teachers see that a change that they have made in instruction has indeed improved student learning.

The degree of a mathematics specialist's success is related to how she works with teachers—not only those who want to work with her, but also those who are reluctant to do so. This chapter addresses only some of the potential challenges that the mathematics specialist might face. Although the specialist's role is complex, her continued work permits schools and teachers to transform their challenges into opportunities for excellence.

Reference

Guskey, Thomas R. "Professional Development and Teacher Change." *Teachers and Teaching: Theory and Practice* 8, nos. 3–4 (2002): 381–91.

Defining the Elementary Mathematics Specialist Position

Debra J. Delozier and Fiona C. Nichols

When a school district decides to add the position of elementary mathematics specialist, the first step is to develop a detailed job description for the position, aligned with the district's vision of the mathematics program. A comprehensive job description establishes, or at least suggests, the boundaries of what the specialist will or will not be expected to do. When a school district has multiple specialists, defining the role of each one up front helps to alleviate misuse of any specialist, whether he is based solely in a school or spends part of his time at the central office. A job description clarifies expectations and can minimize shifts that may cause the position to morph gradually in unintended ways.

Developing the Job Description

An elementary mathematics specialist's job description has two components and, through these, serves two purposes. First, it sets forth the qualifications and essential knowledge and skills that a candidate needs to perform the duties of the mathematics specialist. This part of the job description communicates a minimum standard that enables both applicants and reviewers to determine whether a potential fit exists between a job seeker and the position. Second, a job description defines the roles and responsibilities of a mathematics specialist. This part of the job description communicates to prospective and practicing specialists, as well as administrators, teachers, and parents, how the specialist will support mathematics teaching and learning within a building. A well-crafted job description also helps to maintain uniformity among schools across the district. Further, it makes evaluating the effectiveness of the elementary mathematics specialist possible. Such an evaluation is nearly impossible unless expectations for the position have been clearly established.

When developing the job description for a mathematics specialist, some school districts find it helpful to organize a task force or focus group consisting of teachers, building-level administrators, central-office mathematics leaders, parents, and community members. The facilitator of this group can share current findings or professional literature identifying the necessary skills or abilities of effective mathematics specialists, as well as the goals that the district hopes to achieve by creating this position.

Conveying qualifications through a job description

School districts often describe the qualifications for the position of elementary mathematics specialist after considering job expectations and licensure criteria set by the state. Because these differ across states and districts, no single listing of qualifications applies to all locations. The Association of Mathematics Teacher Educators (AMTE) has published standards for elementary mathematics specialists that may serve a district as a reference when considering what background knowledge and experience to require of an elementary mathematics specialist (AMTE 2010). Figure 13.1 presents a description of appropriate qualifications and background knowledge for a full-time elementary mathematics specialist who will be placed in one school, with full release from classroom teaching. This list assumes that the state has an endorsement or some form of licensure for mathematics specialists, but this is not the case across the United States.

Position title:	K–5 Mathematics Specialist
Reports to:	Building-level principal
Primary responsibility:	Provide leadership and expertise in mathematics teaching to building-level administrators, instructional staff, and parents in support of improved instruction and increased student learning in mathematics.

Qualifications:

1. Licensure in elementary education, a master's degree in education (or have completed at least 24 semester hours of mathematics courses, mathematics pedagogy courses, and leadership/coaching courses applicable to the state's mathematics specialist endorsement), and a state-issued mathematics specialist endorsement.
2. Evidence of participation in a significant number of professional development sessions addressing mathematics and mathematics education.
3. At least five years of successful, full-time K–5 classroom teaching experience.
4. Experience in working with multiple grade levels (preferred) and differentiated instruction.
5. Experience in providing professional development addressing mathematics content, mathematics instructional strategies, and use of assessment to inform instruction.

Knowledge, skills, and abilities:

1. Ability to work cooperatively with all instructional staff to plan and implement appropriate mathematics instructional programs.
2. Ability to relate positively with parents and community representatives.
3. Ability to make appropriate use of written and verbal communication.
4. Effective time-management and organizational skills.
5. Ability to identify and use appropriate pedagogical skills.
6. Knowledge of the development of mathematical understanding and mathematical proficiency.
7. Knowledge of current theory and practices in mathematics instruction, current mathematics curriculum programs, and a variety of assessment strategies.
8. Ability to assess student needs and performance and to interpret results to inform instructional planning.
9. Ability to develop and present quality mathematics professional development for all instructional staff.

Fig. 13.1. Prerequisites for an elementary mathematics specialist position, as listed in a job description

Conveying roles and responsibilities through a job description

One critical consideration that school districts must address when defining the mathematics specialist position is the distinction, if any, between the role of the elementary mathematics specialist and the roles of other specialists within the district. For instance, in many districts reading specialists who are assigned to schools remove students from their regular classroom setting for remediation purposes, but these specialists may or may not fulfill a coaching role with classroom teachers. The primary responsibility of reading specialists is typically teaching *students*. By contrast, the mathematics specialist's role is typically defined as working within the confines of classroom settings to enhance and modify the mathematical content, pedagogical knowledge, and instructional practice of *teachers*. Elementary mathematics specialists have the responsibility of coaching teachers, as well as programmatic responsibilities.

If these kinds of distinctions exist among the roles of specialists in a school district, they should be made clear in the job descriptions. Further, communication with all stakeholders (mathematics specialists, classroom teachers, school-level administrators, and district-level administrators) should highlight the differences. But no matter what responsibilities are assigned to mathematics specialists within schools across a district, their roles should be shared in a straightforward manner with all staff members in a school as soon as the specialist is placed in the school and ready to assume those responsibilities.

Seek the principal's help in clarifying your role to your school's staff.

In my school, the principal told the staff that they were lucky to have me and that he was excited about the opportunity. He spoke with them at a faculty meeting in the fall before the students arrived, describing not only what I would do, but. perhaps more important, what my job description did *not* entail. This squelched the notion that I would be gathering students for remediation groups, as the reading specialist did. Instead, he told them that I would be meeting with them to plan, to observe students, to co-teach with them, to model teaching, and to help them find resources. Because the teachers were told up front what my role would be, they were not upset when I did not do what the reading specialist did. They soon found out that I did many other things that would help them in their teaching and in their efforts to meet the needs of their students.

—Reflections from a mathematics specialist

Because of tradition and legal precedents, each school district has its own views about the optimal format and level of detail for a listing of the roles and responsibilities of a position. This listing will also differ from district to district, depending on the configuration of responsibilities that the school district has established for the mathematics specialist position. For example, a specialist may be assigned to serve one school or to move among multiple schools. She may have full release from classroom teaching so that she is available to work in classrooms with teachers all day. Or she may have a partial teaching load that requires her to be the teacher of record for one or more class periods each day. These distinctions influence the number, type, and intensity of duties that a specialist assumes. Figure 13.2 presents a sample listing of duties that could frame the job description of a full-time elementary mathematics specialist working in one school, with full release from classroom teaching.

Key duties and responsibilities:

1. Promote enhanced mathematics instruction and student learning by coaching and working with teachers to develop more effective mathematics teaching practices and by sharing information addressing the way in which students learn mathematics.
2. Support the professional growth of elementary mathematics teachers by strengthening classroom teachers' understanding of mathematics content.
3. Collaborate with the building-level administrators, building-level staff, and district-level personnel, addressing the development and implementation of programs and strategies for the improvement of student achievement in mathematics.
4. Collaborate with grade-level teachers and grade-level teams of teachers to review and further develop mathematics curriculum maps, pacing guides, and instructional plans to enhance the success of their students.
5. Develop and present job-embedded and other ongoing professional development for teachers, using strategies such as demonstration teaching, co-teaching, co-planning, classroom observation, and debriefing.
6. Plan and coordinate the implementation of opportunities for school-based parent participation in mathematics.
7. Collaborate with teachers to create common assessments and to facilitate data interpretation sessions analyzing student data and collaborate with teachers to develop plans and designs for appropriate instruction based on those interpretations.

Fig. 13.2. Roles and responsibilities of an elementary specialist position, as listed in a job description

Organizational Configurations

The elementary mathematics specialist position has many organizational configurations. The specialist may, for example, be—

- fully released from classroom teaching and serving one school;
- fully released from classroom teaching but serving more than one school;
- serving as a classroom teacher for half the day and as the school's mathematics specialist for the other half of the day; or
- serving as the district's mathematics coordinator for half the day and as a particular school's elementary mathematics specialist for the other half of the day.

The discussion that follows focuses on the configurations for two groups of specialists: those who are partially released from teaching and serve at one school and those who are fully released from teaching and serve at more than one school.

Partially released from classroom teaching and serving one school

An elementary mathematics specialist may be required to teach one or two classes each day and then serve as the school's elementary mathematics specialist for the remainder of the day. To understand what a typical day might be for a partially released mathematics specialist, consider the case of Ms. Clark.

Ms. Clark begins her day by teaching two fifth-grade mathematics classes. She teaches these students five days a week and is responsible for all aspects of their mathematics instruction. Although she is responsible for grading papers on her own time, each week she and the fifth-grade mathematics team meet, allowing her to plan lessons for her students and coach the other fifth-grade teachers at the same time. For the remainder of the school day, Ms. Clark works as a building-level mathematics specialist. She generally structures these partial days so that she is working with only one grade level each day. Because she is available to work with teachers as a specialist for only part of each day, her principal has established as her main focus the teachers of those grade levels that participate in the state's high-stakes standardized mathematics achievement tests. This means that Ms. Clark works less frequently with the teachers from kindergarten through grade 2.

Ms. Clark meets with the grade-level mathematics teams, co-teaches lessons, makes classroom observations, coaches individual teachers, and occasionally teaches demonstration lessons. Ms. Clark tries to adjust her work with teachers on the basis of results of district or classroom assessments, observations, and requests from individual teachers or grade-level teams. She sometimes expresses concern because she is limited to working with teachers primarily in the afternoon. This makes it very difficult for her to provide the kind of support that she would like to offer to a teacher who has mathematics instruction scheduled in the morning. Over time, Ms. Clark has worked with her principal and the other teachers to adjust the school's instructional schedule so that she can be in more of the mathematics classes across grades 3–5 each week. Many mathematics classes now meet at times that do not conflict with Ms. Clark's teaching duties.

The partial-release configuration can be challenging for the specialist, since she has teaching responsibilities as well as instructional support and coaching responsibilities. All these responsibilities are demanding and time-consuming. A potential challenge of the split responsibilities is that the mathematics specialist often feels overwhelmed by the demands of her job. A district choosing a partial-release configuration should be aware of the inherent challenges that the elementary mathematics specialist faces when she is both teacher and specialist. These challenges should be given special consideration when the district is establishing the roles and responsibilities of the partial-release configuration. This can be a difficult model to implement.

Fully released from classroom teaching and serving more than one school

Schools districts that fully release elementary mathematics specialists from teaching and assign them to serve in multiple schools must give special attention to scheduling to maximize the instructional support that these specialists are able to provide to the teachers at the schools. In addition, the assigned schools must have common curricular goals. State objectives, local pacing guides, and local curriculum guides assist in achieving this uniformity across schools. The configuration in which a specialist is fully released from teaching and serving at more than one school is typically implemented by districts with a limited number of mathematics specialists and multiple schools in need of mathematics support.

A dearth of specialists may result from constraints on either budgets or human resources. Generally, a school's need for a specialist is determined by standardized test data that do not meet a certain benchmark, a reassignment of teachers resulting in a large number of new teachers at the school, or an established need for schoolwide change spanning instructional practices. When a mathematics specialist is assigned to a school because of such a need, the assignment may be for the entire school year or for one grading period. Then the district reevaluates the need and prioritizes needs across the district once again. When a mathematics specialist serves multiple schools, she may be at a particular school only one week a month or two days a week. Many ways of scheduling visits to multiple schools are possible, and each arrangement has advantages and disadvantages. Some mathematics specialists visit particular schools on the same day each week; others spend an entire week in a given school and then move on to the next school the following week. Consider the case of Ms. Castillo, a specialist fully released from teaching and serving two schools.

Ms. Castillo is an elementary mathematics specialist who serves two schools. She has been in this role for five years. Ms. Castillo begins her morning with her cart, or as she calls it, her "rolling office," which contains all the materials that she will need for the day. Ms. Castillo arrives at her first school at 8:30 in the morning. She has a small office area where she parks her cart and gathers the materials she will need for her first visit. Today she is working with Ms. Simpson, a first-year teacher who teaches mathematics to all the third graders in the school.

The previous week, Ms. Castillo and Ms. Simpson planned this week's lessons. Today's lesson involves the use of pattern blocks and partitioning shapes into parts with equal area. Ms. Simpson does not have a high degree of comfort with manipulatives in her instruction. As a coach, Ms. Castillo first targets Ms. Simpson's comfort level. Ms. Castillo teaches the first class of the day, incorporating use of the pattern blocks as she and Ms. Simpson discussed in co-planning the lesson.

Ms. Castillo has provided Ms. Simpson with a "look for" sheet to focus her observations of the lesson as taught by the specialist. Using the sheet helps Ms. Simpson to get a sense of the strategies that Ms. Castillo is drawing on to incorporate and manage the use of pattern blocks in the lesson. Working with the sheet also helps Ms. Simpson in noting how Ms. Castillo uses questioning to draw the children's attention to the areas of differing pattern block configurations.

When the second class of the day arrives, Ms. Castillo and Ms. Simpson co-teach the lesson. This provides Ms. Simpson with the opportunity to teach with the support of the mathematics specialist. The third class of the day gives Ms. Simpson her chance to teach the lesson by herself. Ms. Castillo observes and takes notes so she will be able to provide constructive feedback afterward to Ms. Simpson. Before leaving the building that morning, Ms. Castillo also meets briefly with the principal and mentions that she worked with Ms. Simpson that morning. During the meeting, the principal tells Ms. Castillo that she would like her to begin working with the teachers in fifth grade over the next couple of weeks.

At 1:30 in the afternoon, Ms. Castillo arrives at her second school. In this school, all teachers teach all subjects. This requires a little more planning on Ms. Castillo's part. She is working with the fourth-grade team on lesson planning. She meets with the team during their shared team-planning period. Ms. Castillo leads the planning session by helping the teachers clarify the expectations of the content objectives for fraction equivalence and for comparing fractions, as listed for the upcoming unit in the district's planning guide. They begin by talking about what students should know and be able to demonstrate when they have mastered these content standards, as well as what prior knowledge the students bring to the lesson. All team members provide input during the planning session, decide which components will be mandatory in all classes, and suggest various approaches. It will be up to the teachers to take the information from the planning session and create their own lesson plans.

After the planning meeting concludes, Ms. Castillo has a monthly session scheduled with the fifth-grade teachers at which they are going to share their students' work on some jointly planned and assigned mathematics problems addressing the concept of volume. Ms. Castillo has scheduled this session during the teachers' common planning period. This is how she typically works with the fifth-grade teachers because she cannot meet with every teacher individually during the school day and because there are so many after-school scheduling conflicts. She and the fifth-grade teachers agreed that they would meet monthly, with the teachers trying approaches and reflecting on what happened in the interim. In this way, Ms. Castillo hopes to provide some sustained professional development for the fifth-grade teachers.

Ms. Castillo ends her day in an office that she shares with two resource teachers in this school. This is her opportunity to get organized for the next day, when she will reverse the order of her visits to the two schools. She alternates morning and afternoon visits to maximize her contact with and support for teachers in each school.

Like Ms. Castillo, a specialist who is assigned to more than one school may find that his job assignments in each school vary, reflecting the differing expectations of building-level administrators from school to school. When a district has a coherent vision for mathematics, these kinds of differences in expectations are a less significant issue for a specialist who is shared across schools. Another challenge may arise if one school has instructional materials and resources that another school does not have. This difference may occur if schools purchase their own materials. Sometimes the mathematics specialist may need materials that are not available in a school, but the district office has them available for loan. If so, the specialist may have to sign them out, pack them into his car, and bring them with him to the school that does not have them.

The mathematics specialist may be assigned to work with an individual teacher or a few teachers individually on her scheduled day in a school. The specialist may schedule an initial face-to-face planning session with a targeted teacher so that they can co-plan lessons for the upcoming week, as Ms. Castillo did with Ms. Simpson. Their planning may continue through e-mail or by sharing electronic resources as they develop and solidify lesson plans. This arrangement typically occurs when the specialist is assigned to provide weekly lesson plan review and support for particular teachers.

Mathematics specialists may also be asked to work with all teachers at a particular grade level. If the specialist is co-planning with a grade-level team, he should use the same process as with an individual teacher. These planning sessions often involve discussion of the meaning of the mathematics content or curriculum standards. Teachers may be expected to teach co-planned lessons after the specialist has left the school and then to discuss their reflections on those lessons with the specialist when he returns to the building.

Directives from the central district office should ensure that the work of a mathematics specialist in multiple schools has some level of continuity from school to school. Ideally, the specialist should be able to use the same lesson plan format in multiple schools. Additionally, state standards and local learning objectives give focus to mathematics specialists' work. For instance, if standards call for increased emphasis on a particular mathematics process or practice, the specialists across a school district will be working to ensure that teachers in all their assigned schools understand that content, as well as instructional strategies addressing students' development of understanding related to it.

When serving multiple schools, mathematics specialists often provide cross-grade professional development sessions for instructional staff at their assigned schools. These sessions are typically scheduled at a school before or after the instructional day, but they may also occur during the teachers' shared planning period. Another option, though it may involve scheduling challenges, is to use a professional release day to provide a combined professional development session in one school for staff from all the schools served by the specialist.

The mathematics specialist who is fully released from teaching and serves multiple schools has two distinct challenges. First, she must maintain continuity of mathematics content while providing pedagogical support to individual teachers and grade-level teams across multiple schools. To give each teacher realistic expectations—and meet them—requires careful scheduling, frequent communication, and a high level of organization on the part of the specialist. In these settings, it is particularly important for the specialist to have a way of keeping track of scheduled appointments and promises made. She must be up front with teachers about when she is committed to work with another teacher and when she has time in her schedule that is not already committed. Second, when a mathematics specialist works in more than one school, she is subject to the expectations of more than one principal. This may require the specialist to adjust her approach frequently, since the principals may have distinct goals and management styles.

Give priority to developing relationships that will sustain teachers when you cannot be at the school.

When a specialist is not available to a teacher at the hour or on the day she wants her, the teacher may feel that the specialist is not there for her. Relationships are the foundation of any coaching experience. When a mathematics specialist supports multiple schools or serves one school in addition to teaching duties, it is crucial to allot time and energy to developing relationships with the teachers whom she supports.

—Advice from a mathematics specialist

Supporting the Specialist

Defining the role of the elementary mathematics specialist in a job description lays important groundwork that paves the way for a specialist's success. But before the specialist can fully engage in all the work that will lead to success, he must be introduced to the staff, and his role must be explained in a way that promotes his acceptance within a school's culture. This means that district and school administrators need to help a school's administration and instructional staff understand the potential that the mathematics specialist position brings to their school. Although school districts may use different configurations in their assignments of specialists to schools, all those with whom the elementary mathematics specialist works need to have similar expectations about his role.

Launching the elementary mathematics specialist

When a district-level coordinator or principal shares the job description for an elementary mathematics specialist with a school's instructional staff, all staff members have a chance to understand not only the prospective specialist's role, but also the purpose for the specialist's placement in the building. Allowing an opportunity for all staff in a building to learn of the specialist's role can help alleviate future problems, such as questions about the responsibilities assigned to the mathematics specialist. A good time to share the job description is at the beginning of the school year, during the teacher in-service days before the students' first day of school. This allows all teachers to gain an understanding of the specialist's role and to ask questions.

Enlist the principal's help in promoting teacher buy-in.

My principal was very happy to have me in this new position and shared his feelings in a very positive way with the entire staff. As a result, I immediately began to have teachers seeking my help by asking for my input as well as requesting resources. This made it easier for me to establish myself in a position that was completely new to me. My principal's support really opened many doors, and that allowed me to collaborate with teachers.

—Reflections from a mathematics specialist

Teachers radiate the energy of an enthusiastic principal

How teachers perceive and accept a new mathematics specialist initially is highly dependent on a principal's perceived support. When a principal is enthusiastic about this new position and conveys confidence that the specialist will work with the instructional staff in beneficial ways, it can set a tone for trust that may be contagious. As a result of the principal's favorable attitude, teachers are often more accepting and may be more willing to seek out the mathematics specialist for support than they might otherwise be. But if a principal simply attends a district coordinator's presentation to the instructional staff and adds little or nothing when the coordinator concludes his statements about the role of the mathematics specialist, this lukewarm reception can set the tone for restraint or apprehension across the staff. In this case, teachers may take much longer to see that the mathematics specialist is a knowledgeable colleague and partner in their learning, rather than a person who is serving in an evaluative or reporting role.

Use an introduction from the principal as the first step in promoting collaboration.

The mathematics specialist role was new to my district. I was concerned that the teachers would view me either as an evaluator who would report back to administration or as "a reading specialist for mathematics." But my principal and I arrived at a common understanding before the start of school. I was introduced to the staff as an instructional support person, and they were told that they should feel comfortable turning to me with questions. The result of this introduction was that the staff perceived me as their professional equal, and this perception made it easier for them to collaborate with me.

—Reflections from a mathematics specialist

Although a job description defines the role of the specialist and the place of this new position in the district's vision of its mathematics program, the principal's attitude—and specifically, level of enthusiasm—is critical in supporting the successful implementation of this position. At the same time, the configuration determined by the district or school and conveyed in the job description has a significant impact on how the specialist organizes her day and supports teachers.

Leadership Expectations and Negotiating with the Principal

Vickie L. Inge, Carol S. Walsh, and Jeannie Duke

Schools are complex organizations, but if each student enrolled in a school is to be successful, all members of the professional staff must work collaboratively. This means that not only do all members of the professional team have to meet the responsibilities associated with their positions, but also that the purpose of every member's position should be recognized by all other team members. Team members must recognize the principal as the designated instructional leader of the school team; it is the principal who has the responsibility for leading all programs in the school, including mathematics. The other members of the school team must understand that the principal has this role and that her position as leader interacts in specific ways with their positions. But when a mathematics specialist joins the staff, a new position is added to the team. The fact that the school's team members, including the principal, may be unsure of how the mathematics specialist position fits into their established structure is to be expected. New specialists must be self-confident and realize that at the beginning of their tenure, other members of the instructional staff are questioning the new position, not the specialist as a person.

It is natural for teachers to have questions and concerns about the impact of the new position on their roles. A number of questions that might be running through a teacher's mind:

- "What will the new specialist do in the school?"
- "What will the new specialist expect of me?"
- "Who will have authority for the mathematics program?"
- "Will the new specialist be evaluating me?"

These are just a few of the questions that teachers are likely to be asking themselves as the new specialist begins her work with them—and as she begins planning with the principal. This chapter presents ideas for the specialist to consider as she works with the principal to develop a partnership in which she and the principal will share leadership for the school's mathematics program and will plan together how she will support teachers.

Developing Partnerships and Sharing Leadership

In their respective roles, the principal and the specialist have the responsibility to support teachers' instruction so that all students learn mathematics with understanding. Both the principal and the specialist may want to see changes in the mathematics program that lead to increased student learning. However, the specific changes that they envision may be different—as will be the forms of leadership that they will employ to support those changes.

Developing a shared understanding

The new specialist brings his ideas about what mathematics is important for students and what teachers need to do so that students learn that mathematics with understanding. The principal may have different beliefs about what it means to be successful in mathematics and how teachers can help students be successful. Conversations between the principal and the specialist allow them to uncover and discuss any differences in beliefs about teaching and learning mathematics as they explore their perspectives about what changes may be necessary to improve the school's instructional program. Further, these conversations can address what the specialist will do to support the teachers. Negotiations about a vision for the school's mathematics program and the role of the specialist will strengthen the principal-and-specialist partnership. Without these negotiations, problems may arise because the principal and specialist lack a shared understanding about how they will work together.

How well the school team works together depends on how well each of the members understands everyone else's role and the degree of mutual trust and support that exists in the team. A new mathematics specialist needs the principal's support as well as the teachers' trust and respect to carry out her job effectively. When different expectations for the school's mathematics program are overtly conveyed by the principal and the specialist, the teachers will suppose that the principal does not support the specialist, or vice versa, and they will resist working with the specialist. Sometimes, such a discrepancy arises from rushed communication, either by the principal or the specialist, without prior discussion. This is the situation in the vignette about Mr. Thomas, a newly assigned elementary mathematics specialist.

All summer Mr. Thomas was excited about his new role as a mathematics specialist at Dogwood Elementary School, where he would be working with Ted Jones, a principal who had a reputation as a dynamic leader. Mr. Thomas was looking forward to his new role and to the opportunity to provide leadership to help the teachers improve their instruction. He believed that the most challenging part of his job would be working with teachers, so throughout the summer he thought about how he would build his rapport with them. Finally, Mr. Thomas met with Mr. Jones on the first morning of the contracted new school year for teachers.

Mr. Jones provided Mr. Thomas with the teachers' schedules and told him that after the faculty meeting the assistant principal would show him around the building and point out the location of his office. Mr. Jones then let Mr. Thomas know how excited he was to have a mathematics specialist. Because the state test scores at

Dogwood had been lower than the district average for the past two years, he wanted Mr. Thomas to focus on improving the scores. Before Mr. Thomas could ask questions about the school's mathematics program, the assistant principal dropped in and announced that the teachers were gathered in the library for the faculty meeting. The principal quickly introduced Mr. Thomas to the assistant principal and shared with both of them the news that Mr. Thomas would be taking over the data analysis for the mathematics program and would be developing a benchmark-testing program for the school, modeled on the state assessments.

During the faculty meeting, Mr. Jones introduced Mr. Thomas as the new mathematics specialist. He let the teachers know that Mr. Thomas was there to help them and that one of the first things that he was going to do would be to meet with each grade-level team to go over the results of the state mathematics test. Mr. Jones reminded the teachers that the school scores were below the school district's average, and he stressed the urgency of bringing up the scores. He proceeded to say that one of Mr. Thomas's responsibilities would be to create benchmark tests for each grade, compile the data after each test administration, and go over the results of the tests with the teachers and the administrative team.

Mr. Thomas knew that this was not a good way to start building rapport with the teachers. Would they think that his only responsibility was for assessment? How could he help teachers focus on helping students making sense of the mathematics when Mr. Jones wanted to focus only on increasing test scores? Mr. Thomas knew these two goals were closely connected, but he wanted to learn more about the school's mathematics program and more about the students' performance on the state test so that he could discuss his ideas with Mr. Jones—ideas for improving teaching and learning in ways that that he believed could have a significant positive impact on student achievement. He knew that he wanted to have more in-depth conversations with the principal because he would need the support of Mr. Jones, as well as the assistant principal, to succeed in developing trusting relationships with the teachers. Now Mr. Thomas needed to think carefully about his next moves.

Building the Foundation for Working Together

It is important for the principal and specialist to meet during the summer before the school year begins. A meeting before the teachers' return to school could have allowed Mr. Thomas and Mr. Jones to become acquainted with each other's beliefs about mathematics learning and their visions for a school's mathematics program. Together, they could have explored the end-of-year assessments and collaborated to identify ways through which Mr. Thomas could support teachers. They could also have begun to plan how the principal, assistant principal, and Mr. Thomas could work together. A specialist does not need to wait for the principal to initiate a meeting; she may take the lead by contacting the principal's administrative assistant to set up an hour-long appointment.

This initial meeting can be very valuable to the new specialist, who can—

- ask questions about the school's mathematics program;
- learn what the principal sees as the strengths and weaknesses of the program; and
- find out what school initiatives are in place in mathematics and in other areas.

At this meeting, the principal and the specialist can begin to discuss how the specialist will support the teachers. The meeting should end with a plan to come together again after both parties have had time to digest the information gained.

The follow-up meeting can be just as valuable to the specialist as the first meeting. It can provide an opportunity for the specialist to begin negotiating with the principal to clarify—

- how the principal and the specialist will share leadership for the mathematics program at the school;
- how the specialist's role will be fashioned, through joint actions of the principal and the specialist;
- how the teachers will learn of the specialist's role; and
- what structures the principal will put in place to enable the specialist to work effectively with teachers.

As Mr. Thomas learned, meeting during the week before school did not allow the principal and the specialist to have a meaningful and collaborative conversation about these ideas. As a result, they did not have time to discuss why test scores might have been low and what other data might be valuable to examine. They did not consider how the specialist, the principal, and the assistant principal could work together to support teachers. However, for Mr. Thomas, all is not lost, but he does need to schedule a follow-up meeting. For this meeting to be mutually beneficial, the specialist must—

- learn as much as he can about the school's mathematics program;
- carefully plan his questions to ask the principal;
- prepare information he would like to share; and
- support any suggestions he may have with research-based evidence.

Establishing the vision for the school's mathematics program

The work of the specialist has greater impact when the school's staff has a shared vision for the mathematics program. Conversations between the principal and the specialist are a first step in developing the vision. If the school has an assistant principal, then he should also be involved in the conversations. It is important for the principal and specialist to take time to share each other's mathematics philosophies, experiences, and expectations. The specialist must learn about the principal's vision for the mathematics instructional program as a first step toward forming partnerships built on true collaboration with administrators and teachers.

Once the specialist and the principal have a unified, well-understood vision of their mathematics program, they can collaborate to identify expectations for instruction. The specialist plays a crucial role in helping a school realize its vision for mathematics teaching and learning. Everyone knows that the way to increase academic achievement is to have the best people in front of students, but sometimes even the best teachers need some support. That is where the mathematics specialist comes in.

Be open to negotiating productive compromises with the principal.

I have been fortunate as a mathematics specialist to have worked with two principals who were willing to have the crucial, and at times uncomfortable, first conversations. My current principal used to be a reading specialist and has remarked several times that my position is similar, though obviously focusing on mathematics rather than reading. She envisioned me pulling out small groups of students for remediation, whereas I envisioned working alongside the teachers to improve instructional practices. She was willing, however, to observe me working with teachers. After watching me co-teach and plan with teachers during grade-level meetings, she told me, "Yeah, keep doing what you are doing. By working with the teachers you are helping all of the students." Since then she has decided to alter the schedules of our reading specialists to include more co-teaching and modeling during whole-group instruction.

As a compromise, I pull out three small groups of students for thirty minutes each week. To be honest, I love it. The time I spend with these small groups brings back the intrinsic reward of teaching that at times is missing for a specialist. This successful compromise was reached because the principal and I were open, honest, and willing to change in order to help our students.

—Reflections from a mathematics specialist

Preparations before the specialist arrives on the scene

Ideally, the principal sets the stage with the teachers for the specialist's entry into the school. The principal can build anticipation by letting teachers know that someone is coming to the school—someone whose sole purpose is to be a resource for them. If this message does not get out before the arrival of the specialist, as in the case of Dogwood Elementary School, the specialist and principal can collaborate to transmit it to teachers at the beginning of the school year. Teachers want knowledge and support. A specialist knows that teachers want their students to be successful, and she can share the most up-to-date instructional techniques and insights. The principal promotes the mathematics specialist position to the faculty by presenting the specialist as a knowledgeable, "here-to-work-with-you" resource. When a specialist works with this purpose in mind, she can reinforce the promises made by the principal.

Crafting a Strong Partnership with Teachers

It is critical for teachers to know that the specialist is going to be at the school in a support role rather than an evaluative one. Only then can a specialist begin to establish rapport with the teachers. The specialist can work with the principal to plan how he will share the vision for the mathematics program. But if the specialist is introduced to the staff as a working partner in the effort to make the vision a reality, the reception typically will be warmer than if the specialist is presented as a manager. After the principal presents the specialist as a working partner, it is then up to the specialist and the principal to nurture instructional partnerships with teachers through coaching and co-teaching experiences, faculty meetings, team meetings, and committee meetings.

Highlight the fact that a mathematics specialist is a resource for teachers.

Schools have been increasingly successful at getting resources and services for students, but what about resources and services for teachers? What if, instead of focusing on remediating students after they do not "get" something, schools actually added to the staff a mathematics specialist who can teach teachers how to make learning more exciting, engaging, and rigorous?

—Advice from an elementary school principal

Another way in which a principal can help facilitate his partnership with the specialist is to collaborate with her in identifying a few teachers for the specialist to work with intensely during the school year. Co-teaching or coaching a teacher over a semester or the full school year increases the intensity of the collaboration. Having those sustained relationships helps the staff understand the nature of the specialist's coaching or co-teaching role.

There are several ways to choose the collaborating teachers. Some teachers, through their own admission, are weaker in the area of mathematics instruction and welcome the assistance and support of a mathematics specialist. Another way to cultivate partnerships is to identify a strong teacher for collaboration. When a successful teacher collaborates with the specialist in a long-term coaching or co-teaching relationship, teachers understand that the specialist is not there to "fix" teachers but to support and work with them. In addition, working alongside strong teachers enables the specialist to develop additional building-level leadership in mathematics.

The specialist as a supporter, not an evaluator

In her conversations with the principal, it is important that the specialist clarify her role. Her role is to offer support and does not include evaluating teachers, even though her work can lend itself naturally to doing that. The teachers must understand from the beginning that they will not be judged by how much help they need or request, either by the principal or the specialist. This point is important, because teachers already feel the pressure of being evaluated. The pressure to improve student performance is ever increasing, with value-added models emerging as the method of evaluation in many states. Teachers need to know that in the mathematics specialist, they have someone working with them in a non-evaluative role to improve instruction.

For example, consider the case of a specialist who urged teachers to step out of their comfort zone and ask their students to find the value of $2/3 + 1/4$ before students ever learned an algorithm for adding fractions with unlike denominators. She found that teachers were willing because they knew she was there to support them and would not judge them if their students could not figure out an answer. The mathematics specialist, when introduced to the faculty in the right way, becomes a soft place where the teacher can fall. Teachers and a specialist can celebrate success or commiserate together, but either way, a teacher is not evaluated, and the teacher has an opportunity to grow.

This important understanding of the specialist's role was missing when Mr. Thomas was first introduced to the teachers at Dogwood Elementary. When the principal makes clear to the teachers that the specialist is not an evaluator but is there to support and collaborate with them, he also begins to establish a sense of mutual respect and understanding that will promote his work.

Establishing the value of the specialist

A culture of professional respect does not grow automatically. The principal can elevate the visibility of the specialist by facilitating opportunities for the specialist to work directly with teachers. Once the specialist has direct access to teachers, he must seize the opportunities orchestrated by the principal and actively earn the teachers' respect. The nonthreatening, supportive presence of the specialist in the school alleviates teachers' apprehensions and increases their interest in having the specialist stay in their school. When teachers begin to see their students having greater success and developing stronger thinking skills, they will seek out the specialist to support them.

Establish and maintain confidentiality, exercise discretion—and avoid gossip.

I have concluded that principals and teachers like to talk about teachers and principals. I have a rule. I simply do not engage in, nor will I listen to, these conversations. Many times, the teachers start to talk to me about others on staff and then say, "Oh yeah, your rule, never mind." They understand that I cannot be included in these discussions or I lose trust.

—Reflections from a mathematics specialist

Negotiating How the Specialist Will Work with Teachers

It is critical that a specialist be highly visible and accessible. A mathematics specialist who is tucked away in a remote office is not positioned for success. The specialist should negotiate for an office or workspace in a centrally located area. The specialist should also collaborate with the principal to set an expectation for regularly scheduled grade-level planning meetings, long- and short-term co-teaching, and coaching. A specialist who asks to present an instructional strategy at each monthly faculty meeting, facilitate vertical team meetings, or participate with the principal at grade-level team meetings communicates that she is in a unique position to share knowledge with the teachers and the staff.

Be accessible.

One of the most special things about my mathematics specialist is her ability to offer help to teachers in a nonthreatening way that gets them excited about her being in their rooms. They see her in the hallway, find her in a classroom, or send her a "Help!" e-mail, and she is there. That delivery of service and willingness to do whatever it takes to help a teacher makes her a huge success at our school!

—Reflections from an elementary school principal

Managing confidentiality

The specialist has the greatest impact on teachers when they see him as a partner and a teammate. During conversations with the principal, the specialist must negotiate how he will communicate with the principal. They should reach an agreement on what kinds of information the specialist will communicate from teachers as well as what other sorts of information he will treat as confidential and not transmit to the principal. When teachers think that the specialist is sharing everything they say with the principal, the consequences can be detrimental to the specialist's effectiveness. If teachers believe the specialist is reporting what is going on in their classrooms to the principal, doors that were once open may close. Refusing the specialist entrance into classrooms puts a stop to any exchange of ideas between the teacher and the specialist, ultimately affecting the progress of student learning. The trusting relationship that the specialist works to build and maintain with teachers every day can be broken, and once broken, can be very difficult to repair. Teachers who feel that their trust has been betrayed may grow reluctant to ask for help. When teachers do not seek help or communicate, a specialist sometimes develops a false sense that everything is fine in their classrooms, when his help is actually needed.

Be known as a supporter—not an evaluator or a talebearer.

Having regularly scheduled weekly meetings with my principal is an important part of my routine. This time allows me to share positive events I have seen in the school as well as express any concerns I may have. We have a mutual agreement that we don't use names unless the well-being of a student or the learning process is being affected. This anonymity is also important in communication with other teachers. I have found myself in the position of being asked by other teachers what is happening in another classroom and have nicely avoided answering them. Being seen as a supporter and not an evaluator is important so teachers continue to welcome me into their classrooms.

—Reflections from a mathematics specialist

Occasions do arise, however, when the specialist would like to break the pact of confidentiality because he wants to share something from the classroom that will provide an opportunity for the principal to expand her knowledge of mathematics and her understanding of the various ways in which children can think about a problem. For example, one teacher had given her first-grade students the following problem:

> **Mario took 43 steps to reach the door, and Sara took 39 steps to reach the door. How many more steps did Mario take than Sara?**

The students had used different ways to think about the problem as they worked with the number line, alternative algorithms, and pictorial representations to find their solutions. Some students had added, and some had subtracted. The specialist asked the teacher for permission to share this classroom work with the principal. Checking beforehand is one way to communicate classroom specifics to the principal without violating a teacher's trust.

Partnering with the principal to address a problem

The mathematics specialist moves in and out of many classrooms during the school year. This connection with the teachers and the students allows her to develop a "big picture" of the general teaching philosophy within the school as well as the instructional methods employed by teachers. If a time comes when the specialist believes that the principal should be aware of something about the mathematics program at the school, the specialist must tread lightly. The specialist can arrange a private meeting with the principal to talk in general terms about her concern, carefully avoiding any negative comments about specific teachers. The tone of this meeting can be kept positive by keeping the focus on the mathematics program and the students and by introducing constructive ideas to improve instruction.

Above all, a mathematics specialist should remember that it is not his place to report on teachers. Rather, his role is to try to improve what is going on in the mathematics program, with the aim of improving student learning. If the principal is making routine classroom observations throughout the year, he may already be aware of issues that the specialist is seeing. However, some principals may not be knowledgeable about research-based best practices for teaching mathematics, or they may not be aware of what these practices look like when they are observing students in the classroom. The specialist can increase the principal's awareness about what to look for during observations or walk-throughs by sharing and discussing articles (Nelson and Sassi [2006] offer useful information) or by exploring the indicators in a classroom observation instrument (Kanold, Briars, and Fennell [2012] can be helpful).

Depending on interest, time, and availability, the specialist can select a commercial video of mathematics instruction to view with the principal (see, for example, classroom videos from *Lenses on Learning Supervision: Focusing on Mathematical Thinking* [Grant et al. 2005] and *Inside Mathematics* [Noyce Foundation; http://www.insidemathematics.org]; it is best not to use a video of teachers in the school). The specialist can identify one or two aspects to focus on as she and the principal watch the video together. This experience enables the two of them to have a rich discussion, increasing the principal's understanding about some of the things that he should see students and teachers doing in an effective mathematics classroom.

The specialist as a member of the teaching team

The specialist must take steps to cement and sustain a trusting relationship with teachers. When a specialist collaborates with the principal to establish regularly scheduled grade-level meetings that focus on mathematics and then conducts well-planned meetings addressing upcoming mathematics lessons or student work, the teachers will know that the specialist is a team member who values their time and needs.

In addition, from the initial teacher workdays at the beginning of the school year until the last teacher-contract day, the specialist can align herself with the instructional staff, conveying to them in many ways that she is part of their team. During faculty meetings, she should sit with the grade-level teachers rather than with other specialists or administrators. In settings such as school social events, she should spend time with the teachers while limiting time with the principal. She should participate in a school's team-building activities, such as grade-level breakfasts and lunches, and also volunteer to help as part of the teaching team in schoolwide activities, such as field day, carnivals, and assemblies. Above all, the specialist must realize that she is in the teacher's classroom and be respectful of that. The specialist's job is to support the teachers in their jobs as they provide valuable mathematics instruction. By supporting the teachers, the specialist is supporting the students, the principal, and the entire school.

Convey the message that classroom observations are learning opportunities, not evaluations.

In my school, I always enter a classroom with only the resources, materials, and activities needed for the lesson. I avoid taking notes, especially while the grade-level teacher is teaching, to keep from being seen as an evaluator. Anything that requires me to make a note during the lesson I show to the teacher during our debriefing meetings about the lesson. Debriefing meetings provide time with the teacher to discuss, not evaluate, what worked in the lesson, what didn't work in the lesson, and how to adapt the lesson to make it better. These discussions are between the classroom teacher and me, and I do not discuss them with the administrative staff.

—Reflections from a mathematics specialist

Providing Leadership on Current Policies and Educational Practices

An important part of a specialist's job is to stay up to date on state and local mathematics education policies as well as research. Keeping the principal as well as the teachers current on policies and research in mathematics education is essential for good instruction.

State and local education policies

State and local education policies and procedures directly affect how, what, and when for mathematics instruction in public schools. Time away from school to attend local and state mathematics meetings is often difficult for the specialist to arrange; however, these meetings can provide her with vital information that she can then share with the teachers and administrators in her building. At these meetings, the mathematics specialist has the opportunity to ask questions that directly affect her school. After the meeting, the specialist and principal should meet to discuss the information and identify possible implications for the school's mathematics program. In particular, teachers and administrators need to know of any upcoming changes in state standards and assessments.

Stay up to date to help teachers and administrators make transitions to new mathematics standards.

When my state revised its mathematics standards and student assessments, I attended many of the sessions addressing updates in mathematics, particularly in the fall of the school year. I was sent to these informational meetings since my attendance did not disrupt instruction or require hiring a substitute teacher. When I returned to school, my principal made sure I had time to convey the new information and to discuss it with the teachers during faculty, vertical-alignment, and grade-level meetings. The teachers trusted that I would provide them with the correct and most up-to-date information that they needed to provide appropriate mathematics instruction to their students. And if I didn't know the answers to their questions, I made sure I found them, contacting our state mathematics coordinator, if necessary.

—Reflections from a mathematics specialist

Additionally, the specialist should set aside time once a week to review his state's department of education website. This website will provide updated information regarding educational policies and procedures particular to mathematics.

Research in mathematics education practices

Along with staying up to date on educational policies, a specialist should continue to keep abreast of new research in the area of mathematics education. Specialists can develop their knowledge by reading professional journals and attending conferences. In doing so, a specialist will learn about new research, deepening her understanding of how students learn, and broadening her understanding of effective instructional practices. When the principal and specialist collaborate to make decisions about new curriculum materials or discuss ways to improve the school's mathematics program, the specialist can then share information in the research literature. Knowing what has been tried, what worked, and what didn't work also helps guide a specialist's interaction with teachers.

Developing Leadership Skills to Function in the Organization

The culture of a school and a school district determine how a specialist can function. Developing an awareness of the school's and district's organizational culture is important for a new mathematics specialist. This awareness becomes even more important if the specialist is working with both the building principal and a central office leader, such as a mathematics supervisor. An organization's culture is defined by norms that are recognized or presumed, and these will determine whom the specialist should take his questions to first, who is responsible for evaluating the specialist, and who provides materials and resources for the specialist. If the specialist works with both a principal and a mathematics supervisor, he will at times find that he must negotiate with the principal to meet the central office directives about the mathematics program while simultaneously addressing the principal's vision for what he is to do in the school building. When the specialist is in the school building, he is a member of that school's team and has responsibility to assist the principal in supporting his efforts to improve mathematics instruction. As Mr. Thomas realized in the vignette, a specialist must develop skills to negotiate with a principal so that they can form an effective partnership for change.

Preparing for a meeting with the principal

The specialist must always be well prepared for meetings. When the specialist requests a meeting with the principal, she should specify its purpose and the expected duration. By asking to meet for no more than one hour during the summer and thirty minutes during the school year, she demonstrates consideration for the principal's busy schedule. Developing a plan for the meeting in advance, with a goal that can reasonably be accomplished in the requested time, also shows her commitment to making good use of the principal's time—and her own.

When the principal requests a meeting, the specialist should find out the topic before the meeting. The specialist should arrive at the meeting on time and be prepared to speak knowledgeably, providing facts and explicit data.

In meetings with the principal, the specialist can identify one or two key points to emphasize and be prepared to discuss questions that the principal may raise about these key points. Most important, when the principal speaks, the specialist must be a nonjudgmental listener. The first goal is to understand the principal's point of view, and then, after collaborative examination of data and facts based on best-practice research, the next goal is to reach a decision about how the specialist can support the teachers and how the principal can support the specialist. Principals appreciate the efforts of a specialist to stay on topic during a meeting and to end it at the agreed-on time. If more time is needed to resolve an issue, the specialist can request another meeting.

Effective negotiating

Effective negotiation requires a new specialist to be knowledgeable not only about mathematics content and instruction, but also about the school and its community, its prior and current mathematics achievement data, and its mathematics program. This information, coupled with a specialist's knowledge of effective mathematics teaching, informs his conversation with the principal. For example, during a follow-up conversation with his principal, Mr. Thomas could negotiate how he will work with teachers, thus responding to the principal's desire to improve test scores while conveying his ideas about teaching mathematics for understanding.

Negotiation may seem a bold expectation for a new specialist trying to build a relationship with a principal whom she does not know or may have known in a different role. But negotiation is critical to establishing a partnership that can have a positive impact on student learning. If the specialist is to work successfully, she and her principal must come to an understanding about how they will share leadership for the mathematics program and how they will identify expectations for teaching and learning. At the same time, when collaborating with the principal, the specialist can learn a great deal about ways to enhance her own leadership skills and to approach the teachers in the school.

References

Grant, Catherine M., Barbara S. Nelson, Ellen Davidson, Annette Sassi, Amy S. Weinberg, and Jessica Bleiman. *Lenses on Learning Supervision: Focusing on Mathematical Thinking.* Parsippany, N.J.: Pearson Learning, 2005.

Kanold, Timothy D., Diane J. Briars, and Francis (Skip) Fennell. *What Principals Need to Know about Teaching and Learning Mathematics.* Bloomington, Ind.: Solution Tree Press, 2012.

Nelson, Barbara S., and Annette Sassi. "What to Look for in Your Mathematics Classrooms." *Principal Magazine* 11 (November/December 2006): 46–49.

Induction to a New Position Involves Transitions

Aimee J. Ellington and William E. Haver

It is important for an experienced elementary teacher to realize that taking on the role of a mathematics specialist represents a major change on a personal level. The newly minted mathematics specialist continues to report to work in an elementary school building, and although this may or may not be the same school where the specialist was a classroom teacher, otherwise everything is different. Recognizing that this change often will result in dissonance and stress is the first step in meeting this challenge.

Changes on Many Levels

The changes that novice mathematics specialists experience are not surprising, but nonetheless they are real and significant. Moreover, they occur in many aspects of the job.

From expert to novice

Most new mathematics specialists are expert, accomplished teachers. They would not have been selected to prepare for this new role if they were not. Yet, by the very fact that they have accepted their new position, they are now novices. They probably have performed many aspects of their new job: supporting other teachers, studying curricular materials, and communicating with principals. But they are brand-new at performing the overall duties of the position and are beginning as novices.

This change from expert to novice can be very disconcerting on a personal level. For example, a mathematics specialist who has taught in the fourth and fifth grades might have little experience with the difficulties that first graders experience in recognizing that the numbers 11 to 19 are composed of a ten and some ones. Likewise, a specialist with experience in the early grades may not have worked directly with children who are perplexed by the notion that any multiple of a/b is a multiple of $1/b$, much less connecting this insight to understanding what it might mean to multiply a fraction by a whole number. The mathematics specialist is typically responsible for the mathematics program at all grade levels in her school building, so developing an understanding of the entire curriculum is important. But doing so can cause the specialist to feel uneasy.

From children to adults

Although classroom teachers often deal with adults (for example, peers, supervisors, and parents), children are the primary and direct focus of their work. Indeed, it is not rare to hear new specialists speak of feeling sad or guilty because they no longer have the responsibility or privilege of working with a classroom of children. This personal reaction is most pronounced in their first weeks on the job, when virtually all new specialists report that they miss having their own classrooms of students. This feeling does subside after time passes and the specialist begins to experience the personal rewards of the new position. Although the primary focus of the mathematics specialist's responsibility is to work with the teachers involved in mathematics instruction, the specialist does interact with children. In fact, she works with a large number of children in multiple classrooms. As one first-year specialist reports (Donovan 2011, p. 3), students initially had trouble with her name:

> They hit on calling me Mrs. Math—so that is who I became. In most classrooms, at least with the younger students, I am now Mrs. Math. And I love it! ... My main message is that "Math Rocks—and we use it everywhere" and thus began my connection with the students.

That said, working with teachers remains the main focus of the specialist position. Indeed, while having a relationship with children does provide some emotional support, an effective specialist works with students as a means of supporting the classroom teacher, rather than working directly and primarily with students. This is the case even, though working directly with students, for their own sake, might feel personally more rewarding and comfortable, at least at first.

From telling to encouraging

Mathematics specialists work with adults who are the experts in their own classrooms. This is one reason why using words of encouragement and providing positive examples of how different instructional methods help children learn may be more effective than simply telling teachers what to do. This is especially true for new specialists working in grade levels that they may have never taught themselves. In a survey of Virginia mathematics specialists (Standley et al. 2011), one respondent gave the following advice:

> Do not tell the teachers the best way to do something: ask them to reflect on the goals of the lesson and the expected student outcomes. Then ask them how the activity will result in those outcomes being achieved. What you know and what you have to offer is individual, and each person has to arrive at an understanding on their own time. You can only be the mirror that provides an honest, sometimes uncomfortable, reflection. The hard part is that it is not about you!

This advice underscores the fact that although a specialist works as a facilitator to support and encourage teachers' efforts to change, he or she cannot, and should not attempt to, control the actions of others. At the same time, a specialist's inability to cause change and, in that sense, to control his or her own agenda, can be very stressful.

From teaching to leading

Classroom teachers use many tools to lead and enable students to grow and to learn. When they do so in their role as the teacher, the children view them as being in a position of authority—as "my teacher"—not that this authority is never challenged. By contrast, the mathematics specialist position does not confer clearly defined authority. Specialists lead teachers in many ways, but telling someone to do something "because I am the mathematics specialist" is not one of the ways.

Use the teacher's behavioral strategies to gain authority in the classroom.

I found that meeting with the teachers to discuss their classroom behavior plans prior to visiting their room and then using their strategies with the students was a successful way to gain authority with the students in their classrooms. It also showed the teachers that I respected them and their classroom environments. It has amazed me how many different techniques teachers use to control their classrooms, from "Give me five" to color-coded chart systems.

—Advice from a mathematics specialist

From Having a Schedule to Working around the Schedules of Others

Even within schools that are tightly administered, teachers have a great deal of autonomy within their own classrooms and can plan their day within certain parameters. Specialists have no autonomy, and although they can plan the details of their day, their schedule frequently changes. It is important for the specialist to be flexible and available to the teachers. For example, one specialist (Race 2007, p. 15) describes what happened as she was starting down her "to do" list one morning:

> Suddenly, a teacher appears at my office door with a puzzled look on her face. She says, "Yesterday, I taught my students the rule that when you divide fractions you just invert the second fraction and multiply, but my students asked why that works and why the answer is larger than the numbers you started with, unlike division of regular numbers." After we work through the concept, drawing pictures and making models, and she goes off to meet her first class, I reflect on what her question tells me about her own mathematical understanding of the concept, the teaching strategies she uses, and her openness to exploring new ideas.

Clearly, responding to this teacher's needs at this particular time was crucial. But it required the specialist to be flexible about her schedule to meet the demands of this teacher's schedule.

Recognize that flexibility is the key to the job.

As I was preparing to go into a fifth-grade classroom, I noticed the teacher had a distressed look on her face. She related how "horribly" her first class had gone when she introduced the visual model for the distributive property. We discussed where she thought things went wrong. She asked if I would mind teaching the lesson to the next class as she observed, to clarify her confusion. Although I wasn't fully prepared to teach the lesson, I did it. The class went well, and we met to discuss it afterwards. It turned out that although she knew how to do the distributive property, she was still uncomfortable with the visual model. The teacher felt that after observing she had a better understanding of how the model worked and was able to identify what confused her when she taught it the first time. If I had not been flexible and willing to teach, the teacher may have experienced more frustration and confusion.

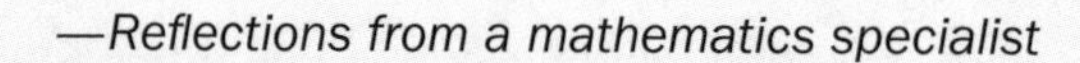
—*Reflections from a mathematics specialist*

Surviving the novice stage

Although mathematics specialists must develop strategies and meet long-term goals, for a novice specialist, the position presents many uncertainties and stresses. Perhaps if the specialist remembers the uncertainties and stresses that he experienced in his first year of classroom teaching, the knowledge of the positive outcomes that emerged from those early teaching experiences will help sustain him through the first year in this new role.

Becoming a Member of the School Community

Being the new person in the building isn't easy. When a teacher arrives at a newly assigned school, she can acclimate to her surroundings gradually by getting to know the other teachers at her grade level first and by having those teachers help her learn the names of the other teachers and introduce her to other personnel in the school. When a new mathematics specialist arrives at a school, where should she turn for help in meeting people and learning the ways of the community that she has joined? How does she get to know her colleagues? How does she ensure that they know she is a team player? And, perhaps most important, how does she help the members of the school community become comfortable with the role that she will play in the school building? The key to a successful beginning in this new job is to spend time building relationships.

Offer to read students a math-related story as a way to gain access to classrooms.

Spending time in the first week or so of school reading a mathematics story to each class at the new school is a way for the mathematics specialist to introduce herself to the students as well as the teachers. The specialist can spend a few minutes talking about mathematics and her role in the school before reading a grade-appropriate mathematics story to the children. This can be a nonthreatening way to gain access into the classrooms at the school.

—Advice from a mathematics specialist

Even as a specialist is making the transition from the role of teacher to the role of specialist in the same school building, he needs to help the classroom teachers and other school personnel acclimate to his different role in the school building.

Recognize the challenges of changing roles from teacher to specialist in the same school building.

One of my transitions was coping with being viewed differently by my colleagues. For ten years I was one of them, dealing with the same stresses and schedules. Starting this year, I had to prove to them that I am not part of the administration, that I do not think that I am "above them," and that I can assist them in teaching mathematics more effectively for their students. Over the last two weeks, my school has given mathematics benchmark exams. One of the fifth-grade teachers received higher scores than she had expected to see from several students. She responded by telling the principal that she couldn't wait to tell me. The principal asked her why, and she said, "Because he is in this with us."

—Reflections from a mathematics specialist

Spend time building relationships

Relationships with classroom and resource teachers are significant in the work of the mathematics specialist. The connections that the specialist is able to build with the other members of the school's instructional team are the foundation for the experiences that take place during the ongoing professional development that the specialist is able to provide. As one practicing mathematics specialist notes, "It is critical to establish trust and confidentiality with each teacher" (Race 2007, p. 17). This is true for resource teachers as well as regular classroom teachers. Special education teachers are responsible for helping identified children understand mathematical concepts. So it is especially important for the mathematics specialist to develop relationships with this group of teachers. Although the specialist may think that she will not be spending much time interacting with the teachers of English language learners or with curriculum and assessment specialists, the mathematics specialist often is asked to conduct professional development for these groups as well as for the teachers in self-contained classrooms. As one practicing specialist recommends, "Build personal relationships with the entire staff, everyone from the administration to the custodial staff and so on. It is important for teachers to see that you are a 'part' of their school and not a separate entity" (Standley et al. 2011).

Spending time during the first year building these relationships provides the foundation for important work that the specialist can do not only during that year in the role of mathematics specialist, but also for many years to come.

Engage in non-mathematical tasks

One way for a mathematics specialist to show that he is a team player and has an interest in the overall function of the school is to volunteer for some of the tasks that are not part of the mathematics program. Teachers will appreciate his willingness to help with the day-to-day operations of the school. It should be noted that in some school districts, mathematics specialists are expected to participate in these kinds of tasks, and this work is not voluntary. The specialist could offer his services for morning or afternoon bus duty or as a car greeter. These tasks allow the specialist to get to know the children, and possibly meet parents, while also giving him an impromptu opportunity to interact with the other teachers who are taking their turn in these activities. Seeing the specialist "out there" and available provides an opportunity for a teacher to ask a question about how to teach a mathematical concept or help a child understand a particular topic. In this environment, some teachers might be more willing to open up about their concerns and questions.

At this point, a word of caution is important about participating in the day-to-day non-mathematics-related tasks of the school. Although this work is a wonderful way for the mathematics specialist to show that she is an integral member of the school's professional team, she must ensure that these tasks do not fill up her day. These kinds of tasks should not replace the important duties that she has with respect to the school's mathematics program. The specialist must strike a delicate balance between using these tasks as opportunities to show teachers that she is a team player with a great deal to offer, on the one hand, and, on the other hand, having these tasks become a large, overwhelming part of her daily schedule. The specialist should carefully consider which activities to take on and how to balance these activities with her regular duties.

Get to know all aspects of the mathematics program

The mathematics specialist needs to be familiar with all aspects of the school's curriculum. If a new specialist previously spent all her time as a classroom teacher in a particular grade before assuming the role of specialist, she will be comfortable with teaching the mathematics content at that grade level, and perhaps the grade levels above and below it, but she may not have a deep understanding of teaching the mathematics content at the other grade levels in her school building.

Pedagogical activities that are included in a mathematics specialist professional development program can help the specialist become familiar with the entire elementary mathematics curriculum. However, the specialist realizes the scope of the curriculum only when her daily work begins. The specialist should make time to familiarize herself with the mathematics and curricular materials that are available in the school building. She should lead grade-level mathematics team meetings where she will hear about how different teachers present mathematical lessons and how the teachers in a grade level share information. She should also spend time observing mathematics instruction at all grade levels. This will allow the specialist to become comfortable with the curriculum, gain familiarity with the instructional styles of different teachers in the school building, and explore ideas about what she can do to support teachers.

Developing a Relationship with the School Principal

The relationship between the mathematics specialist and the school's principal is an important ingredient in the school mathematics program. Indeed, this handbook has two chapters devoted to this relationship. Chapter 14, "Leadership Expectations and Negotiating with the Principal," describes leadership expectations and issues that need to be negotiated between the mathematics specialist and the principal. Chapter 17, "The Principal and the Elementary Mathematics Specialist Work Together," can double as a stand-alone piece for the mathematics specialist and the principal to read and discuss as they consider the importance of a shared vision of good mathematics teaching. As described in that chapter, the collaborative process of creating such a vision takes time. By contrast, the current chapter deals with the reality that in many cases, the school year begins before the newly assigned mathematics specialist and the principal have begun collaborating, let alone developed a shared vision.

Establishing contact prior to the week before school starts

If at all possible, the mathematics specialist and the principal should meet for a planning session sometime in the summer, before the busy week before the start of school. School systems that have established a mathematics specialist program typically have a one- or two-day (or longer) workshop for all principals and specialists. These sessions include discussions of the system's expectations of mathematics specialists and important details about the system's mathematics program.

The initial contact between specialist and principal is best initiated at the system level or through assignments in a preparation program for mathematics specialists. However, if no external decision is made to arrange for such a session, it is important that either the specialist or the principal initiate an introductory session. An important topic to discuss is how the principal will introduce the specialist to the rest of the school community. Ideally, the specialist and the principal could prepare for the session by reading chapter 17 and then devote their time to a discussion of the topics raised in this chapter. Realistically, however, this may not always be feasible.

Introduction of the specialist to the school community

The mathematics specialist should be introduced to the entire school community as early as possible in the week before the start of school. This is particularly important for a first-year specialist and even more important if the principal is new to the school or the school has not had a mathematics specialist in previous years. As outlined in chapter 17, it is important that the principal describe the role of the specialist in enhancing the school's mathematics program and in improving student learning. In addition, the principal should emphasize that the specialist is not an evaluator.

Establishing a plan for regular interaction

Before the start of the school year, in a perfect world, the principal and the specialist would have established—

1. the role of the specialist;
2. the expectations of classroom teachers for interacting with the specialist; and
3. the vision for the school mathematics program.

The reality is that in many situations this will not have occurred. At the very least, however, a schedule can and should be set up for regular meetings between the specialist and the principal to work on these and other issues. They should plan to meet every two weeks, and these meetings should not involve other types of specialists or teachers. For at least half of these meetings—that is, once a month—the pair should choose a topic to discuss in advance. In other words, these meetings should be about more than just the mathematical crisis of the moment in the school building.

Being Invited to a Teacher's Classroom

Most mathematics specialists assume that coaching-related activities will fill a large part of their school day. Chapter 3, "Coaching Individual Teachers," is devoted to this important topic. How does the mathematics specialist, as a new person in the school building, find a teacher with whom to begin coaching-related duties? How can he encourage teachers to allow him to co-plan, model, or co-teach a lesson with them? Chances are good that the principal has in mind particular teachers who could benefit from working with the specialist. Unless the principal is also new to the building, it is very likely that she will already be aware of particular teachers who have mathematics-related areas in which they could improve or particular groups of students who could benefit from different forms of instruction.

However, starting from a list made by the principal creates two problems for the mathematics specialist. First, it may suggest that the specialist's hidden agenda is to serve as an evaluator who will automatically and frequently report to the principal on her interactions with the "teachers on the list." Second, because it is often assumed that the principal would identify only teachers in need of improvement as determined by some administrative evaluation, teachers so identified may be reluctant to work with the mathematics specialist because doing so communicates to the entire professional staff that their teaching has been deemed wanting.

Chapter 17 suggests some responses that a mathematics specialist may offer if her principal expects to identify the teachers with whom the specialist will work. Assuming that the principal will not be identifying all the teachers on whom a mathematics specialist will focus, the specialist can use other approaches to find her way into a teacher's classroom. Some examples are provided below.

Advertise, advertise, advertise

Who could be better at explaining how teachers might find a mathematics specialist helpful as they prepare and present mathematics lessons to students than the specialist herself? No one! A new specialist should make opportunities to sell the values of this important role in the school building—and it doesn't take an advertising agency with glossy posters and commercials to do the job. The following brief vignette illustrates one way of spreading the word.

Ms. Kim is a first-year mathematics specialist in an elementary school in a rural corner of a school district. Her school has never had a mathematics specialist until this year. Ms. Kim has found a unique way to inform teachers of what she has to offer. Each month, she writes three one-page newsletters and places them in the mailboxes of all the teachers in the school building. One newsletter is for the K–2 teachers, another is for third- and fourth-grade teachers, and the last is for the fifth-grade teachers. In this particular building, some fifth-grade students are studying sixth-grade mathematics, so the newsletter to the fifth-grade teachers covers both grade levels. Ms. Kim ensures that even the resource teachers who work with students of different grade levels receive copies of the newsletters. In these newsletters, Ms. Kim outlines ideas for teaching those mathematics topics that are the focus of the school curriculum that month. She "advertises" a mathematics manipulative in one corner of each newsletter and makes direct connections to topics that the manipulative can help children understand.

A newsletter can help teachers become familiar with what the mathematics specialist can offer, but the specialist should not spend an inordinate amount of time developing these kinds of materials. This work must not overshadow more important duties, such as coaching teachers or leading grade-level mathematics meetings.

Consider featuring the "manipulative of the month" in a newsletter for teachers.

Part-whole rational number relationships are an important topic for third graders to grasp. For a newsletter during the month that this topic will be covered in the curriculum, a specialist might feature pattern blocks as the "manipulative of the month." The lesson idea discussed in the newsletter might highlight the importance of part-whole relationships and how pattern blocks can help children make connections between the concrete objects and the abstract idea behind the fraction notation. Establishing one block as the whole allows children to explore the part-whole relationships by making connections between that particular block and the other blocks in the set. For example, if the yellow hexagon is the whole, then the green triangle is one-sixth of the whole, and the red trapezoid is one-half of the whole. Multiple blocks can be considered as a part as well. For example, what is the value of two yellow hexagons, one red trapezoid, and one green triangle if one red trapezoid represents a whole unit? (The story of Ms. Sneider and the Funky Cookie [Ellington and Whitenack 2010] delves deeper into the use of pattern blocks in helping children develop the idea of part-whole relationships.)

—Advice from a mathematics specialist

Start with an interested teacher

Although beginning by coaching those teachers suggested by the principal might appear to be easy, or the path of least resistance, this approach may end up shining a spotlight on particular teachers in an unflattering way. If this approach represents one extreme, the other extreme is the specialist who is newly placed in a school but does not have any guidance about whom to work with or where to start. Because of this lack of direction, he may try to work with every teacher responsible for mathematics instruction in the school building during the first year. However, many practicing specialists (Donovan 2011; Sinclair 2007) who have attempted to visit every mathematics classroom during their first year in a school have noted the challenges associated with this approach. Even if the school community is fairly small, scheduling time with every teacher will be an overwhelming amount of work for any mathematics specialist. At the same time, because visiting every teacher means that the time to work with any one teacher will be limited, the chances are greater that the specialist's visits will be interpreted by teachers as simply an opportunity for him to "check up on them" and to evaluate the teachers' instructional methods. As a result, the visits may not be meaningful learning experiences for anyone.

Many mathematics specialists have found that an approach that yields positive results is to start early in the first school year after placement and select a teacher who is open to having the specialist model or co-teach a lesson. This teacher does not necessarily need to have significant mathematical or instructional weaknesses. Indeed, working with someone who has a solid understanding of mathematics and who has an in-school reputation as a strong mathematics teacher can have benefits both for the teacher and the specialist, while simultaneously communicating the message that the specialist is able to provide collegial, knowledgeable support to other members of the school's instructional staff.

For example, if class time with the specialist is devoted to inquiry-based lessons, the teacher may be surprised at what she learns from the experience. She may also learn something new about what her children are able to do, what they are able to explain, or how they are able to reason unexpectedly with mathematical concepts. In turn, when this teacher—the first to work with the specialist—reports the benefits associated with the sessions, she becomes an advocate for the importance of the work of the specialist. She can spread the word to other teachers in formal and informal ways.

Distribute a "How Can I Help?" form.

I distribute a "How Can I Help?" form with my monthly calendar. Teachers use it to request support on a particular content topic, lesson plan, instructional strategy, resource material, and so on. They also use the form to let me know when they are willing and available to meet with me. It helps me make a plan to collaborate with teachers who are open to the opportunity.

—Advice from a mathematics specialist

Spend Time in All Grades—Even Those without High-Stakes Tests

As all teachers are well aware, the results from high-stakes testing drive much of what happens in the school. This is also true for mathematics specialists. The new specialist will be strongly encouraged by administrators to spend much of her time in the tested grades. While work in these grades is important, the specialist must not neglect the teachers and students in grades at which state standardized tests are not administered. Spending time in these grades will have value too—after all, these students will be tested at some point in the future. They will benefit from the increased effectiveness of the teachers both in their current grade and in future grades, as their learning builds on prior knowledge. A teacher in the primary grades who is interested in working with the new specialist can serve as an entry point for the mathematics specialist to begin working with other teachers, both in assessed grades and in grades that are not assessed.

Organizing the Day, the Month, the Year

The mathematics specialist has a variety of responsibilities, ranging from coaching-related duties, to organizing professional development sessions for different groups of teachers, to playing a significant role in the school's assessment program. Successfully completing tasks related to so many varied aspects of the school's mathematics program requires organization. As one practicing mathematics specialist recommends, "STAY ORGANIZED! Things can get out of hand very quickly because you will be pulled in many different directions" (Standley et al. 2011). Mathematics specialists remain individuals, and so each one has a different organizational routine or system. Adopting one particular approach is not important, but it is necessary for a specialist to have a structure that she is comfortable with and can maintain throughout the year. For example, color coding the calendar may be one method for remembering different duties, with one color for the specialist's daily or weekly meetings with teachers and grade-level groups, another for monthly or quarterly assessment programs, and a third for details about professional development meetings.

A specialist may be able to keep all his scheduling information in an electronic calendar that he can gain access to from a computer or cell phone. Using an electronic calendar may also make it easier to share the calendar with the principal, thus keeping her informed about how he is spending his time and when he may be available for meetings.

One aspect of organization that is often neglected is the need to follow up. With coaching, the follow-up is often called *debriefing*. Because of time constraints, a debriefing session sometimes doesn't take place immediately after a coaching experience, and sometimes, unfortunately, it doesn't take place at all. Chapter 3, "Coaching Individual Teachers," discusses the necessity of the debriefing aspect of coaching. New specialists should take particular care to get into the habit of completing all aspects of the coaching process when working with teachers. Another way of following up is making contact with a teacher after any type of classroom visit. This follow-up could take the form of a short note to the teacher or a brief conversation. Remember to provide positive feedback as well as constructive ideas for improving instructional practice.

Work and Learn as a Member of a Team

The mathematics specialist is a member of the team working to help children develop a solid understanding of mathematical concepts. Although she is a leader of the school's mathematics program along with the principal, she is also one member of a large school-based team in which each member is working toward the same goal. The time spent building relationships with school personnel, beginning a meaningful collaboration with the school principal, and finding entry points for the coaching-related parts of the position will develop the foundation for the first year on the job and beyond. The specialist will not immediately know everything that she needs to know to be successful, and the first year will include change, stress, and dissonance. It is important that the specialist develop a support system. A mathematics specialist must be a willing learner. A great deal of learning will take place in the first year as she moves from the role of expert in her own classroom to novice in a new school building.

References

Donovan, Kathy. "Year 1: Why Am I Here?" *Virginia Mathematics Teacher* 38, no. 1 (2011): 2–3.

Ellington, Aimee J., and Joy W. Whitenack. "Fractions and the Funky Cookie Story." *Teaching Children Mathematics* 16 (May 2010): 532–39.

Race, Kristen. "Beyond the Textbook: Lessons Learned from Two Years as a Mathematics Specialist." *Journal of Mathematics and Science: Collaborative Explorations* 9 (2007): 15–20.

Sinclair, Elizabeth. "The Mathematics Specialist: A Personal View." *Journal of Mathematics and Science: Collaborative Explorations* 9 (2007): 57–60.

Standley, Candace, Carolyn Doyle, Sebrina Davis, Sylvia Haliburton, and Linda Jaeger. *A Survey of Graduates of Virginia's Mathematics Specialist Masters Degree Programs.* Unpublished data, 2011.

Personal and Professional Growth and Development

Reuben W. Farley, Tracy L. Gaither, and Vandivere P. Hodges

Because the demands on a mathematics specialist are many, she can easily be overwhelmed by the day-to-day responsibilities of the job. However, it is critical that a mathematics specialist take time for herself. Maintaining personal and professional growth is crucial to continuing success as a specialist. Meaningful professional learning endeavors might include—

- enhancing her own mathematical understanding as well as her knowledge of teaching and learning mathematics;
- strengthening her leadership skills and ability to work with adult learners;
- extending her willingness to learn from others, thus building a collaborative community of learners;
- increasing her credibility as a strong teacher by continuing to improve her own instructional skills when working with students;
- gaining respect by exemplifying the importance of continuous learning; and
- maintaining her own emotional stability by doing something professionally that she enjoys.

Admittedly, that is quite a list, so how might a specialist find these resources for professional growth?

Recognize the demands of the job while maintaining a balance between personal and professional responsibilities.

After a couple of months on the job, I realized that I had no idea about the responsibility associated with this position. I thought I just needed to love teaching mathematics, but it is a whole lot more. The position of mathematics specialist is huge, and balancing the demands of this job with family and professional growth is so important.

—Advice from a mathematics specialist

Taking Classes and Attending Professional Meetings

A mathematics specialist is responsible for maintaining and expanding her own professional growth while overseeing the professional development of others. A mathematics specialist can gain access to formal professional development through a number of avenues.

Enrolling in college courses

One avenue that is open to mathematics specialists for professional development is enrollment in graduate-level coursework. A specialist might take a course that is focused on an area that he knows quite a bit about but finds particularly interesting or a course that is in an area that he considers a personal or professional need. Depending on the specialist's previous background and experiences, he may want to learn more about working with gifted and talented students, students with special needs, or English language learners. Other areas of interest may include professional or curricular topics such as integrating mathematics and science, writing across the curriculum, leading instructional change, or using new technologies effectively. Content-specific classes can stretch a specialist's mathematical thinking or help him to consider students' understanding of mathematical ideas more deeply. For many years, for example, Mount Holyoke College has offered a summer residential institute (https://www.mtholyoke.edu/cpd/summermathteachers). Many colleges and universities offer classes for teachers on evenings or Saturdays, through summer institutes, or, increasingly, online courses. A specialist might enroll individually in a class, but some courses are also conducive to group enrollments. By enlisting colleagues to complete a course with him, a specialist can create a collaborative learning team. The team will then be in a powerful position to bring new ideas and strategies back to the school or school district.

Attending professional conferences

Conferences sponsored by educational organizations provide professional development opportunities for specialists and teachers. Participating in these can give a specialist a chance to learn from colleagues about the new instructional strategies, materials, assessments, and political changes that are having an impact on mathematics teaching and learning. Attending conferences with school colleagues can build camaraderie, especially if teachers have the opportunity to travel away from home for a few days. As one specialist noted, sharing a hotel room for two nights with three teachers is a bonding experience that can last a lifetime! Without the distractions of home, teachers can meet immediately after sessions or at the end of the day to share and debrief what they learned. This allows the message and the enthusiasm to grow, making the experience much more likely to be shared with other colleagues back at school.

Professional education conferences and workshops range from a few hours on one day to several days. At conferences sponsored by the National Council of Teachers of Mathematics (NCTM) or its Affiliates, specialists and teachers may attend sessions addressing best practices for teaching mathematics while gathering up-to-date information and insights about pressing issues in mathematics education. The timing and locations of these conferences vary. Conferences sponsored by local NCTM Affiliates may be offered once or twice a year on an evening or a Saturday with local speakers, conferences arranged by state Affiliates may be scheduled annually in different in-state locations, and the NCTM regional and national meetings are held annually in locations across the country (go to http://www.nctm.org/meetings).

Another resource for professional growth is the annual conference of the National Council of Supervisors of Mathematics (NCSM), an organization that focuses on pragmatic approaches and research-based insights related to leadership issues in mathematics education (for conference information, go to http://www.mathedleadership.org/events/conferences).

Numerous conferences on coaching provide exceptional learning opportunities for mathematics specialists. Sponsors include the Educational Development Center (Boston, Mass.; http://ltd.edc.org/professional-development#Instructional), the Teachers Development Group (Portland, Ore.; http://www.teachersdg.org/institutes.asp), or the national staff-development organization Learning Forward (Oxford, Ohio; http://www.learningforward.org/learning-opportunities#.USIXtehMH9A).

Other conferences that specialists might find relevant include those offered by ASCD (formerly, the Association for Supervision and Curriculum Development), attended by many principals and school-district administrators (http://www.ascd.org/conferences.aspx). Conferences addressing the effective use of technology are available from the International Society for Technology in Education (go to http://www.iste.org/conferences/iste-conference).

Find good professional organizations to provide support.

I remember sitting in my first mathematics specialist course and wondering what standards the teacher was talking about—"Process Standards," "Principles and Standards," "Content Standards"—all I knew about were the state standards. I kept thinking, "How am I going to share all of this with the teachers in my school when I don't even understand myself?' I didn't understand "NCTM," "NCSM," or any of the other acronyms that came up during that first course. Within the school, the mathematics specialist doesn't have a partner or team to discuss these things with, so finding good professional organizations that support what the mathematics specialist is learning and doing is imperative.

—Advice from a mathematics specialist

Typically, the offices of the department of education within each state offer conferences and workshops. Generally, these sessions address new initiatives spanning curriculum standards, mandatory assessments, and educational policies. These meetings often employ a train-the-trainer model: after attending, the mathematics specialist is expected to present the information that she has learned to her colleagues in her district or region. For example, one state offered a set of workshops at four locations, detailing expectations for mathematical practices in the classroom. At these state-sponsored meetings, grade-band teams developed detailed facilitator's guides that participants took back to their school districts to share at regional workshops. It is not unusual for school districts to bring a team of teacher leaders representing each grade band to participate in these types of state-sponsored workshops, with the expectation that these teams will return to their district and share a very similar program. Elementary mathematics specialists may be called on either to lead or be participants on these teams, so that they may learn for themselves and also acquire information to share.

Participating in online learning opportunities

A variety of online possibilities are available for professional development. Many universities, professional organizations, and state departments of education maintain informative websites posting current research and articles of interest to the mathematics community. In addition, both NCTM and NCSM offer webinars. These online presentations and workshops provide opportunities for both specialists and teachers to participate in a professional development session as it is broadcast live or to record the session and review it when time permits. Further, the mathematics sections in state departments of education frequently provide videos and lesson plans illustrating techniques for teaching concepts that students often find difficult or demonstrating appropriate ways to use new technology in the classroom.

Searching the Internet under "resources for mathematics specialists" will generate an extensive listing of current online sites with the potential to assist a mathematics specialist in locating appropriate research, resources, and networking connections. Helpful sites include those maintained by the Virginia Mathematics and Science Coalition (http://www.vamsc.org), the Elementary Mathematics Specialists & Teacher Leaders Project at McDaniel College (https://sites.google.com/site/emstlonline/home), and the Mathematics and Science Partnership Network (MSPnet; http://hub.mspnet.org).

Accepting a Leadership Role in a Professional Organization

Being part of a professional organization of volunteers who love working with students, teaching mathematics, and sharing their enthusiasm and knowledge with others can be an energizing experience for a specialist. Opportunities for participation are numerous and range from the local to the national level.

Serving at the local level

Boards of directors, typically composed of elected officers and grade-level representatives spanning elementary, middle, and high-school placements, lead NCTM Affiliate groups. In addition, a strong cadre of appointed members usually assumes leadership for various committees. These members take responsibility for everything from newsletter and website development to conference arrangements, programs, and publicity. If a mathematics specialist finds this kind of service rewarding and desires to be increasingly active professionally, his opportunities are numerous—local and state NCTM Affiliates are frequently looking for volunteers. Serving on a committee and completing a small job can lead to positions of greater responsibility and influence.

Join a professional organization to share a common passion.

I joined my local NCTM Affiliate because I wanted to be a part of something where everyone else was as passionate as I was about teaching mathematics. Sharing the joys of teaching with others was fun and energizing. I helped organize the fall and spring conferences. I was in charge of food, decorations, prizes, and presenters for the three years I was on the committee. I made friends with high school and middle school teachers whom I never would have met by just attending conferences. The networking was a nice benefit to being involved, but it was not the main reason that I volunteered. The main reason was to spend time with people who enjoyed mathematics and teaching mathematics to children.

—Advice from a mathematics specialist

Presenting at local conferences

Another way for a specialist to share his leadership skills and grow professionally is by presenting at a local conference. Giving a presentation may seem intimidating at first, but often it can be accomplished by simply varying a professional development session delivered at the school level. Presenting with a colleague, possibly another elementary mathematics specialist or a teacher from the school, can make the task less intimidating and can also help build strong collaborative relationships. A specialist who invites colleagues to co-present sends the message that she admires their work and sees them as strong and valued teacher leaders. This signal can, in turn, help to encourage their leadership at the school. Since local conferences are usually in the evening or on a Saturday, professional leave is not typically required. However, keeping the principal informed is a good idea and will increase his awareness of events in the mathematics community while also validating for him the specialist's extended professional commitment to mathematics education.

Serving at the state level

By moving beyond the local NCTM Affiliates to the state-level groups, the mathematics specialist can find additional ways to grow. Generally, a state NCTM Affiliate has a board of directors with elected members and representatives from each region in the state. In addition, members volunteer to serve on a wide variety of committees, including those responsible for selecting recipients for scholarships, grants, or teacher-of-the-year awards; setting up arrangements, publicity, or the program for the annual conference; producing a newsletter; developing a website; serving as a liaison to NCTM; or making recommendations to the board regarding policy.

Learn through serving in a professional organization.

I agreed to work at a booth selling NCTM materials at the state conference for a few years, and this experience allowed me to learn firsthand about new professional resources. I also gained experience and confidence in promoting new products as I used my creativity to design new promotional materials for the organization.

—Advice from a mathematics specialist

For example, a mathematics specialist agreed to help a colleague and friend when she was elected president of their state's NCTM Affiliate. He began assisting with conference arrangements and performing other duties, and he gradually took on major tasks, working with vendors and arranging conference venues at universities and hotels. Along the way, he made personal contacts that led to invitations to help teach summer courses and write curricular materials. His leadership skills were recognized by the membership, and he now serves as president of the state organization.

The confidence and knowledge that a specialist stands to gain through volunteer professional service can enable her to develop understanding and skills that help in supporting teachers. The enthusiasm and sense of pride gained from this type of service are also likely to generate an even greater commitment to school and district-level work.

Attending and presenting at state conferences

Presenting at the state level often requires an administrator's approval because these conferences frequently overlap with school time. The mathematics specialist should develop a clear rationale for presenting at a state conference, clearly articulating her goals to her principal. Sharing a positive story about the mathematics program in their school is likely to be an aim that the principal will support. If appropriate, the specialist could also invite her administrator to attend the conference, and, even better, persuade him to co-present with her.

Embrace opportunities to present professional development.

If I were speaking to a new mathematics specialist, I would say, "Jump right into the presenter's role." When I first took this position, the mathematics specialists in my county participated in weeklong training on a new textbook series. After that, we each had to plan and then deliver a full day's training for all the teachers in the county at a particular grade level. Not long after that, we had to present at a regional conference in the state. By the spring of that first year, we were all required to present at the state conference. Looking back, I realize that I probably learned a whole lot more than anyone who sat in my sessions! I would say, "Research your topic thoroughly. Be confident in the information you are sharing. Talk to other mathematics specialists and teachers to get ideas on the topic, and then just do it!"

—Advice from a mathematics specialist

Serving at the national level

Giving a presentation at the national level may seem daunting. But since mathematics specialists gradually gain experience by providing multiple professional development sessions at their schools, and perhaps at local and or state meetings, a national experience might not feel very different. Generally, the goal is still to share information about a project, program, or strategy that a school has found successful. Applications are submitted up to a year in advance. It is important to bear in mind that a presentation that engages the audience opens the door to conversation, and the knowledge that participants gain from a conference session comes from the group attending the session—not just from the person presenting the session. (Chapter 5, "Supporting Groups of Teachers across Grades," offers additional suggestions on planning professional development.)

If possible, the specialist making his first foray at the national level should present with a team of colleagues, after securing the approval of his principal. Travel expenses will need to be worked out well in advance, in accordance with school district procedures. Professional groups for teachers generally cannot afford to pay presenters, so the reward is in the networking that occurs, the confidence that the mathematics specialist gains as he builds leadership skills, and the satisfaction that he derives from knowing that he has made a contribution to the greater mathematics education community.

Presenting outside the mathematics community

In addition to sharing within the mathematics community, a mathematics specialist should consider presenting to groups who are not as familiar with her work or the work of elementary mathematics specialists in general. One possibility might be to present a session at an elementary reading conference. These conferences are generally very popular, so presenting a session that ties mathematics instruction to reading instruction can be a powerful way to reach elementary teachers who feel more comfortable teaching reading than mathematics.

Another group that a specialist might consider is a professional organization of elementary principals. A specialist could share information about her role or share information about a program that has helped raise student achievement in her school. Principals are the instructional leaders in their school, and programs must have their support to be truly effective. The specialist should be sure to include references to data in this work and, if possible, present with her principal.

Serving the state department of education

An experienced mathematics specialist who has facilitated effective professional development within his building and at the district level may be asked by coordinators in his state's department of education to help plan and present at statewide professional workshops. These may, for example, be related to implementation of the Common Core State Standards for Mathematics (National Governors Association Center for Best Practices and Council of Chief State School Officers 2010) or new assessment strategies. Working on a state team allows the specialist to gain a broader perspective about the interpretation and implication of policies and initiatives. The audiences may also differ from the colleagues in the school with whom a specialist has developed a sense of community and trust. Just as specialists and teachers differentiate instruction for students, they must adjust presentations and facilitations to fit the needs and requirements of an audience. Careful planning and thoughtful listening to participant responses and questions are critical. These experiences will help build a specialist's leadership skills and foster a better understanding of the needs of others in the profession.

Creating and Leading a New Mathematics Specialist Organization

Creating a mathematics specialist organization is another way for a specialist to take on a leadership role. This very rewarding possibility can offer the specialist the opportunity to network with other mathematics specialists from other counties and school districts and to collaborate with people who have similar interests and passions. For example, mathematics specialists in Virginia are in the planning stages of creating an organization specifically designed to support networking, provide relevant professional development, afford access to resources, and address the many needs of mathematics specialists. A project such as this needs a leader to set the tone and stay focused on the goals. The organization under development in Virginia is intended to be a vehicle for establishing mathematics conferences that provide professional development and support for the role of mathematics specialists. The ultimate goal is to provide a way for the mathematics specialists across Virginia to stay connected and to help sustain them in their work.

The benefits of taking part in a project such as this may include establishing relationships, building trust, and fostering communication. By her participation, a specialist can improve her skills in communication, organization, and planning. There is never a dull moment for the specialist in search of opportunities for growth and leadership.

Teaching Roles

Most mathematics specialists began their professional career as classroom teachers, and teaching remains the core of their positions as specialists. The work of a specialist offers many opportunities to teach.

Working with students

In the transition from classroom teacher to elementary mathematics specialist, one of the first things that a mathematics specialist misses is the emotional reinforcement that comes from having his own group of students. Teaching teachers is just not the same as teaching students. Thoughtful adults may offer praise for a job well done or say thank you for helpful resources, but there is nothing like a child's hug. One way for a specialist to ensure that she will not miss student feedback is to select a class to work with on a regular, if not a daily, basis. Working collaboratively with a strong classroom teacher to provide mathematics instruction for her class gives the mathematics specialist not only positive emotional reinforcement, but also a secure and comfortable setting in which to try new strategies and to use new materials and resources.

The collaboration model has the advantage of sending the message that the specialist works with all teachers, not just those who may be struggling. Another possibility is for the mathematics specialist to teach a class assigned to him alone, although this model may take even more time away from his direct work with teachers. However, in either of these cases, seeing the mathematics specialist as a teacher proves that he understands and can relate to the everyday challenges and pressures of a classroom teacher. He can "walk the walk and talk the talk." The trick is to be sure that working regularly with one teacher and his classroom of students, or serving as the mathematics teacher for a single group of students, does not detract from a specialist's time in working with the other teachers in the school. Clear communication with the principal and the teachers about the roles and responsibilities of the specialist can help him maintain a balance between working with students and performing his other duties. (Chapter 14, "Leadership Expectations and Negotiating with the Principal," and chapter 17, "The Principal and the Elementary Mathematics Specialist Work Together," provide more information about working with the principal to clarify roles and responsibilities.)

Another possibility that the specialist might consider is varying the grade level that she collaboratively teaches from one year to another, sending the dual message that all grade levels are equally important and that the specialist is comfortable working with any grade.

Working with teachers in their schools

The mathematics specialist is first and foremost a teacher of teachers—planning, teaching, and debriefing with teachers individually or in groups—with the goal of fostering teachers' improved practice. Other chapters explain these roles in detail; suffice it to say here that the structure of this work should provide rewards as a mathematics specialist notes each teacher's successes. Taking time to reflect on this work and to appreciate each teacher's accomplishments is an important component of a specialist's professional and personal growth. Working one-on-one with a teacher allows a mathematics specialist to focus her work on that specific teacher's needs. Grade-level teams and even vertical teams within a building offer an opportunity to build a collaborative learning community.

Additionally, a mathematics specialist may be called on to work across the district with teachers from a particular grade level. The challenges of facilitating these conversations can be great because the specialist usually does not know these participants well. Nevertheless, this work can be quite rewarding, since the specialist has a chance to build a common understanding across all the schools in the district.

Working with teachers beyond the school setting

At times, opportunities arise for a mathematics specialist to be part of a teaching team at a university or community college. These can be exciting experiences, allowing the specialist to think more deeply about mathematics, mathematics instruction, and leadership styles. Teaching with a team of professionals, university mathematicians, mathematics educators, and school-district supervisors can broaden the mathematics specialist's thinking and highlight the important work that he does. He should not hesitate to put himself forward, letting university faculty members know that he is interested in co-teaching courses. Though teaching at the college level can be demanding, the rewards can be great.

Teaching "specialists in training"

Opportunities may present themselves to specialists to team-teach courses for future cohorts of specialists. Sometimes funding is available to support multiple instructors in this kind of preparation program, and their experiences of teaching in specialist preparation courses have proven valuable. Courses in such a program might focus on pedagogical content, addressing mathematics teaching and learning, and educational leadership. By teaming with mathematicians and mathematics educators in the planning and delivery of these courses, specialists deepen their understanding while gaining valuable insights. Although these opportunities are not universally available, they are likely to become more plentiful as the mathematics specialist movement expands and grows.

Taking Time for One's Self

For a successful mathematics specialist to stay successful, she must find ways to take care of herself both personally and professionally. Teachers who strive to be mathematics specialists are by nature extremely committed and passionate about teaching mathematics in ways that will help all students learn. The work of the specialist can be exhausting. Taking classes can help prospective and practicing specialists gain knowledge, and involvement in professional organizations—whether through attending conferences, presenting at conferences, or serving on a committee—can provide camaraderie and leadership opportunities. Teaching teachers allows specialists to see others grow as the result of their work. These are significant opportunities for professional growth and can offer emotional satisfaction. But to serve others well, each specialist must remember to take time for self-reflection, relaxation, and enjoyment of family and friends. Doing so is not selfish.

Reference

National Governors Association Center for Best Practices and Council of Chief State School Officers (NGA Center and CCSSO). *Common Core State Standards for Mathematics. Common Core State Standards (College- and Career-Readiness Standards and K–12 Standards in English Language Arts and Math).* Washington, D.C.: NGA Center and CCSSO, 2010. http://www.corestandards.org.

The Principal and the Elementary Mathematics Specialist Work Together

Vickie L. Inge, Debbie Arco, and Duffie Jones

An exciting opportunity emerges for the school's mathematics program when a school acquires a mathematics specialist: a principal and a mathematics specialist, by working together, create a powerful leadership team! It is through the specialist that teachers, students, principals, parents, and the community gain a resource with mathematical expertise. The primary responsibility of a mathematics specialist is to "ensure that all students receive high-quality mathematics instruction from teachers with a deep understanding of mathematics content and pedagogy" (Kanold, Briars, and Fennell 2012, p. 79). But it is difficult for a specialist to meet this responsibility unless he and his principal engage in a series of planning sessions before the school year begins. As a team, they need to set the goals for mathematics instruction for the coming year, clarify the roles and responsibilities that the specialist will assume, and plan how the specialist will support teachers. These meetings set the stage for the specialist and the principal to work together.

This chapter provides information for the principal and the mathematics specialist to discuss before the school year begins. This conversation will naturally lead them to think about their school and to plan how they can share the leadership of the mathematics program in a way that will improve teachers' instructional practices and ultimately enhance student learning. The authors have assumed that the school has just one principal. However, if a school has an assistant principal, the principal is encouraged to include him in these discussions as well, to ensure a clear understanding among all three leaders about how they will work together, as well as how the specialist will interact with the teachers.

Sharing a Common Vision

With a mathematics specialist on staff, the principal no longer is the sole building leader responsible for working directly with teachers to develop their mathematics content knowledge and advance their

This chapter can also serve as a freestanding piece for specialists and principals to read together soon after a specialist is assigned to a school. The information provided can be particularly useful to specialists who are new to the position and to principals who have never before had a specialist assigned to their school. The piece is also available in electronic form at nctm.org/more4u, where readers can print it out for personal and professional use.

instructional abilities. Now he shares that charge with the specialist. However, having a mathematics specialist does not diminish the role of the principal. The principal is still the instructional leader for the school. But the specialist brings additional strengths to the school to assist in the leadership of the mathematics program. When the principal and the specialist begin planning, their first discussion should be about a vision for the school's mathematics program. By starting the school year with a common vision and a shared understanding of what achieving it will require, the principal and the specialist are determining the direction that the school will take as they make decisions about the mathematics program. This vision will be important throughout the school year, shaping discussions with teachers, parents, and the community. It will embody the purpose of the mathematics program, guide decisions about instruction, and serve as the foundation for the approaches that the specialist will use to support teachers.

Goals for the school's mathematics program

Whether the specialist is assigned by the district office or selected by the principal, and whether the specialist was a teacher in the school where she is now placed or transferred from another school, the principal and the specialist should address the objectives that the mathematics specialist will be expected to achieve. But before they can do that, they will need to discuss a vision for the school's mathematics program, since this discussion will lead to a specification of goals, and then, depending on those goals, to a defining of roles and responsibilities.

During the first meeting, the principal should initiate a conversation in which both she and the specialist offer images of what mathematics teaching and learning might look like in classrooms and what components of the school's mathematics program would support and sustain that vision. It is not sufficient for the principal simply to describe her vision. Instead, it is critical that the principal and the specialist engage in a meaningful discussion about their visions. Each party will bring unique, individual knowledge and background to the conversation. The principal is familiar with the current state of the school's mathematics program. She is also aware of any existing or upcoming school-level or district-level initiatives that may affect the mathematics program. The mathematics specialist brings to the conversation his specialized knowledge as a "content-focused" mathematics coach (West and Staub 2003, p. 3) and his expertise in research-based best practices in mathematics education. This knowledge allows the specialist to help the principal reflect on the strengths and weaknesses of the current mathematics program. As their discussion continues, the conversation should focus on the important mathematics experiences envisioned for students, rather than on individual teachers or a specific curriculum.

The next step is to identify specific student goals or learning outcomes. Resources such as the Common Core State Standards for Mathematics (National Governors Association Center for Best Practices and Council of Chief State School Officers 2010) will be useful in determining these goals. Although raising student achievement may be the ultimate intent, this broad goal is open to multiple interpretations. For the principal and the specialist to establish specific goals for the school year, they must reach agreement about which indicators to use to characterize student achievement. This shifts the discussion to the mathematics content that students must know, how they may learn it most effectively, and how they may demonstrate their understanding. Then the conversation can consider what this agenda might imply for teaching and what aspects of it will require support for and engagement of teachers. The implication of this discussion is that the principal and the specialist share responsibility for influencing change in mathematics instruction.

Be sure that everyone is focused on one goal when moving to new standards—improving learning.

Our school is in the midst of change surrounding revised curriculum standards for mathematics. My principal has reset scheduling so that I can provide professional development for teachers, allowing us to study the revised standards and address ways of making a transition to more rigorous expectations for our students. He has arranged teachers' schedules to include regular meetings with me, and he has let me know what he considers to be areas of need. Because everyone understands that we have the same goal—improving students' learning—I feel that I am getting more cooperation from teachers. They have a greater willingness to use me as a resource.

—*Reflections from a mathematics specialist*

Figure 17.1 shows a sequence of questions that can help the principal and the specialist work toward a mutual understanding of what constitutes a high-quality mathematics program. A shared vision emerges through discussion framed by questions such as these. The specialist and the principal can consider what kinds of mathematical practices students should be engaged in during a mathematics class by asking not only, "What should students be doing during the study of mathematics?" but also, "What do teachers need to do to enable students to engage with mathematics in that way?" This question moves the conversation to the work that the specialist will do to support the teachers as well as the work that the principal will do to support both the specialist and the teachers.

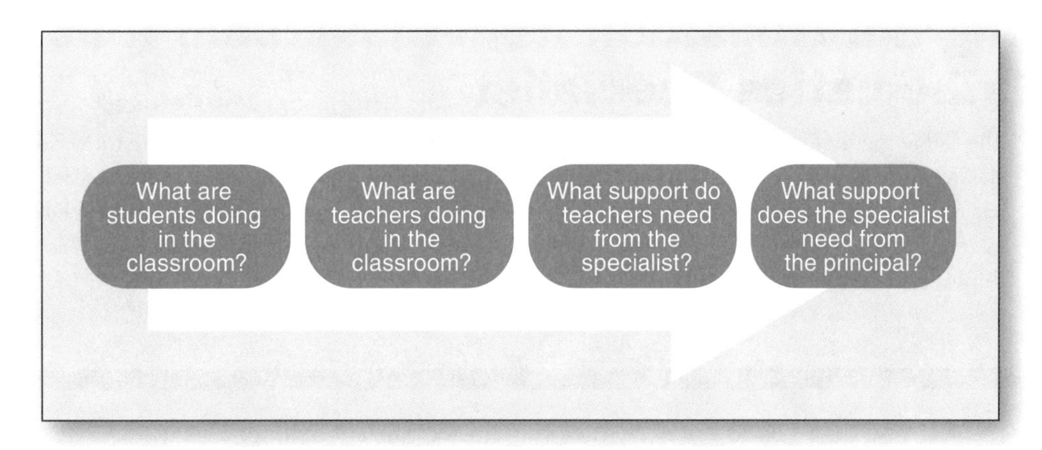

Fig. 17.1. Developing goals for the mathematics program

Defining the roles and responsibilities of the mathematics specialist

Every conversation between a specialist and a principal is a learning opportunity. Regularly scheduled meetings allow the two of them to continue to develop their partnership throughout the year.

Woleck (2012) suggests that engaging in regular conversations allows a principal and a mathematics specialist to develop a shared understanding of what constitutes effective classroom practices. At the same time, it allows them to negotiate expectations for the specialist and to clarify the access and support that the specialist will need to enhance teachers' understandings and instructional practices.

Recognize that the specialist supports the principal's professional growth by deepening the principal's understanding of mathematics learning and teaching.

Having a mathematics specialist in my building has enabled me to gain valuable insight into how children process mathematics concepts. I understand that it is important for teachers to listen to students' discussions and examine students' work to learn about students' mathematical understandings and misconceptions. More important, our conversations and interactions have facilitated a process through which I can confidently and effectively provide necessary instructional guidance for teachers in a manner that acknowledges the best practices necessary to support student achievement.

—Reflections from an elementary school principal

Making the Transition from Classroom Teacher to Mathematics Specialist

The following first-person account illustrates some of the challenges involved in the transition from classroom teacher to mathematics specialist. Ms. Pasquale is an experienced classroom teacher who has recently accepted the position of elementary mathematics specialist in her district. She has been assigned to a school where she was not a teacher. She speaks about this transition, as well as about the important role that the principal can play in making it a smooth one.

It was daunting to enter my new role as a mathematics specialist and to face the many challenges set before me. Moving from classroom teacher to mathematics specialist came with many personal and professional challenges. Not only did I leave my own classroom where I worked exclusively with students, but now my target audience had shifted to teachers. The thought of working primarily with teachers was an intimidating one. I soon realized that by investing time in building a trusting relationship with each teacher, I could make the work run more smoothly as the school year progressed. I realized that teachers wanted to know that I would be a mathematics specialist who would work with them and be not only knowledgeable about mathematics and mathematics teaching, but also trustworthy. They also wanted to know what I would be doing and how I would be helping them.

What exactly is the role of a mathematics specialist? My school had never had a specialist before, so Ms. Jackson, my principal, realized that the staff might have many misconceptions and questions about the role. She decided to address the possible concerns through the school handbook. As we worked together to define what my role would be, we both recognized that mathematics specialists shoulder abundant responsibility, not only to the students and teachers, but also to administrators and the community as well. A mathematics specialist's duties cover both content and pedagogy. The broad responsibilities for a mathematics specialist that Ms. Jackson listed in the handbook for teachers included the following:

- Works with administrators, teachers, students, parents, and the community to reach common mathematics goals.
- Collaborates with individual teachers and teams of teachers through co-planning, co-teaching, and coaching.
- Collects and analyzes data in an effort to improve student achievement as well as mathematics curriculum and instruction.
- Promotes successful, research-based instructional strategies.
- Organizes and delivers professional development opportunities for all teachers.
- Assists in aligning curriculum and assessment resources to support and increase student achievement.
- Conducts non-evaluative observations of teaching and learning to improve student achievement and mathematics instruction.
- Provides mathematics leadership that stimulates sustained systematic change and improvement in mathematics instruction.

Ms. Jackson then took the time to discuss these responsibilities during the first faculty meeting.

Clearly, a mathematics specialist wears many hats. This list provided teachers with a description that gave them valuable insight into what my job entails and encompasses. The description made clear that my primary responsibility was to work with teachers rather than pulling students out of the classroom to work with them.

During the first faculty meeting before the beginning of the school year, Ms. Jackson provided teachers with copies of the handbook and discussed with them how I would support them. Because the teachers had never had an opportunity to work with a mathematics specialist before, the job description provided important information and gave me a reference point as I talked with teachers about my new role. Ms. Jackson also made clear her expectations for the mathematics program for the upcoming school year. I knew that entering another teacher's classroom would be difficult, not only from my perspective, but also from each teacher's perspective as well. But thanks to the framework that was shared at the faculty meeting, I found that the teachers were willing to work collaboratively with me. They understood from the job description that I was there to support them and not to evaluate them each time I visited their classrooms.

During that faculty meeting, I was asked many questions. When would I find time to observe classrooms, co-teach, and analyze and interpret data? How and when would I collaborate with individual teachers and groups of teachers to plan research-based lessons and provide ongoing professional development? Some of these questions were easy to answer because, in addition to the job description in the handbook, Ms. Jackson provided the staff with a copy of my schedule for the first six weeks of school. By laying out when I would be visiting each teacher's classroom, this schedule allowed me to begin working with teachers in the very first week of school. I also learned that it is important to allow for flexibility in a mathematics specialist's schedule.

From the beginning I knew that Ms. Jackson supported my work as a mathematics specialist. By presenting her expectations to the faculty and staff at the beginning of the school year, she laid the foundation for my successful first year as a mathematics specialist. She paved the way for me to work with every teacher from the beginning of the school year. From that beginning, as teachers became more comfortable with me, they began to seek me out in the teacher's lounge, at the mailboxes, on the bus ramp, and in the hallway. Because I was visible and accessible, teachers became comfortable enough to pull me aside to chat about their upcoming lessons, to elicit my help in planning and implementing lessons, or to share something exciting that a child or their class had accomplished that day in mathematics. I believe that by working collaboratively with teachers I was instrumental in helping them change their mathematics instruction and increase their students' achievement.

Scheduling the Specialist's Time

In her account, Ms. Pasquale indicates that Ms. Jackson provided a valuable foundation for her work. After setting clear expectations for how the specialist and the teachers would work together, Ms. Jackson established a way for Ms. Pasquale to work in all teachers' classrooms early in the year by preparing a schedule for her first six weeks. At the end of that period, Ms. Pasquale set her own schedule, allowing flexibility in how she used her time.

A principal can support both of these scheduling needs by providing a fixed schedule for the first six weeks and then supporting the specialist's need to have more autonomy to develop her own schedule so that she can more easily accommodate teachers' requests. This does not mean that when the specialist develops her own schedule, she is working in isolation. Certainly, she should stay informed about particular areas that the principal wants to be her focus. She should also share her calendar with the principal. In addition, the regularly scheduled meetings with the principal provide opportunities for the specialist and the principal to use the specialist's calendar to reflect together on—

1. how the specialist is spending her time;
2. what the specialist has been doing with the teachers;
3. what teachers the specialist has been working with; and
4. the changes that the specialist's work is making in the instructional program, as well as the continuing needs of the mathematics program.

Allow scheduling priorities to emerge.

I have found that having some sort of schedule is important for me, my teachers, and my principal. But when that schedule is tightly defined and highly structured, it can be too confining. Having the principal map out the entire year in advance would set a schedule that would be tough to keep up with.

—Advice from a mathematics specialist

Before the school year begins, the principal and the specialist should commit to meeting regularly, decide how often they will meet, and put these meetings on their respective calendars. The principal should share his expectations for what the specialist will bring to each meeting. Having ongoing, regular, reflective conversations enables the specialist and the principal to collaborate to identify and prioritize areas that need additional focus and discuss any upcoming events that may affect the specialist's work with teachers. It is extremely important in these conversations that the specialist maintain teacher confidentiality. For example, rather than reporting that Ms. Jones is weak in her understanding of fractions, the specialist could focus the conversation on the need to spend more time helping the fourth-grade teachers examine different ways to teach fraction concepts to meet the needs of all learners more effectively.

The work of the elementary mathematics specialist

It is not unusual for the specialist to take on various responsibilities in the school, but both the principal and the specialist need to be mindful that the more engagement teachers have with the specialist, the greater the impact will be on their beliefs about teaching and learning mathematics (Campbell and Malkus 2010). Focusing on this fact can be useful when the specialist and the principal work together to define the specialist's responsibilities and to ensure that the specialist has sufficient time and opportunity to engage with teachers. Awareness of the importance of this engagement can help the principal think about boundaries of the specialist's work and how to convey those boundaries to teachers.

The broad categories in the job description that Ms. Pasquale presents are just that—broad. A specialist will not be able to perform in all these categories on a given day, or perhaps even in a given week, but he may fulfill responsibilities in all of them over the course of the school year. As the principal and the specialist plan how the specialist's time will be allocated, they need to remember that the first year will be a learning period for everyone—the principal, the specialist, and the teachers.

The new specialist may be very familiar with the mathematics content and the curriculum at the grade level or levels that she has taught, but she will be less familiar with the mathematics and curriculum for the other grade levels. This means that the specialist will need time for research and strategic planning as she prepares to work with all grade-level teachers in the building and perhaps even other specialists in the building. In addition, the mathematics specialist is getting to know the mathematics teachers as people—not just as instructors. She is also learning about the other staff members in the building, figuring out how she can work with the other resource teachers and specialists. She is learning what resources are available in the building and where they are located and getting to know the school's culture and figuring out how to become a team player. Being a team player as well as building and maintaining good rapport with teachers are crucial to her success. Knight (2011) provides suggestions for how a coach or specialist can establish and use a partnership approach with teachers.

Prioritizing the specialist's work

Working as partners, the principal and the specialist should prioritize what the specialist will do and how he will be allocating his time for various responsibilities. As priorities change over the course of the school year, the time allocated for certain responsibilities will change to accommodate those priorities. Events such as standardized testing, the arrival of new curricular materials, the emerging needs of first-year teachers, or an extended leave for a teacher can have an impact on a specialist's responsibilities, causing them to shift and re-form. So it is important to revisit these allocations several times during the year to evaluate how much of the specialist's time is being spent on particular activities and which activities are likely to have the greatest impact on teachers' instruction.

Evaluate activities in relation to a teacher's "impact meter."

In my work as a mentor for a group of mathematics specialists, we came up with the idea of an "impact meter" as a tool for talking about how likely a particular activity was to have an impact on teacher practice. Our meter measured from 0 to 1, with 0 representing no impact and 1 representing great impact. This tool became important when we were thinking about the specialists' work. Not everything that specialists do is at the upper end of the meter for the degree to which it helped teachers improve their instruction, but the specialists worked hard to keep most of their work at the upper end. The specialists found that the meter turned out to be a great tool for planning with their principals. Why? Because sometimes a principal would ask a specialist to do something that was on the low end of the impact meter. This was a way for the specialist to be aware of the trade-off in terms of potential teacher impact and to decide whether the requested action should be discussed with the principal.

—Reflections from a mathematics supervisor

Creating circle graphs at different points in the year to depict proportions of time spent on various activities can be an effective way for a specialist to track her work. Each graph illustrates by category the activities in which she has recently engaged and shows, on average, the percentages of time spent on activities in different categories. Creating the graphs provides an opportunity for the specialist to reflect on her work and to think about how the activities she has carried out fit into the categories defined in her job description. It can be enlightening for the specialist to look across a period of time and figure out how much time she has spent on each category. Sometimes, the proportions will surprise her because she can easily lose sight of how time on a particular activity accumulates when she looks only at time spent day by day or week by week. Additional insight can come from comparing graphs constructed at different points in the school year. Consideration of such graphs should lead to conversations between the principal and the specialist about changes in instruction, the current state of the mathematics program, and how the specialist should move forward to schedule her time over the next few months.

Set priorities to know what the focus is.

During my first year as a mathematics specialist, I found myself completing a wide variety of tasks. Although many of these were directed at enhancing teacher instruction and improving student learning, some of the tasks were not. Now, with my principal's support, I am more focused on the tasks that best support teachers and students.

—Advice from a mathematics specialist

Why the Principal and the Specialist Should Partner

The relationship among the elementary mathematics specialist, the teachers, and the principal has the potential to become a powerful instructional partnership if it is built on trust. A principal is an instructional leader and also the evaluator of mathematics instruction. However, the principal may or may not have a background in mathematics, so partnership with the mathematics specialist can help build an essential knowledge of what good mathematics instruction should look like in a classroom. Further, the more the principal understands the mathematical needs of teachers and students, the better the principal can allocate resources and support for meaningful instructional feedback. But this partnership between a specialist and a principal does not extend to the evaluation of teachers. Teachers are much more likely to seek support if they trust that the specialist will not be participating in their evaluations.

The success of the mathematics specialist is largely dependent on the health of the different partnerships within the school. The principal's investment in time to foster healthy relationships among the specialist, the teachers, and himself can reap great benefits.

Establishing a framework of expectations

By establishing a framework of expectations for both the arrival of a mathematics specialist and the partnerships between a specialist and teachers, the principal plays a critical role in the mathematics specialist's success. A principal can take steps to optimize the impact of the specialist on teachers' practice and student learning (Grant and Davenport 2009). How the principal introduces the specialist to the teachers and establishes expectations for teachers' interaction with the specialist establish how the partnerships will work for the remainder of the year. In addition, the structures that the principal puts in place can support or hinder the specialist's opportunities to work with teachers. Consequently, the principal has many questions to consider:

- When will mathematics classes be taught?
- Will grade-level teams have a common planning time?
- Will grade-level teams be expected to meet and plan regularly with the mathematics specialist?
- Will the specialist have an office that is in a centrally located area for easy access by teachers?
- Will the specialist have a computer, a telephone, and a budget for materials and supplies?

Planning for the arrival of the elementary mathematics specialist

After learning that an elementary mathematics specialist will be joining the school's staff, the principal can plan productively for her arrival. Mr. Smith, whose first-person account follows, had been the principal at Elm Street Elementary School for five years when he learned, in July, that a mathematics specialist, Ms. Anders, would be assigned to his school's staff to help teachers increase their students' understanding of mathematics. His account details his planning and its results.

When I learned that Ms. Anders would be coming to Elm Street Elementary, I thought, "What a great opportunity for me and the teachers!" I wanted to build a strong partnership with my new specialist. Although I had some ideas about how to improve the mathematics program, I also wanted to hear Ms. Anders' ideas. Having a specialist in the building to coach and support the teachers would be a big change for the teachers. I wanted them to understand that the specialist was there to help and be a valuable support person. Because change is not easy and by nature people respond to it differently, I began to think about what I needed to do to get the teachers on board and excited about this new resource. Some are always ready to embrace change, others approach it with caution, and still others are immediately skeptical and resistant. As I planned for this change, I considered the needs of my faculty and thought about three Ps: *purpose*, *picture*, and *part*.

Some of the Elm Street teachers would need only to understand the *purpose* for the placement of the mathematics specialist to be on board with the idea of a specialist in the building. Others would need to have a *picture* of what a partnership with a specialist would look like, and, specifically, a sense of what would be their *part* in the partnership. As I thought about this, I realized that understanding the expectations of each other's role in the partnership would be important for both the teacher and the mathematics specialist. I considered questions that the new specialist and teachers might raise:

- "Will the mathematics specialist co-teach with me?"
- "Will the mathematics specialist model lessons for me?"
- "Will the mathematics specialist be working with everyone?"
- "Will the mathematics specialist observe in an informal or a formal way?"
- "Are all teachers expected to plan with the mathematics specialist?"
- "Will the principal set the schedule?"
- "Is the specialist a mentor, a coach, or an evaluator—or is the specialist supposed to assume a combination of these roles?"

It was going to require a lot of work and planning to prepare the teachers for the arrival of the specialist before the new school year began. I wanted to be able to do three things:

1. Communicate the *purpose* of having a mathematics specialist at Elm Street Elementary
2. Provide a *picture* of what the specialist would be doing with the teachers, by sharing a vision of how the partnership might look on a daily basis
3. Clarify everyone's *part* in the partnership by sharing my expectations for myself, as the principal, as well as for the specialist and the teachers

To begin this work, I believed it was important for me to help Ms. Anders learn about our school and for Ms. Anders and me to figure out together how she could best help our teachers. But first, she and I needed to meet and get to know each other.

I invited Ms. Anders to come to school several weeks before the teachers returned so that she could see her office and learn about the resources that were available for her to use. I took her around the school, which allowed us to get to know each other, and it also gave me an opportunity to share what I considered to be the strengths of our school. Then it was time to get to work. Over the course of several meetings, we began planning her introduction to the teachers, identifying her responsibilities, and determining how we would work together to share leadership for the mathematics program. These meetings proved to be invaluable. Throughout the school year, we revisited the foundation that we had built during the summer and referred back to the early decisions that we had made when questions arose about Ms. Anders' role in the building or when actions were called for in the mathematics program.

During our first meeting, we talked about the school's mathematics program and what I considered to be its strengths and weaknesses. We also talked about a vision for the mathematics program. These conversations led us to discuss what we believed was important for Elm Street students to know and be able to do as a result of what they learned in their mathematics classes. We agreed that improving our state test scores in mathematics was important, but we wanted more for our students. After some discussion about our vision for the mathematics program, we brainstormed to come up with some questions that we would need to address at our next meeting:

- What should we see in an effective mathematics classroom?
- What should be included in a good lesson?
- What are key elements in a comprehensive K–12 mathematics curriculum?
- What structures and schedules could we put in place to facilitate collaboration between the specialist and the teachers?
- What support do teachers need to help them rethink and change their instruction?
- What should the role of technology be in a mathematics classroom?
- How can we share leadership, how will we communicate with each other, and what support do we need from each other?
- What are our long-term goals for mathematics instruction, and what are our short-term goals for next year? How will we know if instruction is changing?

We continued our meetings and used the questions that we had developed to guide our conversations. We needed open discussions to push our thinking, so we set up norms for our conversations. We decided that we would—

1. ask questions of each other;
2. push each other to share our thinking; and
3. listen and understand each other's perspective.

We agreed that these were critical to reach a shared understanding and to have one clear message when we communicated with teachers.

I think we both found this process rewarding. As we discussed each other's questions, we had the opportunity to reflect on our individual beliefs about what is important for students to know and accomplish in mathematics and what kind of instruction is necessary for students to understand mathematics. As a result of these discussions, we reached an agreement on how we would share leadership for the mathematics program. We recognized that Ms. Anders would naturally be in a position to work more closely with classroom teachers on instructional design and delivery and assessment of student understanding. We agreed that teachers must trust her if they were going to take risks or become vulnerable, since true growth often comes from a place of uncertainty and depends on taking risks and learning from mistakes. Clearly, teachers would have a difficult time taking risks and changing practice if Ms. Anders were evaluating them. For this reason alone, we agreed that she would not evaluate teachers and that I would make that clear to the teachers. We also agreed that I would not ask Ms. Anders to provide me with information for any teacher evaluations.

Organizing the School for the Specialist's Work with Teachers

Establishing the expectation that teachers will work with the specialist is a critical first step, but the principal and the specialist must take other important steps to facilitate a successful working partnership between the specialist and the teachers. Developing a structure for their work and finding time for the specialist to provide professional development presents a challenge to the principal, the mathematics specialist, and the teachers. Observing in classrooms and reviewing assessment data are important activities for the specialist, since these allow her to learn about the school's instructional program and students' performance on summative assessments. Co-teaching, coaching, and one-on-one planning with a teacher are valuable forms of professional development for teachers as they work to improve their instruction. Grade-level meetings, schoolwide workshops, and faculty meetings can also be important forms of professional development for groups of teachers.

Grade-level meetings

Grade-level planning sessions are a crucial aspect of a mathematics specialist's job, since these support direct contact with teachers. In these sessions, teachers and the mathematics specialist collaboratively plan how to facilitate change in mathematics instruction and in student achievement. An effective way for a specialist to support teachers is meeting each week or every other week with a group of teachers. The small groups may be teachers of the same grade or vertical-grade-level teachers with common planning time built into the school schedule. When the principal and the specialist review the school schedule, they can determine which is more realistic—one planning period each week or a planning period every other week. At the beginning of the year, it is important for the principal to help teachers understand the purpose of these grade-level meetings, provide the year's schedule for grade-level meetings, and describe expectations for feedback from the meetings.

The specialist then assumes responsibility for planning and facilitating the meetings. Providing teachers with an agenda and a clear goal can keep each meeting productively focused on students and their learning. A specialist can invite the teachers to partner in the management of the meeting by asking them to summarize any decisions made, offer suggestions for the next meeting's agenda, and take turns keeping notes. When the specialist maintains a notebook of the agendas and the notes and makes the notebook available at all grade-level meetings, she and the teachers can refer to it when questions arise. In addition, the principal can read the agenda and notes when she is unable to attend a meeting.

Meeting with small groups of teachers enables the mathematics specialist to collaborate and use the school's curricular materials to co-plan lessons that the teachers will use. They can then share their experiences of teaching the lessons with one another at future meetings. When teachers bring in student work samples, the specialist can use the student work to keep the focus on student learning, asking questions such as the following:

- "What is the mathematics in the lesson?"
- "What did students understand, and what confusion do they still appear to have?"
- "What next instructional steps will address students' misunderstandings?"
- "How is the mathematics in the lesson connected with other mathematics content?"

As a result of conversations growing out of these questions, a professional learning community focused on instruction can be established and nurtured. Staub and West (2003, p. 129) report that the "long-term goal of coaching is to create a collaborative and professional community." By keeping the focus on the mathematics and the students, the specialist can take the spotlight off individual teachers as they move through the change process.

Ms. Pasquale recounts that as she worked with classroom teachers and specific grade-level groups of teachers, she realized that change does not happen overnight. Change in teachers' instructional practices occurs in small increments over the course of the year. Just as students need to have their instruction differentiated according to their level of understanding, the specialist will need to differentiate work with individual teachers depending on their readiness for new instructional practices. To differentiate effectively, the specialist must identify the needs of individual teachers so that he can tailor his planning for grade-level meetings to address the needs of all teachers. But when he talks with the principal, he should highlight teachers' growth toward particular goals as a group, not as individuals.

Inviting the principal to join a grade-level meeting is one way for teachers to share their classroom experiences with him. Through the discussions that occur, the principal learns about effective mathematics lessons and what they should look like. When the principal attends a grade-level meeting, he is able to witness the collaborative relationship among the classroom teachers and the mathematics specialist. In addition, his presence at a grade-level meeting lets teachers know that he sees them as important and that he supports the specialist's work with them.

Identifying teachers for the specialist to work with

The mathematics specialist is expected to spend time working with individual mathematics teachers. However, during the first year of a specialist's placement in a school, identifying teachers for co-teaching and coaching in such a way that the specialist does not appear to be working just with the weak teachers is a challenge. When a specialist is assigned to work only with the weak teachers, both the specialist and the teachers begin to feel that she is there to "fix" them. Such a situation does not inspire the teachers to respect or trust the specialist. The specialist is not in the building to fix anyone but rather to work with teachers to design and teach lessons and to coach teachers as they work to change their practice. So the specialist and the principal must work together to target teachers who need the mathematics specialist's support to strengthen their practice as well as teachers who are strong and have the potential to become leaders themselves.

Consider the benefits of long-term co-teaching with a strong teacher.

Before I became a mathematics specialist, I was a K–1 teacher, so I was anxious about working with upper-grades teachers. For that reason, I decided to ask my principal if I could spend a year co-teaching with a fourth- or fifth-grade teacher. At first the principal was hesitant, but she finally agreed to ask her fifth-grade lead teacher for mathematics if she would be willing to work with me. As a result, we developed a great friendship that has continued during my five years in the school. She helped me learn about fifth grade, and I had students to work with every day. Today, we continue to get together when we can to talk about mathematics. The biggest payoff is that she became my biggest cheerleader. At the end of that first year, other teachers came to me to ask if I would co-teach with them the next year!

—Reflections from a mathematics specialist

Structures that the principal puts in place can help the specialist work with individual teachers without losing the trust of the teachers. For example, the principal can establish an expectation that all teachers will engage at some point with the specialist in co-teaching or coaching. She can share the various reasons for this expectation, including a goal of supporting teachers as they implement new lessons, supporting teachers' efforts to develop new research-based instructional practices, or allowing the specialist to become familiar with students across all the grade levels. The principal can also put in place a schedule that distributes mathematics instruction throughout the day, maximizing the specialists' opportunities to coach or co-teach in teachers' classrooms.

Encouraging reluctant teachers

It is inevitable. A specialist will encounter teachers who are reluctant to work with him. This can be very discouraging for the mathematics specialist. Ms. Pasquale found in her first year that even though she was expected to work with all teachers, some were more willing than others. However, because her principal set working with Ms. Pasquale as an expectation, she was able to visit every teacher's classroom. The support provided by her principal was essential in gaining access to all teachers, including those who were reluctant. Access is the first step. Once the initial contact is made, a specialist must look for opportunities to develop rapport and gain the trust of reluctant teachers. This means that a specialist will need to find a way to involve the teacher and build her confidence. Knight (2009) offers a perspective that a principal and a specialist might discuss to gain some understanding of the reasons why teachers resist change.

Be assured that patience and persistence do pay off.

Betty was my most reluctant teacher. She always seemed to have a reason not to meet with me to plan, even though I kept going by her room and checking in with her. As usual, she did not make any contributions at the grade-level meeting on Monday. Imagine my surprise when she came by my office Tuesday morning and sat down. With a catch in her voice, she told me that she had never been good at mathematics and dreaded each day when it was time to teach the subject. She thanked me for what we did in the grade-level meetings, since she realized that the reason she hated mathematics was that she never understood why the rules work. So in school, she could never remember the rules. The unit on fractions was coming up, and she asked if I could help her plan some lessons. I couldn't say yes fast enough! I know I need to go slowly so that I do not overwhelm her with my enthusiasm, but this breakthrough is the best reward for a mathematics specialist.

—*Reflections from a mathematics specialist*

Principal and specialist in partnership for success

In his account, Mr. Smith proactively defines how he and the mathematics specialist will work together and how the specialist and the teachers will work together. He collaborates with the specialist on these decisions, and together they plan for her introduction to the teachers. This process of collaborative planning is critical because the principal and the specialist have equal responsibility for the success of the specialist (Killion and Harrison 2006, p. 116). Furthermore, as found in a survey of principals with a mathematics specialist (Blount and Singleton 2007), when a principal with vision and stature partners with a confident and knowledgeable specialist, a "noticeable synergy" (p. 71) emerges that influences the quality of the mathematics specialist's work. The proactive principal helps every teacher and staff member understand his vision for the mathematics program and his expectations that classroom activities will support the vision. An influential mathematics specialist takes the lead in supporting teachers as they align their instructional practice with the school's vision for their mathematics program.

Take Time to Celebrate

Once the school year is under way and the principal and the specialist have established their partnership, they will be ready to work as a team, advancing toward a shared target: students receiving high-quality mathematics instruction from teachers who are developing a deep understanding of mathematics content and pedagogy. Throughout the year, the team will encounter challenges and setbacks to their change efforts. But more important, they will encounter successes. Some will be small successes, and others more substantial. In the process of planning, the principal and the specialist should take time to establish some modest interim goals. Progress toward these goals will give frequent opportunities for celebration. Realizing growth and celebrating progress provide momentum to work past the challenges and setbacks. It is important to make celebrations public, invite the teachers to participate, and sometimes invite the students to celebrate and be a part of their own success.

References

Blount, David, and Judy Singleton. "The Role and Impact of the Mathematics Specialist from the Principals' Perspectives." *Journal of Mathematics and Science: Collaborative Explorations* 9 (Spring 2007): 69–77.

Campbell, Patricia F., and Nathaniel N. Malkus. "The Impact of Elementary Mathematics Specialists." *Journal of Mathematics and Science: Collaborative Explorations* 12 (2010): 1–28.

Grant, Catherine, M., and Linda R. Davenport. "Principals in Partnership with Mathematics Coaches." *Principal* 88 (May/June 2009): 36–41.

Kanold, Timothy D., Diane J. Briars, and Francis (Skip) Fennell. *What Principals Need to Know about Teaching and Learning Mathematics*. Bloomington, Ind.: Solution Tree Press, 2012.

Killion, Joellen, and Cindy Harrison. *Taking the Lead: New Roles for Teachers and School-Based Coaches.* Oxford, Ohio: National Staff Development Council, 2006.

National Governors Association Center for Best Practices and Council of Chief State School Officers (NGA Center and CCSSO). *Common Core State Standards for Mathematics. Common Core State Standards (College- and Career-Readiness Standards and K–12 Standards in English Language Arts and Math).* Washington, D.C.: NGA Center and CCSSO, 2010. http://www.corestandards.org.

Knight, Jim. "What Can We Do about Teacher Resistance?" *Phi Delta Kappan* 90 (March 2009): 508–13.

———. "What Good Coaches Do." *Educational Leadership* 69 (October 2011): 18–22.

West, Lucy, and Fritz C. Staub. *Content-Focused Coaching: Transforming Mathematics Lessons.* Portsmouth, N.H.: Heinemann, 2003.

Woleck, Kristine Reed. *Moments in Mathematics Coaching: Improving K–5 Instruction.* Thousand Oaks, Calif.: Corwin Press, 2010.

Appendix A

Who Are Mathematics Specialists?

Mathematics Specialists are teacher leaders with strong preparation and background in mathematics content, instructional strategies, and school leadership. Based in elementary and middle schools, mathematics specialists are former classroom teachers who are responsible for supporting the professional growth of their colleagues and promoting enhanced mathematics instruction and student learning throughout their schools. They are responsible for strengthening classroom teachers' understanding of mathematics content, and helping teachers develop more effective mathematics teaching practices that allow all students to reach high standards as well as sharing research addressing how students learn mathematics.

The overarching purpose for Mathematics Specialists is to increase the mathematics achievement of all the students in their schools. To do so, they

- Collaborate with individual teachers through co-planning, co-teaching, and coaching;
- Assist administrative and instructional staff in interpreting data and designing approaches to improve student achievement and instruction;
- Ensure that the school curriculum is aligned with state and national standards and their school division's mathematics curriculum;
- Promote teachers' delivery and understanding of the school curriculum through collaborative long-range and short-range planning;
- Facilitate teachers' use of successful, research-based instructional strategies, including differentiated instruction for diverse learners such as those with limited English proficiency or disabilities;
- Work with parents/guardians and community leaders to foster continuing home/school/community partnerships focused on students' learning of mathematics; and
- Collaborate with administrators to provide leadership and vision for a school-wide mathematics program.

From Virginia Mathematics and Science Coalition, Richmond, Virginia, http://www.math.vcu.edu/MathSpecialists.

The Virginia Mathematics Specialist Program

Megan K. Murray and Loren D. Pitt

For the last decade, a partnership in the state of Virginia has worked to develop a common program for K–8 mathematics teacher specialists. The resulting program, although constantly evolving in space and time, reflects the community's best thoughts on an optimal master's program for mathematics specialists. This article describes this program and its current implementation at the University of Virginia. Virtually identical programs are offered at five other Virginia universities.

In the early 1990s, Virginia's community of mathematicians and mathematics educators began advocating for the placement of mathematics teacher specialists in all elementary and middle schools (Critchfield 1992). In the fall of 2002, the Virginia Mathematics and Science Coalition (VMSC) created the Mathematics Specialist Task Force, charged with preparing the case for mathematics specialists in elementary and middle schools and with producing a report that included recommendations on job descriptions, competencies, preparation, and licensure. The task force was composed of university mathematicians and mathematics educators, as well as school mathematics leaders.

The Virginia Mathematics and Science Coalition Task Force Report (2005b) and the recommendations that it contained were groundbreaking and became the foundation for the subsequent work on mathematics specialist programs that has occurred in Virginia since that time. The recommendations were endorsed by the Virginia Council for Mathematics Supervision (VCMS) and the Virginia Council of Teachers of Mathematics (VCTM). The recommendations also became the basis for Virginia's licensure endorsement for mathematics specialists for elementary and middle education that went into effect in 2007.

While the endorsement proceeded toward approval in the Virginia Department of Education and the state legislature, a partnership of universities, school divisions, VMSC, VCMS, and VCTM was developing a series of courses intended for a master's degree program for K–5 mathematics specialists. The Virginia endorsement is for K–8 mathematics specialists, but most of the work done in the project has focused on K–5 specialists. How this K–5 program can be modified and strengthened mathematically to meet the needs of middle school specialists is the focus of a current NSF Mathematics Specialist Partnership project. Variations in the programs have been implemented at the partner institutions of higher education, but these programs are in fact remarkably similar. This appendix sketches the original recommendations and then describes the strands and courses of the program that was implemented and has evolved into its current form at the University of Virginia.

The University of Virginia Program

Some background is helpful in understanding the current degree program for mathematics specialists at the University of Virginia. Descriptions of each of the courses required to complete the program can flesh out this understanding. Texts currently used in each course are listed at the conclusion of the appendix.

Early efforts leading to the University of Virginia mathematics specialist program

To understand the Virginia Mathematics Specialist Project, it is important to understand the job of mathematics specialists as they function in Virginia. The following description appears in the executive summary of the task force report, which appeared in the VMSC journal (Virginia Mathematics and Science Coalition Task Force 2005a, pp. 3–4):

> A Mathematics Specialist is a teacher in the elementary or middle school who has interest and special preparation in mathematics content, scientifically based research in the teaching and learning of mathematics, diagnostic and assessment methods, and leadership skills. School-based Mathematics Specialists serve as resources in professional development, instructing children with learning difficulties, curriculum development, mentoring of new teachers, and community education.
>
> Mathematics Specialists assume multiple leadership roles in schools. Some Specialists work primarily providing job-embedded staff development for teachers. Others work in teaching roles with students in either pullout programs or in co-teaching situations. Another essential role of the Specialist is supporting the work of the classroom teacher, and in developing a high-quality, research-based mathematics program that ensures the success of all children in learning mathematics.
>
> The Specialist role requires a comprehensive and rigorous preparation. Mathematics Specialists require deep knowledge of mathematics and how children learn mathematics, of the use of various assessments in diagnosing student difficulties in learning mathematics, and of designing instruction for diverse learners. Individuals in Specialist positions require graduate-level preparation including significant coursework on school mathematics.
>
> Programs to prepare Mathematics Specialists must include appropriate school mathematics content and model pedagogy essential for teaching that content.

The Virginia Mathematics Specialist Project has attempted to design a complete program to prepare specialists to perform the job that was envisioned by the task force. To do this, the designing team based its work on three integral components: (1) robust visions of the essential content in the K–8 mathematics strands, (2) study of how children build their understanding of this mathematics and how teachers can support their students' learning, and (3) effective knowledge and skills for working with teachers and administrators in schools to enhance students' mathematical learning and performance.

The task force recognized that this content, knowledge, and skills form a highly complex whole and that mastering this material in its entirety is the work of a very full graduate program. An important difficulty in teaching within this program is that many beginning students do not recognize the complexities, both mathematical and pedagogical, of school mathematics. Today, a majority of those who have spent a great deal of time developing the program would probably say that the graduates are not masters of this material but that they have acquired a solid foundation that is sufficient to support highly successful careers.

Mathematics content courses

The mathematics content of the program is divided into three strands: numbers and algebra, geometry and measurement, and statistics and probability. In each strand, the mathematics courses focus on a core of essential content and give particular attention to the ways in which children learn this material. The issues encountered in shaping the program can be illustrated by looking carefully at the numbers and algebra strand.

Numbers and algebra

The numbers and algebra sequence consists of three linked courses: Numbers and Operations; Rational Numbers and Proportional Reasoning; and Patterns, Functions, and Algebra. Descriptions of the courses follow an explanation of the rationale for the strand.

Kilpatrick, Swafford, and Findell (National Research Council 2001) provide a good summary of the mathematical landscape of the school number strand. We will restrict our comments to the simple observation that this strand includes counting; the construction of the familiar number systems, starting with the whole numbers and ending with the rational numbers and decimal representations; and an analysis of numbers systems that lead to generalizations about the relationships between quantities and the multiple ways in which these relationships may be represented. Specialists need a deep understanding of whole numbers, integers, and rational numbers. Achieving this requires extensive study of place value and other aspects of the base-ten system. The end result is a vision of the concept of number that is unified and allows specialists to work with numbers as points on a number line. Similarly, it is necessary for specialists to construct an understanding of the number operations that is deep and builds from counting to conceptual understanding of and computational fluency with operations on integers and rational numbers. Ideally, this understanding will be sufficiently robust that algorithms such as that for adding fractions ($a/b + c/d = (ad + bc)/bd$) are seen as naturally extending to quotients of real numbers.

All the mathematics courses, but particularly those in this strand, have a very strong emphasis on student reasoning. The understanding envisioned here is highly conceptual and interconnected. The connections that are often developed by using multiple representations provide both mathematical depth and alternative pathways for solving individual problems and teaching individual topics. By having opportunities for reasoning, students identify connections and build on these to form generalizations. Essential characteristics of the instruction in these classes include representing numbers in different ways and decomposing and recomposing numbers as tools for understanding (especially the meaning of operations).

This work provides a natural link between the work on numbers and the part of algebra called "generalized arithmetic." Furthermore, analysis of the relationships between numbers and how quantities vary provides opportunities to develop reasoning about functions.

Numbers and Operations. This course centers on the number and operations curriculum built around the Developing Mathematical Ideas series of textbooks (Shifter, Bastable, and Russell; see list of texts for courses at the end of this appendix). The course focuses primarily on whole numbers, but integers and rational numbers receive minimal treatment. Participants work through the major ideas of number in K–8 mathematics, study how those ideas build on one another, and examine how children develop these ideas. Special attention is given to student reasoning and the mathematics in the case studies. Mathematical conversations about the case studies lead naturally to generalizations and the development of early algebraic thinking. Developing an understanding of the structure of the base-ten number system, the meaning of the operations, and student reasoning in using number properties are the primary goals of the course. Numbers and Operations is a prerequisite for all other courses in the program.

Rational Numbers and Proportional Reasoning. This course provides a conceptual treatment of the number systems occurring in school mathematics that are not adequately treated in Numbers and Operations: fractions and rational numbers, ratios and proportions, and decimals and percents. The central core of exploratory activities and student thinking receives continued emphasis, but the available case studies and videos are not as rich as those available for the earlier course and receive less emphasis.

Several themes run through the instruction in this course. Fractions are introduced through the idea of equal shares, and they are treated throughout as numbers, as opposed to parts of a whole. Fractions are identified with points on the number line, and many of the mathematical arguments are given a measurement interpretation. This material is intrinsically complex and abstract. Diverse representations, sketches, and manipulatives are used to develop conceptual understanding of fractions and operations on fractions.

Patterns, Functions, and Algebra. This course focuses on developing algebraic thinking. It directs attention first to generalized arithmetic, the generalization of patterns, and developing skills necessary to describe patterns with symbols. Participants develop fluency with algebraic notation. They justify conjectures (for example, that an odd number plus an odd number equals an even number) and prove that they hold, first with models and then symbolically. Participants apply basic properties of arithmetic operations, such as the distributive property, as they manipulate numerical and algebraic expressions and equations. In the second half of the course, activities explore various functions (mostly linear but including some quadratic and exponential functions). Emphasis is given to the connections among multiple representations. This course includes work on how young children can develop an understanding of functions.

Geometry and Measurement

K–8 teachers often do not possess a basic knowledge of the geometry and measurement content, and these subjects are widely neglected in mathematics education and school classrooms. It is critical that mathematics specialists be well prepared to support instruction in this area. To have this preparation, they need rigorous content instruction that includes a strong focus on pedagogy and how children learn geometry and measurement.

In the University of Virginia program, this strand is covered in a single course that addresses the geometry and measurement content that is covered in grades K–8. The course is built around the Developing Mathematical Ideas geometry and measurement curricula, as well as a large collection of exploratory, hands-on lessons and activities. The course features a strong focus on measurement in one, two, and three dimensions, including angular measurement.

The course discusses the van Hiele model of how children develop and advance in their geometric understanding. This discussion includes consideration of the need to scaffold instruction and activities to raise children's understanding of geometry and measurement concepts and skills from a lower level to a higher level. As with other courses in the program, this course maintains a strong focus on student reasoning.

Probability and Statistics

Probability and Statistics is a course that engages participants in developing an understanding of the material in the K–8 content strands of data analysis, statistics, and probability. Participants develop the language, tools, and abilities to formulate and discuss questions of a statistical nature and collect, organize, and display relevant data to address these questions. They participate in a substantial statistical project in which they formulate a question, collect data, and make and evaluate statistical inferences and predictions. The course also includes an introduction to elementary probability.

Leadership courses

To complement the mathematics content courses, future mathematics specialists complete three leadership courses. This series of courses begins with a focus on developing personal knowledge and skills necessary for effective mathematics instruction. Next, participants explore the role of the mathematics specialist as it relates to working with other teachers in the schools. Finally, they consider aspects of the job that require effective communication with various levels of administration and other interested parties. In each of these courses, participants spend a significant amount of time engaging in various mathematical tasks and refining their own mathematical content knowledge, as well as developing their philosophy of teaching and learning mathematics.

Leadership I: Problems and Issues in Mathematics Education for K–8 Mathematics Specialists

Leadership I introduces the participant to the role of the mathematics specialist and rests on the premise that a good mathematics specialist must first have a solid understanding of how to design, deliver, and evaluate mathematics instruction. Thus, course activities include work on developing the specialist's understanding of mathematics content pedagogy, as well as aspects of planning for and diagnosing student understanding. The course gives special attention to students as mathematics learners, with course content that develops an understanding of learning theories related to mathematics instruction and assessment, as well as needs of diverse learners.

Participants in this course analyze what it means for teachers to be learners. They develop skills for self-reflection and identify and use collaboration as a tool for learning. Finally, participants focus on instruction through the design, teaching, and evaluation of inquiry-based lessons.

To meet the goals of this course, participants conduct and analyze student interviews to develop their personal knowledge of students' mathematical reasoning; design a standards-based lesson, reflecting the spirit of national standards; observe another teacher, including a pre- and post-conference with the teacher and a written reflection on the lesson; lead a study group with several colleagues; and analyze samples of student work, using various protocols, and describe how the practice of examining student work serves as an important tool for professional development.

Leadership II: Development and Evaluation of Educational Staff

Leadership II is designed to help prospective mathematics specialists build those skills, understandings, and dispositions required for optimal performance of mathematics education leadership roles in elementary and middle schools. Participants refine their own skills as mathematics instructors by continuing to develop an understanding of mathematics content taught by elementary and middle school teachers, as well as the content pedagogy necessary to develop and teach standards-based lesson plans. At the same time, participants also hone abilities required to work effectively with adult learners, including coaching skills and planning and facilitation skills for leading small group and schoolwide professional development.

For their personal development, as well as to increase their abilities to work with adults, participants in this course must become familiar with the body of mathematics education research related to selected topics within the NCTM strands. Assignments that support the goals of this course include developing a standards-based lesson that focuses on classroom discussion; researching and writing a literature review related to a specific topic in the elementary or middle school classroom; planning, implementing, and critiquing a coaching session; and developing and delivering two professional development experiences.

Leadership III: Curriculum—Advanced Theory for K–8 Mathematics Specialists

In Leadership III, prospective mathematics specialists continue to develop the necessary skills, understandings, and dispositions for a leadership role in an elementary or middle school. Specifically, participants develop and refine knowledge and skills to—

- facilitate a lesson study process;
- create and use formative and summative assessments and use the resulting data to diagnose student understanding and misunderstanding;
- make instructional observations and coach teachers;
- identify problems in teaching or learning mathematics, locate and use resources to address those problems, and evaluate the effectiveness of the research lesson; and
- communicate clearly and effectively, especially through formal presentations.

Through this course, participants develop a deeper understanding of student-centered and inquiry-based mathematics pedagogy, as well as of the mathematics that elementary and middle school teachers teach. To satisfy the requirements for this course, participants write a professional book review; complete a clinical classroom observation as well as a student clinical interview; display and analyze school test data and lead a discussion about the data; build an assessment portfolio that demonstrates their understanding of summative and formative assessment and their ability to write assessment questions; and complete a lesson study cycle.

Electives

Future specialists enrolled at the University of Virginia must complete two electives as part of their degree program. Most students in the program enroll in a course titled Mathematics for Diverse Populations and another course, Supervised Study in Mathematics: Research in Mathematics Education.

Mathematics for Diverse Populations

The overarching purpose of Mathematics for Diverse Populations is to engage the prospective mathematics specialist in developing skills for facilitating best practices in the mathematics classroom. Participants learn to recognize students with diverse learning and cultural needs, and they develop respect for and understanding of equity issues regarding gender, ethnicity, race, social class, and cultural differences. Participants learn to support the mathematics learning of all students by applying skills in using a variety of instructional materials, assessment tools, strategies, and techniques for teaching mathematics. They also learn about key elements of public laws such as the Individuals with Disabilities Education Act and the No Child Left Behind Act.

A major component of the course is the weekly completion of mathematics tasks and reflections papers. Tasks are generally open-ended, and reflections examine how these tasks are accessible to a wide variety of learners at different levels of understanding. Other assignments include the differentiation of an existing lesson, and the development of a professional development activity focused on mathematics for diverse populations.

Supervised Study in Mathematics: Research in Mathematics Education

Research in Mathematics Education offers supervised study designed to help prospective mathematics specialists gain knowledge and skill in identifying, locating, and applying current, relevant research to inform instructional planning, analyze students' mathematics understanding, and respond to curriculum and policy decisions. This course prepares participants with the knowledge and skills to carry out classroom or school-based applied or action research. Participants in this course learn to locate, read, and analyze research for particular purposes, such as to influence instructional and policy decisions (for instance, textbook adoption), to provide insight and guidance about program adoptions, and to inform instructional decision making. The course emphasizes research as a tool for exploring a particular mathematical topic, both to develop a deep and thorough understanding of that topic and to develop research-based instructional tasks. Particular attention is given to identifying learning and teaching trajectories for the purpose of encouraging the participants to consider the complexity of mathematical topics and the opportunities that these complexities provide for instruction. As a culminating activity, participants conduct a literature review that will help them develop and implement their practicum projects.

The practicum

The mathematics specialist practicum serves as an integrative capstone experience. Students implement a planned practicum project after completing a minimum of twenty-seven hours in their degree program. The project, an application in or to a particular topic of interest—for instance, instructional practices to develop early understanding of and fluency in using basic facts—is designed to extend competencies in curriculum development, instruction, or school leadership. Most important, the practicum must move the student forward professionally and therefore must involve some activity that the student has not previously attempted. The entire project includes the preparation of a practicum proposal, developed in consultation with pertinent faculty advisors and school or school division leaders; the implementation of the project described in the proposal; and a reflective evaluation of what the participant learned as a result of completing the practicum. During the practicum, participants are expected to demonstrate that they understand and can summarize current research in their area of specific interest through application of acquired knowledge in this area or discipline focus. Through the practicum, participants demonstrate the various planning, implementation, and assessment skills necessary to improve instruction and inform policy decisions in a school-based setting, as well as effective oral and written communication skills.

Concluding Remarks

It is our belief that this program has proven very successful. Participants in the program learn mathematics and pedagogy, and what they learn is directly linked to the mathematics specialist's job. Considerable research, including that of Campbell and Malkus (2011), provides statistics that indicate that specialists who graduate from the program have a powerful impact on the mathematical success of the students in the schools where they serve. The courses appear to be effective, and the program's dedication to both mathematical rigor and student reasoning appears to be important.

However, over the history of this project, we have learned a great deal about what works and what does not work, and not all of what we have learned has found its way into the program. In the courses, the most obvious place for improvement today seems to be in spaces between strands, where powerful connections might be built or the strands themselves might be integrated. For example, some research-based evidence suggests that measurement activities support the development of students' understanding of fractions and number sense (Fazio and Siegler 2011; Harms 2012), and some observations made during the course of the project suggest that linear measurement activities may be the most powerful avenue available to develop an understanding of fractions as numbers rather than simply as parts of a whole. These same activities lead naturally to the addition and subtraction of fractions and to the development of number sense. The suggestion arising from this is that perhaps both the number strand and the geometry strand could be strengthened by a careful integration of these courses.

In light of the national interest in supporting algebraic success for all students, we see helping teachers in the elementary schools understand the inherent algebraic nature of the K–5 mathematics curriculum as an important function of the mathematics specialist's role in schools. Developing students' algebraic reasoning can often enhance arithmetic instruction; for instance, learning the basic facts for multiplication can be approached as an entry into functional thinking, and early patterning activities can serve as a basis for considering the structure of the number system. As we have recognized the abundance of such opportunities, we have also realized that the program might benefit from highlighting and emphasizing the development of algebraic reasoning as a unifying theme across all courses.

Perhaps one of the best lessons to keep in mind is that our program is for teachers to learn mathematics at a sufficiently deep level that they become capable coaches for other teachers, with the ultimate goal of improving student learning. The methods that teachers employ to deliver effective mathematics instruction are important; however, without a deep understanding of mathematics, great methods produce little more than good activities. Mathematics specialists should help teachers to understand the mathematics they are teaching and the concepts that children build on to create new mathematical understandings, as well as to know how this knowledge will serve as a basis for future learning. To help teachers in this way, the mathematics specialist needs a personal, deep, connected understanding of the mathematics.

References

Campbell, Patricia, and Nathaniel N. Malkus. "The Impact of Elementary Mathematics Coaches on Student Achievement." *Elementary School Journal* 111 (March 2011): 430–54.

Critchfield, Sandra. "Lead Teachers of Mathematics in the Elementary Schools: VCTM Position Statement." *Virginia Mathematics Teacher* 18, no. 2 (1992): 21.

Fazio, Lisa, and Robert Siegler. *Teaching Fractions.* Belley, France: Gonnet, 2011. http://www.unesdoc.unesco.org/images/0021/002127/212781e.pdf.

Harms, William. "Learning about Spatial Relationships Boosts Understanding of Numbers." *University of Chicago News* (June 15, 2012). http://news.uchicago.edu/article/2012/06/13/learning-about-spatial-relationships-boosts-understanding-numbers.

National Research Council. *Adding It Up: Helping Children Learn Mathematics.* Mathematics Learning Study Committee, Jeremy Kilpatrick, Jane Swafford, and Bradford Findell, eds. Center for Education, Division of Behavioral and Social Sciences and Education. Washington, D.C.: National Academy Press, 2001.

Virginia Mathematics and Science Coalition Task Force. "Executive Summary—Building the Case: Mathematics Specialists." *Journal of Mathematics and Science: Collaborative Explorations* 8 (2005a): 3–5.

———. "Mathematics Specialists Task Force Report." *Journal of Mathematics and Science: Collaborative Explorations* 8 (2005b): 5–22.